STORY HOUR READINGS

SIXTH YEAR

BY

E. C. HARTWELL, M.A., M.Pd.

SUPERINTENDENT OF SCHOOLS
BUFFALO, NEW YORK

Illustrations by

George Varian, B. Westmacott, Joseph Franké
E. B. Comstock, and others

AMERICAN BOOK COMPANY

NEW YORK   CINCINNATI   CHICAGO
BOSTON   ATLANTA

PREFACE

THIS Reader undertakes to provide desirable material for work in silent reading without losing sight of the other elements essential to a good Sixth Reader.

SILENT READING is entitled to a larger place in the sixth year than in the previous years because of its relation to the important business of learning how to study. As children progress from grade to grade, they should do an increasingly large amount of silent reading with the purpose of learning to read swiftly, accurately, and intelligently. The establishment of good reading habits is constantly to be kept in mind. Supplemental reading in school libraries and elsewhere should be used to encourage wide and general reading. Teachers should undertake from time to time to test pupils on their speed, accuracy, and ability to gather the chief ideas of the author.

CORRELATION. With plenty of varied and virile material provided, such work is easily made the basis of oral and written English, thus effecting that correlation of activities which all teachers recognize as especially desirable. Much of the material in this reader was chosen because of its close correlation with history and geography, to the enrichment of interest in both subjects.

CONTENT. The selections are both old and new. Character and fitness, rather than the date of production, have governed the choice of the editor. Ample opportunity is offered in the material for drill in oral reading, memorization, word study, dramatization, and reading

3

for appreciation. Wherever the teacher can profitably get the pupils to work in groups, she should take advantage of the coöperative spirit.

ARRANGEMENT BY GROUPS. There is an obvious advantage in grouping kindred reading materials in sections, under captions such as "Old-World Stories" and "The World of Work," etc. Besides affording some elements of continuity, the plan offers opportunity for comparison and contrast of the treatment of similar themes. It also insures a massing of the effect of the idea for which the section stands. Secondarily, the section divisions break up the solid text, and because of this the pupils feel at frequent intervals that they have completed something definite.

The groupings make no pretense to being mutually exclusive. On occasion a selection may well be transferred to another section. For example "The Landing of the Pilgrims" could be used in the "Early Days in America" section or in "Days We Honor." Teachers should have no hesitation in breaking across from one section to another when the occasion or the children's interest seems to warrant.

MECHANICAL FEATURES. Editor and publisher have spared no pains or expense to make this book attractive to children. The volume is not cumbersome or unwieldy in size. The length of line is that of the normal book with which they regularly will come into contact. The type is clean-cut and legible.

CITIZENSHIP. This means more than the passing phase of so-called Americanization. It means a genuine love of country, a reverence for our pioneer fathers, a respect for law, order, and truth. This Reader is rich in patriotic content. It is hoped that the ethical element in the selections will be found to be forceful as well as pleasing. The book emphasizes throughout the worth of individual and social virtues. If it can help teachers to make clean, upright, and loyal citizens of our great Republic, it will not have been made in vain.

Mastery of the printed page is not the sole end and aim of Reading. It is hoped that the devices employed in this Reader, as well as the direction and suggestions in study materials, may assist the teacher to develop, through her own initiative, a method of instruction one result of which shall be a genuine love on the part of her pupils for good books.

ACKNOWLEDGMENTS

In addition to acknowledgments made in connection with various selections in this volume, thanks are due the following authors and publishers:

To Clark Howell for permission to use his "The Man with his Hat in his Hand"; to Mitchell Kennerley, Publisher, for Gerald Gould's poem, "Wanderlust"; to Franklin K. Lane for his "The American Pioneer"; to P. J. Kenedy & Sons for the use of Abram J. Ryan's "Song of the River"; and to Charles Scribner's Sons for "God Give Us Men," by J. G. Holland, and "The Skating Match," from *Hans Brinker, or the Silver Skates*, by Mary Mapes Dodge.

Selections by Emerson, Hawthorne, Holmes, Longfellow, Lowell, Whittier, and Margaret E. Sangster are used by permission of and special arrangement with Houghton Mifflin Company, the authorized publishers of these authors.

Acknowledgment is made to the American Book Company for the use of selections by Frank P. Bachman, James Baldwin, Frank G. Carpenter, Fanny E. Coe, and W. W. Livengood.

CONTENTS

CONTENTS

IN THE OPEN

The outer world, from which we cower into our houses, seemed after all a habitable place; and night after night a man's bed, it seemed, was laid and waiting for him in the fields where God keeps an open house.

— ROBERT LOUIS STEVENSON.

THE ROBBER CRAB (*See opposite page*)

THE ROBBER CRAB

By Frederick O'Brien

One of the fairylands of the world is the island country of the South Seas. There one finds animals and plants strange to us who live in the temperate zone. The following description of a crab was written by a traveler who loves the outdoors and who knows how to describe what he sees.

THESE crabs climb coconut trees to procure their favorite food. They dote on coconuts, the ripe, full-meated sort. They are able to enjoy them by various endeavors demanding strength, cleverness, and an
5 apparent understanding of the effect of striking an object against a harder one and of the velocity caused by gravity. Nuts that resist their attempts to open them, they carry to great heights, to drop them and thus break their shells.

It was a never-failing entertainment on my walks in the
10 Paumotas to observe these creatures, light-brown or reddish in color, more than two feet in length, stalking about with their bodies a foot from the ground, supported by two pairs of central legs. They can exist at least twenty-four hours without visiting the water, of which they carry a
15 supply in reservoirs on both sides of the cephalothorax, keeping their gills moist.

They live in large deep burrows in the coconut groves, which they fill with husks, so that the natives often rob them to procure a quick supply of fuel. These dens are
20 contrived for speedy entry when pursued. Terrifying as they appear when surprised on land, they scuttle for safety either to a hole or to the sea, with an agility astounding in

a creature so awkward in appearance. Though they may be seen about at all hours of the day, they make forays upon the coconuts only at night.

When darkness descends and all is quiet, the robber crab ascends the tree by gripping the bark with his claws. The rays of my electric flash light have often caught him high over my head against the gray palm. Height does not daunt him. He will go up till he reaches the nuts, if it be a hundred feet. With his powerful nippers he severs the stem, choosing always a nut that is big and ripe. Descending the palm, he tears off the fibrous husk, which, at first thought, it would seem impossible for him to do. He tears it fiber by fiber, and always from that end under which the three eyeholes are situated. With these exposed, he begins hammering on one of them until he has enlarged the opening so that he can insert one of the sharp points of his claw into it. By turning his claw backward and forward he scoops out the meat and regales himself luxuriously.

This is his simplest method, along the line of least resistance; but let the nut be refractory, and he seizes it by a point of a claw and beats it against a rock until he smashes it. This plan failing, he will carry the stubborn nut to the top of the tree again and hurl it to the earth to crack it. And if at first he does not succeed, he will make other trips aloft with the husked nut, dropping it again and again until at last it is shattered and lies open to his claws.

It is said that if a drop of oil be placed on the long and delicate antennæ of these crabs they die almost instantly. We have a somewhat similar rumor with respect to salt and a bird's tail. Seldom does a robber crab linger to be oiled, and so other means of destroying him, or, at least, of guarding against his depredations, are sought. With the rat, who bites the flower and gnaws the young nuts, this crab is the principal enemy of the planter. The tree owner who can afford it nails sheets of tin or zinc around the tree, a dozen feet from the earth. Neither a rat nor crab can pass this slippery band, which gives no claw hold. Thousands of trees are thus protected, but usually these are in possession of white men, for tin is costly and the native is poor.

The ingenious native, however, employs another means of saving the fruit of his groves. He climbs the palm trunk in the daytime, and forty feet above the ground encircles it with dirt and leaves. On his mat for the night's slumber, he smiles to think of the revenge he shall have. For the crab ascends and passes the puny barrier to select and fell his nuts, but when in his backward way he descends, he forgets the curious bunker he went over and, striking it again, thinks he has reached the ground. He lets go, and smashes on the rocks his crafty foe has piled below.

— *White Shadows in the South Seas.*

1. Who is the author of this selection? From what book is it taken? Why does this description belong to this section of your reader?

2. Describe the robber crab as to appearance, size, and habits of living.

3. How many methods does this crab use to get coconuts? Explain each.

4. How do the natives keep him from doing damage? What way can the natives not afford to employ?

5. Study the illustration on page 12. Is it a good picture to illustrate the text? Discuss.

(Taken from O'Brien's *White Shadows in the South Seas* by permission of the publishers, The Century Co.)

JUNE

By James Russell Lowell

A ND what is so rare as a day in June?
 Then, if ever, come perfect days;
Then Heaven tries earth if it be in tune,
 And over it softly her warm ear lays;
Whether we look, or whether we listen,   5
We hear life murmur, or see it glisten;
Every clod feels a stir of might,
 An instinct within it that reaches and towers,
And, groping blindly above it for light,
 Climbs to a soul in grass and flowers;   10
The flush of life may well be seen
 Thrilling back over hills and valleys;
The cowslip startles in meadows green,
 The buttercup catches the sun in its chalice,
And there's never a leaf nor a blade too mean   15
 To be some happy creature's palace;
The little bird sits at his door in the sun,
 Atilt like a blossom among the leaves,
And lets his illumined being o'errun
 With the deluge of summer it receives;   20
His mate feels the eggs beneath her wings,
And the heart in her dumb breast flutters and sings;
He sings to the wide world, and she to her nest —
In the nice ear of Nature which song is the best?
Now is the high-tide of the year,   25
 And whatever of life hath ebbed away

Comes flooding back with a ripply cheer,
   Into every bare inlet and creek and bay;
Now the heart is so full that a drop overfills it,
We are happy now because God wills it;
5 No matter how barren the past may have been,
'Tis enough for us now that the leaves are green;
We sit in the warm shade and feel right well
How the sap creeps up and the blossoms swell;
We may shut our eyes, but we cannot help knowing
10 That skies are clear and grass is growing;
   The breeze comes whispering in our ear,
   That dandelions are blossoming near,
     That maize has sprouted, that streams are flowing,
   That the river is bluer than the sky,
15 That the robin is plastering his house hard by;
And if the breeze kept the good news back,
For other couriers we should not lack;
     We could guess it all by yon heifer's lowing, —
   And hark! how clear bold chanticleer,
20 Warmed with the new wine of the year,
   Tells all in his lusty crowing!

                 — *Vision of Sir Launfal.*

   1. Write from memory the lines of the poem that make the most pleasing picture.

   2. What evidences does Lowell give that June is the " high-tide of the year"? Does he omit any that you can think of?

   3. In the following lines use your own words to explain what is meant: 3-4, 15-16, 21-23, page 16; 3-6, 15, 16-17, 19-21, page 17.

   4. June was Lowell's favorite month. He expressed a wish that he might die in that month, and his wish came true.

SONG OF THE RIVER

By Abram J. Ryan

A RIVER went singing adown to the sea,
 A-singing, low, singing,
And the dim, rippling river said softly to me,
 "I'm bringing, a-bringing —
  While floating along —   5
  A beautiful song
To the shores that are white, where the waves are so weary,
To the beach that is burdened with wrecks that are dreary.

  "A song sweet and calm
  As the peacefullest psalm,   10
  And the shore that was sad
  Will be grateful and glad,
And the weariest wave from its weariest dream
Will wake to the sound of the song of the stream,
  And the tempests shall cease,   15
  And there shall be peace."

  From the fairest of fountains
  And the farthest of mountains,
  From the stillness of snow
  Came the stream in its flow;   20
Down the slopes where the rocks are gray,
 Through the vales where the flowers are fair,
Where the sunlight flashed — where the shadows lay
 Like stories that cloud a face of care.

The river ran on, and on, and on,
   Day and night, and night and day;
Going and going, and never gone,
   Longing to flow to the far away.
5   Staying and staying, and never still,
Going and staying, as if one will
   Said, "Beautiful river, go to the sea,"
   And another will whispered, "Stay with me";
   And the river made answer, soft and low,
10   "I go and stay." — "I stay and go."

  1. Read aloud what the river said to the poet.

  2. The river was of two minds. What did each will it to do? Which did it do?

  3. Describe the river's course by reading aloud the lines that tell of its source; its breaking out of the highlands; its travels in the lowlands; its mouth.

FERN SONG

By John B. Tabb

DANCE to the beat of the rain, little Fern,
   And spread out your palms again,
   And say, "Though the Sun
   Hath my vesture spun,
5 He had labored, alas, in vain,
   But for the shade
   That the Cloud hath made,
And the gift of the Dew and the Rain."
   Then laugh and upturn
10   All your fronds, little Fern,
And rejoice in the beat of the rain!

(Used by permission of the publishers, Small, Maynard & Company.)

CAMPING IN THE WINTER WILDERNESS

By H. O. Templeton

ONE winter several years ago I decided to do some
trapping up in northern Maine. During October,
when I was guiding a sportsman on a moose-hunting trip,
I had seen a great many signs of fisher, lynx, fox, and bear,
and so I bought food for about five months and included
blankets and clothing with my traps. Before freezing
weather came I loaded all my duffel into a canoe and
started for Musquacook Lakes, about ninety miles distant.
It took me ten days to go in, as there were several long
portages where I had to tote' everything in packs over
rough trails.

I finally reached my trapping ground and selected for
my camp site a sheltered spot near a good spring. It was
on the north shore of a small lake, well shielded from the
north winds, and there was plenty of bright sunshine in the
daytime. The camp I made of spruce trees chopped down
and cut in twelve-foot and sixteen-foot lengths. I laid the
largest logs at the bottom and notched them at either end
to receive the next log, and so on up until the walls were
seven feet high; then I laid up several end logs, each of
which was shorter than the last, to receive a log lengthwise
of the camp, and in that way the roof was soon finished.

My next job was to cover the roof. I found some large
straight-grained cedars, cut them into three-foot lengths,
and split these short pieces into boards, thin, flat, and
smooth, known as "splits." These I put on the roof like

shingles, but in a double layer, and over them spread boughs, and finally covered the whole with earth to keep the heat inside the camp. The holes between the logs I filled with moss from the ground, driven in hard. I made 5 the door of boards split from balsam, and for a window cut out between the logs a space about nine inches wide and two feet long, over which I stretched a very thin piece of deerskin.

To make my bed I used small logs, raised about sixteen 10 inches from the floor; the bottom was of small springy poles, which I covered about a foot deep with boughs. It was a very comfortable bed and only needed new boughs about every two or three weeks. Everything was now ready for the zero weather that was sure to come soon, 15 and I had to set my lines of traps and bait them, for the fur was getting prime.

These trapping lines are marked by blazing trees on both sides, forming what are known by woodsmen as "spotted lines." They follow across the ridges for many miles, and 20 a trapper usually builds a small camp eight miles or so from his home camp — for eight miles is about as far as he can travel on the shortest days in winter and properly attend to his traps. He puts from three to five traps to the mile for sable and fisher; but for mink, otter, and 25 beaver, which frequent the rivers, streams, and small ponds, he places his sets more thickly.

Usually bears go into their dens about the first of December, but much depends upon how cold the weather is. Some mild seasons they stay out until January. One 30 morning late in December that winter, when it was very cold — almost zero — and the snow was sixteen inches deep I saw the tracks of a large bear just ahead of me. As

I carried my rifle, my ax, and a good supply of food with me, I thought I would follow his trail until I got him. I was wearing snowshoes and the snow was fairly hard, for there had been a thaw and a freeze, and then four inches of light snow had covered the crust. I had one big advan- tage — every time the bear started to run he broke through the crust — so I hurried as fast as I could, trying to catch sight of him, but I couldn't seem to gain on him. I kept at it, however, until late in the afternoon ; my clothing was wet with perspiration, it was nearing night, but still the old bear led me due west, straight away from home.

About four o'clock I was fourteen miles from home — too far to give up the chase and return to my cabin — and so I decided to go on and camp for the night. Bruin's track led me to the bank of a large stream of rapid open water. He had gone straight across and I could see where he had crawled out on the other side and had shaken him- self free of water, but there was no crossing here for me. I had to go upstream for a mile to find still water that was frozen over strong enough to hold me. I got across and circled down until I found his track, but it was so late then that I had to camp.

First I found wood, plenty of it, and carried it to a sheltered spot near by. I then shoveled and scraped away the snow to the ground on a space eight or nine feet long and two or three feet wide and built a fire of fine wood all along this trench. When it was blazing well, I put on some hardwood limbs and split hardwood, and let it burn to coals. Then I gathered balsam boughs — heaps of them — and after raking the biggest burning sticks from my fire to the end of the trench where my feet would be, I piled the green fir boughs on top of the live coals in such

large armfuls that there was no danger of their blazing up, and trod them down by jumping on them. Over all I spread dry decayed wood to lie on. Above my bed I placed some long poles in a lean-to manner, covered them
5 with boughs, and threw on snow to keep the wind out.

At the end of the trench where I had placed the live brands I built up a fire, made my tea, broiled a piece of bacon, thawed out a chunk of bread, and ate my supper. After pulling off my moccasins, unloading my pockets, and
10 letting down my suspenders, I lay down for a rest. With the warm boughs under me and a good fire at my feet I soon became sleepy, and woke up only when the fire got low and I felt chilly. Then I put on some fine dry wood and got a good blaze going, and put on three big hardwood
15 logs with smaller ones to make the big ones burn. Properly laid, the large logs will roll into the center as they burn and the fire will last a long time. I slept warm and comfortably for about eight hours.

At daylight I followed my bear trail for about two miles
20 and found Bruin curled up under some fallen trees where he had made a fine nest for himself some time previously — probably in the early autumn. He was very large and very old. After I had shot him and had skinned him I set out for my home camp. It was about eighteen miles
25 away, but I hurried along with my pelt and arrived there after dark, tired and hungry, but satisfied.

1. Read this story once silently. Then outline briefly: (a) where the events took place; (b) how he built his camp; (c) his bear hunt; (d) how he slept in the open.

2. Make a rough pencil sketch of his camp.

3. Relate some experience of your own in camping out.

(Reprinted by permission from *The Open Road, The Magazine for Young Men*.)

SPRING

By Henry Timrod

Henry Timrod (1829–1867) was a Southern poet whose fame rests on a single volume of nature and love songs of high quality. The following poem describes spring in the South.

SPRING, with that nameless pathos in the air
  Which dwells with all things fair,
Spring, with her golden suns and silver rain,
Is with us once again.

Out in the lonely woods the jasmine burns   5
  Its fragrant lamps, and turns
Into a royal court with green festoons
The banks of dark lagoons.

In the deep heart of every forest tree
  The blood is all aglee,   10
And there's a look about the leafless bowers
As if they dreamed of flowers.

Yet still on every side we trace the hand
  Of winter in the land,
Save where the maple reddens on the lawn,   15
Flushed by the season's dawn;

As yet the turf is dark, although you know
  That, not a span below,
A thousand germs are groping through the gloom,
And soon will burst their tomb.   20

Already, here and there, on frailest stems
Appear some azure gems,
Small as might deck, upon a gala day,
The forehead of a fay.

5   In gardens you may note, amid the dearth,
The crocus breaking earth;
And near the snowdrop's tender white and green,
The violet in its screen.

And there's a sense of blossoms yet unborn
10   In the sweet airs of morn;
One almost looks to see the very street
Grow purple at his feet.

At times a fragrant breeze comes floating by,
And brings, you know not why,
15   A feeling as when eager crowds await
Before a palace gate

Some wondrous pageant; and you scarce would start,
If from some beech's heart,
A blue-eyed dryad, stepping forth, should say,
20   "Behold me, I am May!"

1. What month do you think is described? Why?
2. What evidences of spring are given? What are the first signs of spring you have observed? What signs has the poet omitted?
3. Explain the fifth and tenth stanzas.
4. Define: pathos; jasmine; festoons; lagoons; bowers; gala; azure; pageant; dryad.

A CHILD'S VISIT TO THE MOON

By Agnes Giberne

ONE evening in summer a child stood watching the stars in the sky above him. The moon had just risen in the east, sending its soft light upon the earth.

"Oh, if I could only visit the stars!" he sighed.

Soon he began to feel weary. He sat down and leaned his head against a grassy bank. Then his eyes closed, and he fell asleep. It seemed to him that he had been asleep about three seconds when he heard a clear, sweet voice calling his name. He sprang to his feet and looked around. A little girl dressed in white was standing near him.

Her eyes were blue, her hair was golden like the sunset, and on her shoulders there was a pair of silver wings.

"Don't you wish to go with me?" asked the little girl.

"Where are you going? What is your name?" said the child.

"My name is Stella," was the answer, "and I am going to visit the stars."

"Oh, I should like that better than anything else," said the child. "But how can I go?"

"I think your wings are strong enough to carry you," said Stella.

"Wings!" cried the child; and peeping over his shoulder he saw them there, sure enough, all ready for use. He felt very strange, but he said, "Oh, yes, let us go."

"We will visit the moon first," said Stella.

"Yes, because it is the nearest," said the child. "How soon shall we start?"

"Now. We need not wait a moment."

"But shall we not take some food with us?"

5 "Oh, no," answered Stella. "Those who have wings are never hungry."

"Well, I am ready," said the child.

One! two! three! They spread their wings and rose side by side through the darkness. Below them, everything 10 seemed to sink and fade away. Above them, all seemed to broaden and grow bright.

"See!" said Stella. "We have left the earth behind us. We are flying through space now."

"How far does space reach?" asked the child.

15 "I do not know. If there is anything beyond space, we only know that God is there."

This seemed to the child a wonderful thought.

"Oh, what is that?" he cried, as a small dark body rushed past them towards the earth. Soon it flamed up 20 for a moment like fire, and then was seen no more.

"Only a shooting star," answered Stella. "Have you never watched for shooting stars at night?"

"Yes, yes," whispered the child, "but I did not know what they were like. I hope one will not strike us. Will 25 not that shooting star fall on the earth and kill somebody?"

"No, it will burn up before it reaches the earth. Now, shut your eyes and take my hand. Do not look until I give you leave."

The child obeyed, and on they flew. Once he said, "We 30 are going ever and ever so fast, but I cannot feel the wind."

"There cannot be wind where there is no air," said Stella. "Wind is moving air."

"Then is there nothing here?" asked the child eagerly.

"Nothing that we can see or feel."

Suddenly the child felt himself standing upon his feet.

"Open your eyes," said Stella softly.

"Why, here we are back on the earth again!" cried the 5 child.

"Do you think so? Look around!"

"It's only earth."

It was a strange earth. Here and there were great mountains, casting black shadows upon the plain. The 10 sunshine was so bright and hot that the child could not face it. No grass nor trees nor other plants could be seen anywhere.

"Look up," said Stella.

The child obeyed. 15

The sky was black, not blue. And the sun! Was it the very same sun? A fringe of many-colored lights streamed from it on all sides, and it was far brighter than the child had ever seen it from his earth home.

Then he saw another splendid sight. A shining body 20 like the moon was floating aloft, but it was many times larger than the moon and covered with curious marks.

"That is the earth," said Stella.

"I never knew we had such a shining world to live in," said the child. He could hardly believe it was true. 25

"How do you like this heat?" asked Stella.

"I wonder that I can stand it," was the answer. "I never felt such heat."

"You came with wings," said Stella. "If you had come in any other way, you could not endure it for the tenth part 30 of a second."

Just then a round, hard body came rushing down from

above and struck the ground near where they stood. The ground shook, yet there was no sound.

"Oh!" cried the child, "I did not hear it."

"There are no noises in the moon," said Stella, "for there is no air. Without our wings, we could not hear each other speak. That was only a shooting star."

"A shooting star! But this one did not burn."

"No, there is no air to make it burn. If you will only watch you may see many more."

"I wonder where they come from," said the child.

"Millions and millions of them are always rushing round the sun and moon," answered Stella.

Far away, the child saw a great rocky wall, like a ridge of mountains.

"I wonder what we could see from over there," he said.

"We will go and look," answered Stella. "Come, shall we mount the rocks? Spring upward as high as you can."

The child obeyed; but instead of jumping three or four feet, he easily jumped forty.

"Why, how is this?" he cried. "I never felt so light. I never jumped so far in my life."

"Well, you have not been used to jumping in the moon," said Stella. "Weight here is much less than on the earth."

"Why so?"

"Because the moon is so much smaller than the earth. It does not draw you towards it with so much force."

A few more leaps and some swift climbing and running brought them to the rocky wall. They could see no grass, no trees — only black shadows and a black sky and the fierce, bright sunshine.

"I could not bear to live here," said the child.

"I have not shown you the worst yet," said Stella. "You have yet to learn about the moon's night. Sit down, and let us wait. The sun will set in less than a week, and then night will come."

"A week!" cried the child.

"Less than a week. The moon's day lasts a fortnight of our time; but her day is more than half over now, and we will wait and see the sun set."

So they waited, and watched the sun as it crept slowly down toward the mountain tops and then sank out of sight. Night was upon them. But it was not a very dark night, for the shining earth was brighter than a dozen full moons.

The cold was fearful. The child drew close to his little friend and shivered.

"Have you seen enough, dear?" asked Stella.

"Oh, yes! Let us go home."

"Then take my hand and spread your wings. Shut your eyes and have no fear."

Swiftly they flew from the dreary land of the moon, and before the child thought it possible he was back in the garden by his mother's house.

"Good-by," said Stella, and she faded from his sight.

The child looked up. His mother had come to call him.

1. Imagine yourself in an airplane flying away from the earth, out into space. What would the earth look like directly? Later? How would the sun appear? The moon?

2. What is the moon? Where does it get its brightness from? If people lived in the moon how would the earth appear to them?

3. Of what other planets besides the earth do you know?

THE GLADNESS OF NATURE

By William Cullen Bryant

IS THIS a time to be cloudy and sad,
   When our mother Nature laughs around;
When even the deep blue heavens look glad,
   And gladness breathes from the blossoming ground?

5 There are notes of joy from the hangbird and wren,
   And the gossip of swallows through all the sky;
The ground squirrel gayly chirps by his den,
   And the wilding bee hums merrily by.

The clouds are at play in the azure space,
10   And their shadows at play on the bright green vale,
And here they stretch to the frolic chase,
   And there they roll on the easy gale.

There's a dance of leaves in that aspen bower,
   There's a titter of winds in that beechen tree,
15 There's a smile on the fruit, and a smile on the flower,
   And a laugh from the brook that runs to the sea.

And look at the broad-faced sun, how he smiles
   On the dewy earth that smiles in his ray,
On the leaping waters and gay young isles;
20   Aye, look, and he'll smile thy gloom away.

1. What season of the year is described? Pick out the words that express happiness.

I DIG A DITCH

BY DAVID GRAYSON

This is an extract from a book called *Adventures in Contentment.*
The author and his sister Harriet leave the city, go to the country,
and purchase a farm. There they find real contentment. The author
herein relates his adventure in ditch digging and describes the joy
of it.

I TAKE off my coat and hang it over a limb of the little
hawthorn tree. I put my bag near it. I roll up the
sleeves of my flannel shirt. I give my hat a twirl; I'm
ready for work.

So I dug. There is something fine in hard physical 5
labor, straight ahead; no brain used, just muscles. I stood
ankle-deep in the cool water; every spadeful came out
with a smack, and as I turned it over at the edge of the
ditch small turgid rivulets coursed back again. I did not
think of anything in particular. I dug. 10

A peculiar joy attends the very pull of the muscles. I
drove the spade home with one foot, then I bent and lifted
and turned with a sort of physical satisfaction difficult
to describe. At first I had the cool of the morning, but
by seven o'clock the day was hot enough! I opened the 15
breast of my shirt, gave my sleeves another roll, and went
at it again for half an hour, until I dripped with perspiration.

"I will knock off," I said, so I used my spade as a ladder
and climbed out of the ditch. Being very thirsty, I
walked down through the marshy valley to the clump of 20
alders which grows along the creek. I followed a cow

path through the thicket and came to the creek side, where
I knelt on a log and took a good long drink. Then I
soused my head in the cool stream, dashed the water upon
my arms, and came up dripping and gasping. Oh, but
5 it was fine!

So I came back to the hawthorn tree, where I sat down
comfortably and stretched my legs. There is a poem in
stretched legs — after hard digging — but I can't write it,
though I can feel it! I got my bag and took out a half loaf
10 of Harriet's bread. Breaking off big crude pieces, I ate
it there in the shade.

How rarely we taste the real taste of bread! We dis-
guise it with butter, we toast it, we eat it with milk or
fruit. We even soak it with gravy (here in the country,
15 where we aren't at all polite — but very comfortable), so
that we never get the downright delicious taste of the
bread itself.

I was hungry this morning and I ate my half loaf to the
last crumb — and wanted more. Then I lay down for a
20 moment in the shade and looked up into the sky through
the thin outer branches of the hawthorn. A turkey
buzzard was lazily circling cloud-high above me. A frog
boomed intermittently from the little marsh, and there
were bees at work in the blossoms.

25 I had another drink at the creek and went back somewhat reluctantly, I confess, to the work. I was hot, and
the first joy of effort had worn off. But the ditch was to
be dug and I went at it again.

Down toward the town there is a little factory for barrel
30 hoops and staves. It has one of the most musical whistles
I ever heard in my life. It toots at exactly twelve o'clock:
blessed sound! The last half hour at ditch digging is a

hard, slow pull.   I'm warm and tired, but I stick down to it
and wait with straining ear for the music.   At the very
first note of that whistle I drop my spade.   I will even
empty out a load of dirt halfway up rather than expend
another ounce of energy;   and I spring out of the ditch 5
and start for home with a single desire in my heart — or
possibly lower down.   And Harriet, standing in the doorway, seems to me a sort of angel — a culinary angel!

Talk of joy!   There may be things better than beef
stew and baked potatoes and homemade bread — there 10
may be —

— Adventures in Contentment.

1. How did the author make ready to dig?   How did he rest?
What pleasure did he get from each?

2. What did he expect to have for dinner?   Why was the food
so appetizing to him?

3. Have you ever worked out of doors — hard?   Tell your experience.   Is there a thrill in hard work?   Explain.   Why do most
people miss it?

I KNOW A BANK

By WILLIAM SHAKESPEARE

I KNOW a bank where the wild thyme blows,
   Where oxlips and the nodding violet grows,
Quite overcanopied with luscious woodbine,
With sweet musk roses and with eglantine:
There sleeps Titania sometime of the night,   5
Lulled in these flowers with dances and delight.

— A Midsummer Night's Dream.

THREE SUMMER STUDIES

By James Barron Hope

I

THE cock hath crowed. I hear the doors unbarred;
    Down to the moss-grown porch my way I take,
And hear, beside the well within the yard,
    Full many an ancient, quacking, splashing drake,
5 And gabbling goose, and noisy brood hen — all
Responding to yon strutting gobbler's call.

The dew is thick upon the velvet grass —
    The porch rails hold it in translucent drops,
And as the cattle from th'inclosure pass,
10   Each one, alternate, slowly halts and crops
The tall, green spears, with all their dewy load,
Which grow beside the well-known pasture road.

A lustrous polish is on all the leaves —
    The birds flit in and out with varied notes —
15 The noisy swallows twitter 'neath the eaves —
    A partridge whistle through the garden floats,
While yonder gaudy peacock harshly cries,
As red and gold flush all the eastern skies.

Up comes the sun: through the dense leaves a spot
20   Of splendid light drinks up the dew; the breeze
Which late made leafy music dies; the day grows hot,
    And slumbrous sounds come from marauding bees;
The burnished river like a sword blade shines,
Save where 'tis shadowed by the solemn pines.

II

Over the farm is brooding silence now —
    No reaper's song — no raven's clangor harsh —
No bleat of sheep — no distant low of cow —
    No croak of frogs within the spreading marsh —
No bragging cock from littered farmyard crows,   5
The scene is steeped in silence and repose.

A trembling haze hangs over all the fields —
    The panting cattle in the river stand,
Seeking the coolness which its wave scarce yields.
    It seems a Sabbath through the drowsy land;   10
So hushed is all beneath the summer's spell,
I pause and listen for some faint church bell.

The leaves are motionless — the song bird's mute —
    The very air seems somnolent and sick;
The spreading branches with o'erripened fruit   15
    Show in the sunshine all their clusters thick,
While now and then a mellow apple falls
With a dull sound within the orchard's walls.

The sky has but one solitary cloud,
    Like a dark island in a sea of light;   20
The parching furrows 'twixt the corn rows plowed
    Seem fairly dancing in my dazzled sight,
While over yonder road a dusty haze
Grows reddish purple in the sultry blaze.

III

That solitary cloud grows dark and wide,
    While distant thunder rumbles in the air;
A fitful ripple breaks the river's tide —
    The lazy cattle are no longer there,
5 But homeward come in long procession slow,
With many a bleat and many a plaintive low.

Darker and wider spreading o'er the west,
    Advancing clouds, each in fantastic form,
And mirrored turrets on the river's breast
10   Tell in advance the coming of a storm —
Closer and brighter glares the lightning's flash,
And louder, nearer, sounds the thunder's crash.

The air of evening is intensely hot,
    The breeze feels heated as it fans my brows —
15 Now sullen raindrops patter down like shot,
    Strike in the grass, or rattle 'mid the boughs.
A sultry lull; and then a gust again,
And now I see the thick-advancing rain.

It fairly hisses as it comes along,
20   And where it strikes bounds up again in spray,
As if 'twere dancing to the fitful song
    Made by the trees, which twist themselves and sway
In contest with the wind which rises fast,
Until the breeze becomes a furious blast.

And now the sudden, fitful storm has fled,
   The clouds lie piled up in the splendid west,
In massive shadow tipped with purplish red,
   Crimson, or gold. The scene is one of rest;
And on the bosom of yon still lagoon   5
I see the crescent of the pallid moon.

          — *A Wreath of Virginia Bay Leaves.*

1. What does each of the above studies picture? How much time do the three studies cover? Prove your answer by citing lines from the poem.

2. Which of the scenes is most vividly pictured? Read the stanzas in which you enjoy the picture most.

3. James Barron Hope (1829–1887) spent most of his life in his native state of Virginia. He was a lawyer, a scholar, a journalist, and a poet. His poetry has the fine virtues of clearness, simplicity, and dignity.

(Used by the kind permission of Janey Hope Marr, daughter of James Barron Hope.)

THE SPIDER'S TELEGRAPH WIRE

By J. Henri Fabre

OF THE six Garden Spiders I have noticed, two only, the Banded and the Silky Spiders, stay constantly in their webs, even under the blinding rays of a fierce sun. The others, as a rule, do not show themselves until nightfall. At some distance from the net they have a rough-and-ready 5 retreat in the brambles, a hiding place made of a few leaves held together by stretched threads. It is here that they usually remain in the daytime, motionless and sunk in meditation.

But the shrill light that vexes them is the joy of the 10 fields. At such time, the Locust hops more nimbly than ever, more gayly skims the Dragon Fly. Besides, the sticky web, in spite of the rents suffered during the night, is still in fairly good condition. If some giddy-pated insect allow himself to be caught, will the Spider, at the distance whereto she has retired, be unable to take advantage of the windfall? Never fear. She arrives in a flash. How does she know what has happened? Let us explain the matter.

It is the vibration of the web which tells her, rather than the sight of the captured object. To prove this, I laid upon several Spiders' webs a dead Locust. I placed the Locust where the Spider might plainly have seen it. Sometimes the Spider was in her web, and sometimes she was outside, in her hiding place. In both cases, nothing happened at first. The Spider remained motionless, even when the Locust was at a short distance in front of her. She did not seem to see the game at all. Then, with a long straw, I set the dead insect trembling.

That was quite enough. The Banded Spider and the Silky Spider hastened to the central floor; the others, who were in hiding, came down from the branch; all went to the Locust, bound him with tape, treated him, in short, as they would treat a live prey captured under the usual conditions. It took the shaking of the web to decide them to attack.

If we look carefully behind the web of any Spider with a daytime hiding place, we shall see a thread that starts from the center of the web and reaches the place where the Spider lurks. It is joined to the web at the central point only. Its length is usually about twenty-two inches, but the Angular Spider, settled high up in the trees, has shown me some as long as eight or nine feet.

This slanting line is a footbridge by which the Spider hurries to her web when there is something going on there, and then, when her errand is finished, returns to her hut.

But that is not all it is. If it were, the footbridge would be fastened to the upper end of the web. The journey would then be shorter and the slope less steep.

The line starts from the center of the net because that is the place where the spokes meet and therefore where the 5 vibration from any part of the net is best felt. Anything that moves upon the web sets it shaking. All, then, that is needed is a thread going from this central point to carry to a distance the news of a prey struggling in some part or other of the net. The slanting cord is not only a footbridge; 10 it is a signaling apparatus, a telegraph wire.

In their youth, the Garden Spiders, who are then very wide-awake, know nothing of the art of telegraphy. Only the old Spiders, meditating or dozing in their green tent, are warned from afar, by telegraph, of what takes place on 15 the net.

To save herself from keeping a close watch that would be drudgery and to remain alive to events even when resting, with her back turned on the net, the hidden Spider always has her foot upon the telegraph wire. Here is a true story 20 to prove it :—

An Angular Spider has spun her web between two laurestine shrubs, covering a width of nearly a yard. The sun beats upon the snare, which is abandoned long before dawn. The Spider is in her day house, a resort easily 25 discovered by following the telegraph wire. It is a vaulted chamber of dead leaves, joined together with a few bits of silk. The refuge is deep; the Spider disappears in it entirely, all but her rounded hind quarters, which bar the entrance.

With her front half plunged into the back of her hut, 30 the Spider certainly cannot see her web; she could not even if she had good sight, instead of being half blind as she is. Does she give up hunting during this period of bright sunlight? Not at all. Look again.

Wonderful! One of her hind legs is stretched outside the leafy cabin; and the signaling thread ends just at the tip of that leg. Whoever has not seen the Spider in this attitude, with her hand, so to speak, on the telegraph receiver, knows nothing of one of the most curious examples of animal cleverness. Let any game appear upon the scene, and the slumberer, at once aroused by means of the leg receiving the vibrations, hastens up. A Locust whom I myself lay on the web gives her this agreeable shock, and what follows? If she is satisfied with her prey, I am still more satisfied with what I have learned.

One word more. The web is often shaken by the wind. The signaling cord must pass this vibration to the Spider. Nevertheless, she does not leave her hut and remains indifferent to the commotion prevailing in the net. Her line, therefore, is something better than a bell rope; it is a telephone capable, like our own, of transmitting infinitesimal waves of sound. Clutching her telephone wire with a toe, the Spider listens with her leg; she can tell the difference between the vibration proceeding from a prisoner and the mere shaking caused by the wind.

— Insect Adventures.

1. How did the author prove that spiders have a system of telegraphy? What is the system?

2. Henri Fabre (1823–1915) is a noted French authority on insect life. Most of his life was spent in teaching school, but his interest was in the outdoors. His books are remarkably simple and always entertaining. You will enjoy *Insect Adventures*.

(From J. Henri Fabre's *Insect Adventures*. Copyright, 1917, by Dodd, Mead & Company, Inc.)

LIFE IN THE WOODS

BY HENRY VAN DYKE

THE people who always live in houses, and sleep on beds, and walk on pavements, and buy their food from butchers and bakers and grocers, are not the most blessed inhabitants of this wide and various earth. The circumstances of their existence are too mathematical and secure for perfect contentment. They live at second or third hand. They are boarders in the world. Everything is done for them by somebody else.

It is almost impossible for anything very interesting to happen to them. They must get their excitement out of the newspapers, reading of the hairbreadth escapes and moving accidents that befall people in real life. What do these tame ducks really know of the adventure of living? If the weather is bad, they are snugly housed. If it is cold, there is a furnace in the cellar. If they are hungry, the shops are near at hand. It is all as dull, flat, stale, and unprofitable as adding up a column of figures. They might as well be brought up in an incubator.

But when man abides in tents, after the manner of the early patriarchs, the face of the world is renewed. The vagaries of the clouds become significant. You watch the sky with a lover's look, eager to know whether it will smile or frown. When you lie at night upon your bed of boughs and hear the rain pattering on the canvas close above your head, you wonder whether it is a long storm or only a shower.

The rising wind shakes the tent flaps. Are the pegs well driven down and the cords firmly fastened? You fall asleep again and wake later, to hear the rain drumming still more loudly on the tight cloth, and the big breeze snoring through the forest, and the waves plunging along the beach. A stormy day? Well, you must cut plenty of wood and keep the camp fire glowing, for it will be hard to start it up again, if you let it get too low.

There is little use in fishing or hunting in such a storm. But there is plenty to do in the camp: guns to be cleaned, tackle to be put in order, clothes to be mended, a good story of adventure to be read, a belated letter to be written to some poor wretch in a summer hotel, a game of hearts or cribbage to be played, or a hunting trip to be planned for the return of fair weather. The tent is perfectly dry. A little trench dug around it carries off the surplus water, and luckily it is pitched with the side to the lake, so that you get the pleasant heat of the fire without the unendurable smoke. Cooking in the rain has its disadvantages. But how good the supper tastes when it is served up on a tin plate, with an empty box for a table and a roll of blankets at the foot of the bed for a seat!

A day, two days, three days, the storm may continue, according to your luck. I have been out in the woods for a fortnight without a drop of rain or a sign of dust. Again, I have tented on the shore of a big lake for a week, waiting for an obstinate tempest to pass by.

Look now, just at nightfall: is there not a little lifting and breaking of the clouds in the west, a little shifting of the wind toward a better quarter? You go to bed with cheerful hopes. A dozen times in the darkness you are half awake, and listening drowsily to the sounds of the storm. Are they waxing or waning? Is that louder pattering a new burst of rain, or is it only the plumping of the big drops as they are shaken from the trees? See, the dawn has come, and the gray light glimmers through the canvas. In a little while you will know your fate. 5

Look! There is a patch of bright-yellow radiance on the peak of the tent. The shadow of a leaf dances over it. The sun must be shining. Good luck! And up with you, for it is a glorious morning.

The woods are glistening as fresh and fair as if they had 10 been new-created overnight. The water sparkles, and tiny waves are dancing and splashing all along the shore. Scarlet berries of the mountain ash hang around the lake. A pair of kingfishers dart back and forth across the bay, in flashes of living blue. A black eagle swings silently 15 around his circle, far up in the cloudless sky. The air is full of pleasant sounds, but there is no noise.

The world is full of joyful life, but there is no crowd and no confusion. There is no factory chimney to darken the day with its smoke, no trolley car to split the silence with 20 its shriek and smite the indignant ear with the clanging of its impudent bell. No lumberman's ax has robbed the encircling forests of their glory of great trees. No fires have swept over the hills and left behind them the desolation of a bristly landscape. All is fresh and sweet, calm 25 and clear and bright. — *Fisherman's Luck.*

1. A rainy day in camp is a gloomy day for most people. Why was it an enjoyable day for Dr. van Dyke? What did he do?

2. If you have camped out, what did you do on a rainy day? How can you make a rainy day pleasant anywhere?

3. Appoint three members of your class to report on Dr. van Dyke's life and writings.

ADVENTURE

Life itself is a brave adventure. It is little wonder, then, that we crave the excitement that adventure lends; or next to that, the story of daring achievement. We crown those men heroes who dare risk their lives in a worthy cause; and the tale of their doings excites a lively interest and sympathy in the hearts of its readers.

LOCKSLEY WINS THE ARCHERY CONTEST
(*See opposite page*)

46

THE ARCHERY CONTEST

By Sir Walter Scott

King Richard of England (Richard the Lion Heart) while away on a crusade, left his brother, Prince John, to govern. John attempted to make himself king, by the aid of Norman knights, whom the native Saxon-English hated. The archery contest was a competition between the two parties; for Locksley was really Robin Hood, and a follower of Richard.

"NOW, Locksley," said Prince John to the bold yeoman with a bitter smile, "wilt thou try conclusions with Hubert or wilt thou yield up bow, baldric, and quiver to the provost of the sports?"

5 "Sith it be no better," said Locksley, "I am content to try my fortune; on condition that when I have shot two shafts at yonder mark of Hubert's, he shall be bound to shoot one at that which I shall propose."

"That is but fair," answered Prince John, "and it 10 shall not be refused thee. If thou dost beat this braggart, Hubert, I will fill the bugle with silver pennies for thee."

"A man can do but his best," answered Hubert; "but my grandsire drew a good long bow at Hastings, and I trust not to dishonor his memory."

15 The former target was now removed and a fresh one of the same size placed in its room. Hubert, who as victor in the first trial of skill had the right to shoot first, took his aim with great deliberation, long measuring the distance with his eye, while he held in his hand his bended bow 20 with the arrow placed on the string. At length he made a

47

step forward, and raising the bow at the full stretch of his left arm till the center, or grasping place, was nigh level with his face, he drew his bowstring to his ear. The arrow whistled through the air and lighted within the inner ring of the target but not exactly in the center. 5

"You have not allowed for the wind, Hubert," said his antagonist, bending his bow, "or that had been a better shot."

So saying, and without showing the least anxiety to pause upon his aim, Locksley stepped to the appointed 10 station and shot his arrow as carelessly in appearance as if he had not even looked at the mark. He was speaking almost at the instant that the shaft left the bowstring, yet it lighted in the target two inches nearer to the white spot which marked the center than that of Hubert. 15

"Hubert," said Prince John, "an thou suffer that runagate knave to overcome thee thou art worthy of the gallows!"

Hubert had but one set speech for all occasions. "An Your Highness were to hang me," he said, "a man can but do his best. Nevertheless, my grandsire drew a good 20 bow —"

"Never mind thy grandsire!" interrupted John, "shoot, knave, and shoot thy best, or it shall be the worse for thee!"

Thus exhorted Hubert resumed his place; and not neglecting the caution which he had received from his 25 adversary, he made the necessary allowance for a very light air of wind which had just arisen, and shot so success-fully that his arrow alighted in the very center of the target.

"A Hubert! a Hubert!" shouted the populace, more 30 interested in a known person than in a stranger. "In the clout — in the clout! a Hubert forever!"

"Thou canst not mend that shot, Locksley," said the prince with an insulting smile.

"I will notch his shaft for him, however," replied Locksley; and letting fly his arrow with a little more precaution than before, it lighted right upon that of his competitor, which it split to shivers. The people who stood around were so astonished at his wonderful dexterity that they could not even give vent to their surprise in their usual clamor.

"This must be no man of flesh and blood," whispered the yeomen to each other. "Such archery was never seen since a bow was first bent in Britain."

"And now," said Locksley, "I will crave Your Grace's permission to plant such a mark as is used in the north country, and welcome every brave yeoman who shall try a shot at it to win a smile from the bonny lass he loves best."

He then turned to leave the lists. "Let your guards attend me," he said, "if you please — I go but to cut a rod from the next willow bush."

Prince John made a signal that some attendants should follow him in case of his escape, but the cry of "Shame! shame!" which burst from the multitude induced him to alter his ungenerous purpose.

Locksley returned almost instantly with a willow wand about six feet in length, perfectly straight, and rather thicker than a man's thumb. He began to peel this with great composure, observing at the same time that to ask a good woodsman to shoot at a target so broad as had hitherto been used was to put shame upon his skill. For his own part, he said, and in the land where he was bred, men would as soon take for their mark King Arthur's Round Table, which held sixty knights around it.

"A child of seven years old," he said, "might hit yonder target with a headless shaft; but," added he, walking deliberately to the other end of the lists and sticking the willow wand upright in the ground, "he that hits that rod at fivescore yards — I call him an archer fit to bear both 5 bow and quiver before a king, an it were the stout King Richard himself."

"My grandsire," said Hubert, "drew a good bow at the battle of Hastings and never shot at such a mark in his life — and neither will I. If this yeoman can cleave that 10 rod I give him the bucklers; a man can but do his best, and I will not shoot where I am sure to miss. I might as well shoot at the edge of our parson's whittle, or at a wheat straw, or at a sunbeam, as at a twinkling white streak which I can hardly see." 15

"Cowardly dog!" said Prince John. "Sirrah Locksley, do thou shoot; but if thou hittest such a mark I will say thou art the first man ever did so. Howe'er it be, thou shalt not crow over us with a mere show of superior skill."

"I will do my best, as Hubert says," answered Locksley; 20 "no man can do more."

So saying he again bent his bow, but on the present occasion looked with attention to his weapon and changed the string, which he thought was no longer truly round, having been a little frayed by the two former shots. He 25 then took aim with some deliberation and the multitude awaited the event in breathless silence. The archer vindicated their opinion of his skill; his arrow split the willow rod against which it was aimed. A jubilee of acclamation followed, and even Prince John, in admiration of Locks- 30 ley's skill, lost for an instant his dislike to his person.

"These twenty nobles," he said, "which with the bugle

thou hast fairly won, are thine own; we will make them fifty if thou wilt take livery and service with us as a yeoman of our bodyguard and be near to our person. For never did so strong a hand bend a bow nor so true an eye direct a shaft."

"Pardon me, noble prince," said Locksley, "but I have vowed that if ever I take service it shall be with your royal brother, King Richard. These twenty nobles I leave to Hubert, who has this day drawn as brave a bow as his grandsire did at Hastings. Had his modesty not refused the trial he would have hit the wand as well as I." Hubert shook his head as he received with reluctance the bounty of the stranger, and Locksley, anxious to escape further observation, mixed with the crowd and was seen no more.

— *Ivanhoe.*

1. Only the complete tale of *Ivanhoe* can give you the details of Locksley's further adventures in behalf of King Richard. You will be interested, however, to know that his valiant support later saved the life of the king, and thus caused Prince John's overthrow.

2. Why do you wish Locksley to win in the contest? At what point in the story do you first feel sure he will win? Does John suspect who Locksley is?

3. What kind of man does John show himself to be? Locksley?

4. The name of Sir Walter Scott (1771–1832) is one of the best known and loved in English literature. His *Waverley* novels, of which *Ivanhoe* is one, afford the finest pictures of the age of chivalry that have ever been painted by pen. If you are not acquainted with them, a great pleasure lies ahead of you.

MY FIGHT WITH HANDS

By Robert Louis Stevenson

An island where pirates' treasure was buried had been found. But half the crew of the vessel in search were really pirates, and they rose up in mutiny. The chief battle ground of the two parties was the island; but young Jim Hawkins attempted single-handed to recover the drifting ship from pirate control. A fight for its possession, between the lad and a pirate, is the story that follows.

THE excitement of these last maneuvers had somewhat interfered with the watch I had kept hitherto, sharply enough, upon the coxswain. Even then I was still so much interested, waiting for the ship to touch, that I had quite forgot the peril that hung over my head, and stood craning over the starboard bulwarks and watching the ripples spreading wide before the bows. I might have fallen without a struggle for my life, had not a sudden disquietude seized upon me, and made me turn my head. Perhaps I had heard a creak, or seen his shadow moving with the tail of my eye; perhaps it was an instinct like a cat's; but, sure enough, when I looked round, there was Hands, already halfway towards me, with the dirk in his right hand.

We must both have cried out aloud when our eyes met; but while mine was the shrill cry of terror, his was a roar of fury like a charging bull's. At the same instant he threw himself forward, and I leaped sideways towards the bows. As I did so, I left hold of the tiller, which sprang sharp to leeward; and I think this saved my life, for it struck Hands across the chest, and stopped him, for the moment, dead.

Before he could recover, I was safe out of the corner where he had me trapped, with all the deck to dodge about. Just forward of the mainmast I stopped, drew a pistol from my pocket, took a cool aim, though he had already turned and was once more coming directly after me, and drew the trigger. The hammer fell, but there followed neither flash nor sound; the priming was useless with sea water. I cursed myself for my neglect. Why had not I, long before, reprimed and reloaded my only weapons? Then I should not have been, as now, a mere fleeing sheep before this butcher.

Wounded as he was, it was wonderful how fast he could move, his grizzled hair tumbling over his face, and his face itself as red as a red ensign with his haste and fury. I had no time to try my other pistol, nor, indeed, much inclination, for I was sure it would be useless. One thing I saw plainly; I must not simply retreat before him, or he would speedily hold me boxed into the bows, as a moment since he had so nearly boxed me in the stern. Once so caught, and nine or ten inches of the blood-stained dirk would be my last experience on this side of eternity. I placed my palms against the mainmast, which was of a goodish bigness, and waited, every nerve upon the stretch.

Seeing that I meant to dodge, he also paused; and a moment or two passed in feints on his part, and corresponding movements upon mine. It was such a game as I had often played at home about the rocks of Black Hill Cove; but never before, you may be sure, with such a wildly beating heart as now. Still, as I say, it was a boy's game, and I thought I could hold my own at it, against an elderly seaman with a wounded thigh. Indeed, my courage had begun to rise so high, that I allowed myself a few darting

thoughts on what would be the end of the affair; and while
I saw certainly that I could spin it out for long, I saw no
hope of any ultimate escape.

Well, while things stood thus, suddenly the *Hispaniola*
struck, staggered, ground for an instant in the sand, and
then, swift as a blow, canted over to the port side, till the
deck stood at an angle of forty-five degrees, and about a
puncheon of water splashed into the scupper holes, and
lay in a pool, between the deck and bulwark.

We were both of us capsized in a second, and both of us
rolled, almost together, into the scuppers; the dead red-
cap, with his arms still spread out, tumbling stiffly after
us. So near were we, indeed, that my head came against
the coxswain's foot with a crack that made my teeth rattle.
Blow and all, I was the first afoot again; for Hands had
got involved with the dead body. The sudden canting of
the ship had made the deck no place for running on; I
had to find some new way of escape, and that upon the
instant, for my foe was almost touching me. Quick as
thought I sprang into the mizzen shrouds, rattled up hand
over hand, and did not draw a breath till I was seated on
the crosstrees.

I had been saved by being prompt; the dirk had struck
not half a foot below me, as I pursued my upward flight;
and there stood Israel Hands with his mouth open and his
face upturned to mine, a perfect statue of surprise and
disappointment.

Now that I had a moment to myself, I lost no time in
changing the priming of my pistol, and then, having one
ready for service, and to make assurance doubly sure, I
proceeded to draw the load of the other, and recharge it
afresh from the beginning.

My new employment struck Hands all of a heap; he began to see the dice going against him; and after an obvious hesitation, he also hauled himself heavily into the shrouds, and, with the dirk in his teeth, began slowly and painfully to mount. It cost him no end of time and groans to haul his wounded leg behind him; and I had quietly finished my arrangements before he was much more than a third of the way up. Then, with a pistol in either hand, I addressed him.

"One more step, Mr. Hands," said I, "and I'll blow your brains out! Dead men don't bite, you know," I added, with a chuckle.

He stopped instantly. I could see by the working of his face that he was trying to think, and the process was so slow and laborious that, in my new-found security, I laughed aloud. At last, with a swallow or two, he spoke, his face still wearing the same expression of extreme perplexity. In order to speak he had to take the dagger from his mouth, but, in all else, he remained unmoved.

"Jim," says he, "I reckon we're fouled, you and me, and we'll have to sign articles. I'd have had you but for that there lurch: but I don't have no luck, not I; and I reckon I'll have to strike, which comes hard, you see, for a master mariner to a ship's younker like you, Jim."

I was drinking in his words, and smiling away, as conceited as a cock upon a wall, when, all in a breath, back went his right hand over his shoulder. Something sang like an arrow through the air. I felt a blow and then a sharp pang, and there I was pinned by the shoulder to the mast. In the horrid pain and surprise of the moment — I scarce can say it was by my own volition, and I am sure it was without a conscious aim — both my pistols went off, and both escaped out of my hands. They did not fall alone; with a choked cry, the coxswain loosed his grasp upon the shrouds, and plunged head first into the water.

— Treasure Island.

1. The "I" of the story was only a boy. While the crew were fighting ashore with the pirates, he undertook to save the ship, which was adrift with two drunken pirates aboard. He rowed out to it in time to see Hands slay his fellow pirate in a brawl. Then the lad plays his part.

2. Prove from the selection that the hero is only a boy. How do you know that there had been a fight previously on the ship?

3. What is the climax of the story? What does the boy do or fail to do that keeps your interest held?

4. *Treasure Island* is a book worthy of a place on your library shelves. Robert Louis Stevenson (1850–1894) wrote other books, too, with which you should become acquainted. *The Master of Ballantrae* and *Kidnapped* are fine tales of adventure.

POCAHONTAS

By WILLIAM MAKEPEACE THACKERAY

WEARIED arm and broken sword
    Wage in vain the desperate fight;
Round him press a countless horde;
    He is but a single knight.
Hark! A cry of triumph shrill   5
    Through the wilderness resounds,
    As with twenty bleeding wounds,
Sinks the warrior, fighting still.

Now they heap the fatal pyre,
　　And the torch of death they light;
Ah! 'tis hard to die of fire!
　　Who will shield the captive knight?
5　Round the stake, with fiendish cry,
　　Wheel and dance the savage crowd;
　　Cold the victim's mien and proud,
And his breast is bared to die.

Who will shield the fearless heart?
10　　Who avert the murderous blade?
From the throng, with sudden start,
　　See, there springs an Indian maid.
Quick she stands before the knight —
　　"Loose the chain, unbind the ring,
15　　I am daughter of the king,
And I claim the Indian right!"

Dauntlessly aside she flings
　　Lifted ax and thirsty knife;
Fondly to his heart she clings
20　　And her bosom guards his life!
In the woods of Powhatan,
　　Still 'tis told by Indian fires,
　　How a daughter of their sires
Saved the captive Englishman.

1. Who was "the captive Englishman"? How is he connected with early American history?

2. Read aloud the lines that tell how he was captured. What did the Indians intend to do with him?

3. You probably know from history that Pocahontas married John Rolfe, and that there are many descendants of the family now living.

THE SUNKEN TREASURE

By Nathaniel Hawthorne

SIR WILLIAM PHIPS was a poor man's son who was born in the province of Maine, where he used to tend sheep upon the hills in his boyhood and youth. Until he had grown to be a man, he did not even know how to read and write. Tired of tending sheep, he next apprenticed 5 himself to a ship carpenter and spent about four years in hewing the crooked limbs of oak trees into knees for vessels.

In 1673, when he was twenty-two years old, he came to Boston and soon afterwards was married to a widow lady, who had property enough to set him up in business. It was 10 not long, however, before he lost all the money that he had acquired by his marriage and became a poor man again. Still he was not discouraged. He often told his wife that some time or other he should be very rich and would build a "fair brick house" in the Green Lane of Boston. 15

Several years passed away and William Phips had not yet gained the riches which he promised to himself. During this time he had begun to follow the sea for a living. In the year 1684 he happened to hear of a Spanish ship which had been cast away near the Bahama Islands and 20 which was supposed to contain a great deal of gold and silver. Phips went to the place in a small vessel, hoping that he should be able to recover some of the treasure from the wreck. He did not succeed, however, in fishing up gold and silver enough to pay the expenses of his voyage. 25

But before he returned he was told of another Spanish

ship, or galleon, which had been cast away near Porto de la Plata.   She had now lain as much as fifty years beneath the waves.   This old ship had been laden with immense wealth, and hitherto nobody had thought of the possibility 5 of recovering any part of it from the deep sea which was rolling and tossing it about.   But though it was now an old story and the most aged people had almost forgotten that such a vessel had been wrecked, William Phips resolved that the sunken treasure should again be brought to 10 light.

He went to London and obtained admittance to King James, who had not yet been driven from his throne.   He told the king of the vast wealth that was lying at the bottom of the sea.   King James listened with attention and 15 thought this a fine opportunity to fill his treasury with Spanish gold.   He appointed William Phips to be captain of a vessel called the *Rose Algier*, carrying eighteen guns and ninety-five men.   So now he was Captain Phips of the English navy.

20   Captain Phips sailed from England in the *Rose Algier* and cruised for nearly two years in the West Indies, endeavoring to find the wreck of the Spanish ship.   But the sea is so wide and deep that it is no easy matter to discover the exact spot where a sunken vessel lies.   The prospect 25 of success seemed very small, and most people would have thought that Captain Phips was as far from having money enough to build a "fair brick house" as he was while he tended sheep.

The seamen of the *Rose Algier* became discouraged and 30 gave up all hope of making their fortunes by discovering the Spanish wreck.   They wanted to compel Captain Phips to turn pirate.   There was a much better prospect, they thought, of growing rich by plundering vessels which still sailed in the sea than by seeking for a ship that had lain beneath the waves full half a century.　They broke out in open mutiny, but were finally mastered by Phips and compelled to obey his orders.　It would have been danger- 5 ous, however, to continue much longer at sea with such a crew of mutinous sailors; and besides, the *Rose Algier* was leaky and unseaworthy.　So Captain Phips judged it best to return to England.

Before leaving the West Indies he met with a Spaniard, 10 an old man, who remembered the wreck of the Spanish ship and gave him directions how to find the very spot.　It was on a reef of rocks, a few leagues from Porto de la Plata.

On his arrival in England, therefore, Captain Phips 15 begged the king to let him have another vessel and send him back again to the West Indies.　But King James, who had probably expected that the *Rose Algier* would return laden with gold, refused to have anything more to do with the affair.　Phips might never have been able to 20 renew the search if the duke of Albemarle and some other noblemen had not lent their assistance.　They fitted out a ship and gave the command to Captain Phips.　He sailed from England and arrived safely at Porto de la Plata, where he took an adze and assisted his men to build a boat. 25

The boat was intended for the purpose of going closer to the reef of rocks than a large vessel could safely venture. When it was finished the captain sent several men in it to examine the spot where the Spanish ship was said to have been wrecked.　They were accompanied by some 30 Indians, who were skillful divers and could go down a great way into the depths of the sea.

The boat's crew proceeded to the reef of rocks and rowed round and round it a great many times. They gazed down into the water, which was so transparent that it seemed as if they could have seen the gold and silver at the bottom had there been any of those precious metals there. Nothing, however, could they see; nothing more valuable than a curious sea shrub which was growing beneath the water in a crevice of the reef of rocks. It flaunted to and fro with the swell and reflux of the waves and looked as bright and beautiful as if its leaves were gold.

"We won't go back empty handed," cried an English sailor; and then he spoke to one of the Indian divers. "Dive down and bring me that pretty sea shrub there. That's the only treasure we shall find."

Down plunged the diver, and soon rose dripping from the water, holding the sea shrub in his hand. But he had learned some news at the bottom of the sea.

"There are some ship's guns," said he, the moment he had drawn breath, "some great cannon, among the rocks near where the shrub was growing."

No sooner had he spoken than the English sailors knew that they had found the very spot where the Spanish galleon had been wrecked so many years before. The other Indian divers immediately plunged over the boat's side and swam headlong down, groping among the rocks and sunken cannon. In a few moments one of them rose above the water with a heavy lump of silver in his arms. The single lump was worth more than a thousand dollars. The sailors took it into the boat and then rowed back as speedily as they could, being in haste to inform Captain Phips of their good luck.

But confidently as the captain had hoped to find the Spanish wreck, yet, now that it was really found, the news seemed too good to be true. He could not believe it till the sailors showed him the lump of silver.

"Thanks be to God!" then cries Captain Phips. "We shall every man of us make our fortunes!"

Hereupon the captain and all the crew set to work with iron rakes and great hooks and lines, fishing for gold and silver at the bottom of the sea. Up came the treasure in abundance. Now they beheld a table of solid silver, once the property of an old Spanish grandee. Now they found a sacramental vessel which had been destined as a gift to some favored church. Now they drew up a golden cup, fit for the king of Spain to drink his wine out of. Perhaps the bony hand of its former owner had been grasping the precious cup and was drawn up along with it. Now their rakes or fishing lines were loaded with masses of silver bullion. There were also precious stones among the treasure, glittering and sparkling so that it is a wonder how their radiance could have been concealed.

After a day or two they lighted on another part of the wreck, where they found many bags of silver dollars. But nobody could have guessed that these were moneybags. By remaining so long in the salt water they had become covered over with a crust which had the appearance of stone, so that it was necessary to break them in pieces with hammers and axes. When this was done, a stream of silver dollars gushed over the deck of the vessel.

The whole value of the recovered treasure, plate, bullion, precious stones, and all, was estimated at more than two millions of dollars. It was dangerous even to look at such a vast amount of wealth. A sea captain who had assisted Phips in the enterprise utterly lost his reason at the sight of it.

Captain Phips and his men continued to fish up plate, bullion, and dollars, as plentifully as ever, till their provisions grew short. Then, as they could not feed upon gold and silver any more than old King Midas could, they found it necessary to go in search of better sustenance. Phips resolved to return to England. He arrived there in 1687 and was received with great joy by the duke of Albemarle and other English lords who had fitted out the vessel. Well they might rejoice; for they took by far the greater part of the treasure to themselves.

The captain's share, however, was enough to make him comfortable for the rest of his days. It also enabled him to fulfill his promise to his wife, by building a "fair brick house" in the Green Lane of Boston. The duke of Albemarle sent Mrs. Phips a magnificent gold cup, worth at least five thousand dollars. Before Captain Phips left London, King James made him a knight; so that instead of the obscure ship carpenter who had formerly dwelt among them, the inhabitants of Boston welcomed him on his return as the rich and famous Sir William Phips.

— *Grandfather's Chair.*

1. Who is the author of this selection? What other of his writings have you read? What is the author's nationality? What is the nature of his writing — prose or poetry; novels or short stories?

2. What other story in this section has hidden treasure as its goal?

3. Relate Captain Phips' life under the following heads: his early life; his early manhood; his chief adventure. When and where did he live?

4. Do you consider this adventure as exciting as some of the others in this section? Give reasons for your answer.

CHASED BY WOLVES

DURING the winter of 1844, being in the northern part of Maine, I had much leisure for the sports of a new country. To none was I more passionately addicted than to skating. The sequestered lakes, frozen by intense cold, offered a wide plain to the lovers of this pastime. Often would I bind on my skates and glide away up the glittering river, threading every mazy streamlet that flowed on toward the parent ocean and feeling every pulse bound with the joyous exercise.

It was during one of these excursions that an adventure befell me that I can rarely think upon, even now, without a certain thrill. I had left a friend's house one evening, just before dusk, with the intention of skating a short distance up the noble Kennebec, which, under its icy crust, flowed directly before the door. The air was clear, calm, and bracing. The full moon silvered the lofty pines and the stars twinkled with rare brilliancy from their dark-blue depths. It was a perfect night — one that challenged a skater to go on and on.

I had gone up the river nearly two miles, when coming to a little stream which emptied into a larger I turned in to explore its course. Fir and hemlock trees of a century's growth met overhead and formed an evergreen archway radiant with frostwork.

All was dark within; but I was young and fearless and as I peered into the unbroken forest I laughed in very joyousness! My wild hurrah rang through the woods and

I stood listening to the echo that reverberated again and again until all was hushed. Occasionally from some tall oak a night bird would flap its wings. I watched the owls as they fluttered by and I held my breath to listen to their distant hooting.

All of a sudden a sound arose which seemed to proceed from the very ice beneath my feet. It was low and tremulous at first, and ended in a long yell. I was appalled. Coming on the ear amid such an unbroken solitude, it sounded like a blast from an infernal trumpet. Presently I heard the twigs on the shore snap as if from the tread of some animal.

The blood rushed to my forehead with a bound that made my skin burn, but I felt a strange relief that I had to contend with things of earthly and not spiritual mold. My energies returned. The moon shone through the opening by which I had entered the forest, and considering this the best direction for escape, I shot towards it like an arrow.

The opening was hardly a hundred yards distant and the swallow could not have skimmed them more swiftly; yet as I turned my eyes to the shore I could see two dark objects dashing through the underbrush at a pace nearly double my own. By their great speed and the short yells which they gave, I knew at once that they were of the much-dreaded species known as the gray wolf.

The untamable fierceness and untiring strength of this animal

> "With its long gallop that can tire
> The hound's deep hate, the hunter's fire,"

render it an object of dread to benighted travelers. The bushes that skirted the shore now seemed to rush by me with the velocity of light as I dashed madly onward. The outlet was nearly gained; one second more and I would be comparatively safe; but my pursuers suddenly appeared on the bank directly above me, which rose to the height of some ten feet.

There was no time for thought; I bent my head and darted wildly forward. The wolves sprang, but miscalculating my speed, sprang behind, while their intended prey glided out upon the river. Instinct turned me toward home. How my skates made the light icy mist spin from the glassy surface! The fierce howl of my pursuers again rang in my ears. I did not look back; I thought of the dear ones awaiting my return and I put in play every faculty of mind and body for my escape. I was perfectly at home on the ice and many were the days I had spent on my skates.

Every half minute an alternate yelp from my pursuers told me they were close at my heels. Nearer and nearer they came; I could hear them pant. I strained every muscle in my frame to quicken my speed. Still I could hear close behind me the pattering of feet, when an involuntary motion on my part turned me out of my course. The wolves, unable to stop and as unable to turn, slipped and fell, sliding on far ahead, their tongues lolling out, their white tushes gleaming from their red mouths, their dark, shaggy breasts flecked with foam; and as they slid on, they howled with redoubled rage.

The thought occurred to me that by thus turning aside whenever they came too near, I could avoid them; for from the peculiar formation of their feet they cannot run on ice except in a straight line. I immediately acted on plan. The wolves, having regained their feet, sprang

directly towards me. The race was renewed for twenty
yards up the stream; they were already close on my back
when I glided round and dashed past them. A fierce howl
greeted my evolution, and the wolves slipped upon their
5 haunches and again slid onward, presenting a perfect
picture of baffled, bloodthirsty rage.

Thus I gained at each turning nearly a hundred yards.
This was repeated two or three times, the wolves getting
more excited every moment, until, coming opposite the
10 house, a couple of staghounds, aroused by the noise,
bayed furiously from their kennels. Quickly taking the
hint the wolves stopped in their mad career, turned
skulkingly, and fled. I watched them till their dusky forms
disappeared over a neighboring hill. Then, taking off my
15 skates, I wended my way to the house, grateful to Provi-
dence for my escape and determined never to trust myself
again, if I could help it, within the reach of a gray wolf.

1. Relate in order the events of this story. Where is the highest
point of interest? By what trick did the man finally make his escape?

2. What other skating story do you know? What other stories
of adventure with wolves have you heard?

ATTACKED BY A SUBMARINE

By James Baldwin and W. W. Livengood

"STRANGE craft on starboard!"
It was Spar who had made the discovery. A chill
went up my spine. The captain took a hurried look
through the glasses and gave some sudden orders to the
5 engine room. He called me to his side.

"Looks like trouble," he remarked. "It may not be a U-boat, but we take no chances."

The *Argo* came clean around till her stern pointed in danger's direction. Then we zigzagged ahead as fast as our remaining engines could carry.

"Torpedo on port side!" Macy had come in for honors. The white wake unrolled past us several yards away.

No question about the stranger now. Our wireless shot the message of the attack far and wide. Then our stern gun spoke. The shell fell short. The enemy replied in kind, with the same result. Another and another shot followed. The exchange of compliments was getting lively. But the shells as yet were only stirring up splashes of water between us.

"It looks like a dispute that will be settled by whoever gets in the first shot," observed the captain to me on the bridge. "If he gets us through the hull we will be kindling wood in a second!"

Meanwhile our wireless operator had brought a little encouragement. The captain of the destroyer convoy ahead had picked up our SOS. His reply was, "Hold out. Keep wiring position. Destroyer coming."

That was hopeful, but his help would probably reach us after our fate had been settled one way or the other.

"One thing's sure, Tom," Captain Folger commented. "This ship doesn't surrender!"

"I'm with you on that," I said with emphasis.

But the enemy was gaining on us. He tried to maneuver to get us with a torpedo broadside on, but we changed our course as often as he changed his; and the stern of a ship offers only a small target a few thousand yards away. Suddenly one of his shells sprayed us with water as it splashed harmlessly alongside. Our gunners tried hard to send a shot home, but we had no luck, although we were peppering the water around the U-boat.

In the midst of the excitement I caught a glimpse of a little scene aft that strangely quieted my pulse. Hawkins and Macy were both busy filling their pipes from Hawkins's tobacco pouch, and quietly watching the effect of our shots. I would give much to know their comments. At any rate the two old skippers were as cool as if they were watching a whale instead of a submarine.

The next moment there was a crash, and fragments of shell and flying splinters whirred through the air. I suddenly became dizzy, and everything went black. I could have been down only a few seconds; that I discovered at once on coming to my senses. But it was time enough for a dream to flit through my brain. I thought I was back on the porch at home, cuddled up in a big rocking chair, and Mother was singing an old sea ballad she used to sing. The refrain ran, "Oh, the lowlands low!" in a sort of dying fall.

Blood was running down my right cheek when I came to my senses. Captain Folger was stretched on the bridge, face up, with a ghastly cut on his forehead and a stony stare in his half-opened eyes. I knew without touching his pulse that it was all over with him. A glance aft revealed another sad story. The gun crew was scattered, with three of the men down on deck. Macy was stooping over Hawkins. And our stern gun yawed in its fittings. The enemy had registered an awful hit. He had drawn first blood; but we were still afloat with a forward gun intact.

I was half maddened by the blood around me, but my head was never clearer. The ship's doctor was already kneeling by the captain, and shaking his head to me. I nodded my understanding. The responsibility of what was to follow now rested on my shoulders.

I gave a drastic order and the great ship slowly started to wheel in her course. It looked like certain destruction to bring our broadside to the enemy but it was our last chance. We must bring our forward gun to bear. The gun crew was standing ready and impatient to avenge their fallen comrades.

Then a commotion rose from the hatchway leading up from the engine room. I saw Macy drop Hawkins's lifeless body and pick up a heavy fragment of timber dislodged by the bursting shell. The engine-room force had run amuck, panicky with fear! They were led by the East Indian I had signed from Newport. He had a big pistol in his hand.

Macy let drive at him with his shaft, but it went over the rebel leader's head, downing the man behind him. Instantly the Indian fired, and Macy crumpled up on deck and sat down with his head in his hands.

I have no idea how I got off the bridge so quickly, but scarcely had Macy fallen when I was facing the cowards, and my automatic pistol cut loose. The East Indian let out a yell, made a wild run for the scuppers, and pitched headlong overboard. Spar got the next man with his bare fists, and the remainder took to the hatchway. They had come to their senses. In fairness, let me say that there were only half a dozen men on the rampage, all foreigners. The rest, including my college men, had stuck hard to their posts. Spar followed the rebels with my gun leveled; and there was no more trouble from that direction. The mutiny had been quelled.

By this time our ship was coming round past the broadside. The enemy had been aware of our troubles. He had evidently observed the effect of his shell fire and thought he had us groggy when we tacked. But between his speed forward and our change of course his succeeding shells were now dropping beyond us. Why he did not give us a torpedo on the broadside I do not know, unless he felt so sure of us he thought to save this costly weapon.

I was on the bridge again, after ordering the removal of Captain Folger, Hawkins, and Macy to the captain's apartments for any medical attention that might be offered. Likewise the wounded and dead of the gun crew were borne to my own rooms.

By this time our forward gun had come into play, and I bore the ship down directly on the submarine. Our second shot was a direct hit. Thank God, our luck had changed! A yell went up from the gun crew as the periscope and part of the enemy's upper works went overboard. That evened matters somewhat. At any rate he could not dive now and escape; it was to be a fight to the finish — somebody's finish!

Our fifth shot put his forward gun out of commission. The tide had turned.

We were closing in on him, and the enemy realized his danger. My intention was to ram him if we failed to get a shot home; so I rang the engine room for all possible speed ahead. But I was still aware of the submarine's fangs. His stern gun and his torpedo tubes were yet active. A white trail curled past us uncomfortably close. He was not sparing torpedoes now. But we were closing in, not three hundred yards from him. Twenty seconds more and one of us would be down — maybe both.

A shot took off the other section of his scant upper works. One of his cleaned out our wireless.

We were all but on him now, too close to bring our gun to bear. Our last shot had either seriously crippled the enemy or thrown terror into his crew. "Kamerad!" "Kamerad!" came huskily from a score of throats; but their brotherly petition came too late. Before I could sheer the *Argo* off we cut through the submarine diagonally. Her shell crumpled under the impact of our weight and speed, and there was scarcely a tremor on the bridge of our stanch ship.

— *Sailing the Seas.*

1. The young man who relates this story was first mate on a vessel laden with munitions and bound for France, during the World War. Because of engine trouble the *Argo* had to drop out of the convoy of ships of which she was a member. Then the German submarine attacked.

2. What in the story suggests its recency?

I FIND A FOOTPRINT

By Daniel Defoe

This section of *Robinson Crusoe* relates a thrilling experience he had, long after his landing on the island.

YOU are to understand that now I had, as I may call it, two plantations in the island; one, my little fortification or tent with the wall about it, under the rock, with the cave behind me, which by this time I had enlarged into several apartments or caves, one within another. One of these, which was the driest and largest and had a door out beyond my wall or fortification — that is to say, beyond where my wall joined to the rock — was all filled up with large earthen pots and with fourteen or fifteen great baskets which would hold five or six bushels each, 5 where I laid up my stores of provision, especially my corn — some in the ear, cut off short from the straw, and the other rubbed out with my hand.

As for my wall, made as before with long stakes or piles, those piles grew all like trees and were by this time grown 10 so big and spread so very much, that there was not the least appearance to anyone's view of any habitation behind them.

Near this dwelling of mine, but a little farther within the land and upon lower ground, lay my two pieces of 15 cornland, which I kept duly cultivated and sowed and which duly yielded me their harvest in its season; and whenever I had occasion for more corn, I had more land adjoining, as fit as that.

Besides this, I had my country seat, and I had now a 20 tolerable plantation there also; for first, I had my little bower, as I called it, which I kept in repair; that is to say, I kept the hedge which circled it in, constantly fitted up to its usual height, the ladder standing always in the inside; I kept the trees, which at first were no more than stakes 25 but were now grown very firm and tall, always cut, so that they might spread and grow thick and wild and make the more agreeable shade — which they did effectually, to my mind.

In the middle of this I had my tent always standing, being 30 a piece of a sail spread over poles set up for that purpose, and which never wanted any repair or renewing; and under this I had made me a couch with the skins of

creatures I had killed, and with other soft things, and a
blanket laid on them such as belonged to our sea bedding
which I had saved, and a great watch coat to cover me;
and here, whenever I had occasion to be absent from my
seat, I took up my country habitation.   5

Adjoining to this I had my inclosures for my cattle,
that is to say, my goats; and as I had taken an incon-
ceivable deal of pains to fence and inclose this ground, so
I was so uneasy to see it kept entire, lest the goats should
break through, that I never left off till with infinite labor 10
I had stuck the outside of the hedge so full of small stakes,
and so near to one another, that it was rather a pale than
a hedge and there was scarce room to put a hand through
between them, which afterwards, when those stakes grew
(as they all did in the next rainy season), made the inclosure 15
strong like a wall — indeed stronger than any wall. This
will testify for me that I was not idle and that I spared
no pains to bring to pass whatever appeared necessary for
my comfortable support.

In this place also I had my grapes growing, which I 20
principally depended on for my winter store of raisins and
which I never failed to preserve very carefully as the best
and most agreeable dainty of my whole diet; and indeed
they were not agreeable only, but medicinal, wholesome,
nourishing, and refreshing to the last degree.   25

As this was also about halfway between my other
habitation and the place where I had laid up my boat, I
generally stayed and lay here in my way thither; for I
used frequently to visit my boat and I kept all things about
or belonging to her in very good order; sometimes I went 30
out in her to divert myself, but no more hazardous voyages
would I go, scarcely ever above a stone's cast or two

from the shore, I was so apprehensive of being hurried out of my knowledge again by the currents or winds or any other accident. But now I come to a new scene of my life.

It happened one day, about noon, going towards my boat, I was exceedingly surprised with the print of a man's naked foot on the shore, which was very plain to be seen on the sand. I stood like one thunderstruck or as if I had seen an apparition; I listened, I looked round me, I could hear nothing nor see anything; I went up the shore and down the shore, but it was all one, I could see no other impression but that one. I went to it again to see if there were any more and to observe if it might not be my fancy; but there was no room for that, for there was exactly the print of a foot — toes, heel, and every part of a foot; how it came thither I knew not nor could in the least imagine.

But after innumerable fluttering thoughts, like a man perfectly confused and out of myself, I came home to my fortification, not feeling, as we say, the ground I went on, but terrified to the last degree, looking behind me at every two or three steps, mistaking every bush and tree, and fancying every stump at a distance to be a man.

When I came to my castle (for so I think I called it ever after this) I fled into it like one pursued; whether I went over by the ladder, as first contrived, or went in at the hole in the rock which I had called a door, I cannot remember; no, nor could I remember the next morning; for never frightened hare fled to cover, or fox to earth, with more terror of mind than I to this retreat.

I slept none that night; the farther I was from the occasion of my fright the greater my apprehensions were; which is something contrary to the nature of such things and especially to the usual practice of all creatures in fear; but I was so embarrassed with my own frightful ideas of the thing, that I formed nothing but dismal imaginations to myself, even though I was now a great way off it. Sometimes I fancied it must be the devil. For how should any other thing in human shape come into the place? Where was the vessel that brought them? What marks were there of any other footsteps? And how was it possible men should come there? Unless, indeed, savages from the mainland had come to the shores of my island!

While these reflections were rolling in my mind I was very thankful in my thoughts that I was so happy as not to be thereabouts at that time or that they did not see my boat, by which they would have concluded that some inhabitants had been in the place and perhaps have searched farther for me. Then terrible thoughts racked my imagination about their having found out my boat and that there were people here; and that, if so, I should certainly have them come again in greater numbers and devour me; that if it should happen that they should not find me, yet they would find my inclosure, destroy all my corn, and carry away all my flock of tame goats, and I should perish at last for mere want.

In the middle of these reflections it came into my thoughts one day that all this might be a mere chimera of my own, and that this foot might be the print of my own foot when I came on shore from my boat. This cheered me up a little.

Heartening myself therefore with the belief that this was nothing but the print of one of my own feet, I began to go abroad again and went to my country house to milk my flock; but to see with what fear I went forward, how often

I looked behind me, how I was ready every now and then to lay down my basket and run for my life, it would have made anyone think I was haunted with an evil conscience or that I had been lately most terribly frightened; and so indeed
5 I had.

However, I went down thus two or three days, and having seen nothing I began to be a little bolder and to think there was really nothing in it but my own imagination; but I could not persuade myself fully of this till I should go
10 down to the shore again, and see this print of a foot, and measure it by my own, and see if there was any similitude or fitness, that I might be assured it was my own foot. But when I came to the place, first, it appeared evidently to me that when I laid up my boat I could not possibly be on
15 shore anywhere thereabout. Secondly, when I came to measure the mark with my own foot I found my foot not so large by a great deal; both these things filled my head with new imaginations and gave me the vapors again to the highest degree, so that I shook with cold like one in an
20 ague; and I went home again, filled with the belief that some man or men had been on shore there; or, in short, that the island was inhabited and I might be surprised before I was aware; and what course to take for my security I knew not.

— *Robinson Crusoe.*

1. What had Crusoe done to improve his island home? How many dwellings had he? Describe each.

2. What did he grow? What animals had he?

3. Under what circumstances did he make the discovery of the footprint? What effect did the discovery have upon him? Was his fear justified, or was he merely foolish? Discuss your answer.

CUSTER'S LAST CHARGE

By Frederick Whittaker

The Sioux Indians were on the warpath in 1876. General Custer with 1100 men followed them to Little Big Horn River. He divided his command, and attacked with 277 men. Three thousand Indians came against the little band. Every man of the 277 fell, including Custer and the entire command of the Seventh cavalry regiment.

D EAD! Is it possible? He, the bold rider,
    Custer, our hero, the first in the fight,
Charming the bullets of yore to fly wider,
    Far from our battle king's ringlets of light!
Dead, our young chieftain, and dead, all forsaken!   5
    No one to tell us the way of his fall!
Slain in the desert, and never to waken —
    Never, not even to victory's call.

Proud for his fame that last day that he met them!
    All the night long he had been on their track,   10
Scorning their traps and the men that had set them,
    Wild for a charge that should never give back.
There on the hilltop he halted and saw them —
    Lodges all loosened and ready to fly;
Hurrying scouts with the tidings to awe them,   15
    Told of his coming before he was nigh.

All the wide valley was full of their forces,
    Gathered to cover the lodges' retreat! —
Warriors running in haste to their horses,
    Thousands of enemies close to his feet!   20

Down in the valleys the ages had hollowed,
  There lay the Sitting Bull's camp for a prey!
Numbers! What recked he? What recked those who
    followed —
5   Men who had fought ten to one ere that day?

Out swept the squadrons, the fated three hundred,
  Into the battle line steady and full;
Then down the hillsides exultingly thundered,
  Into the hordes of the old Sitting Bull!
10 Wild Ogalallah, Arapahoe, Cheyenne,
  Wild Horse's braves, and the rest of their crew,
Shrank from that charge like a herd from a lion, —
  Then closed around, the grim horde of wild Sioux!

Right to their center he charged, and then facing —
15   Hark to those yells! and around them, oh, see!
Over the hilltops the Indians come racing,
  Coming as fast as the waves of the sea!
Red was the circle of fire around them;
  No hope of victory, no ray of light,
20 Shot through that terrible black cloud without them,
  Brooding in death over Custer's last fight.

Then did he blench? Did he die like a craven,
  Begging those torturing fiends for his life?
Was there a soldier who carried the Seven
25   Flinched like a coward or fled from the strife?
No, by the blood of our Custer, no quailing!
  There in the midst of the Indians they close,
Hemmed in by thousands, but ever assailing,
  Fighting like tigers, all bayed amid foes!

Thicker and thicker the bullets came singing;
  Down go the horses and riders and all;
Swiftly the warriors round them were ringing,
  Circling like buzzards awaiting their fall.
See the wild steeds of the mountain and prairie,   5
  Savage eyes gleaming from forests of mane;
Quivering lances with pennons so airy,
  War-painted warriors charging amain.

Backward, again and again, they were driven,
  Shrinking to close with the lost little band;   10
Never a cap that had worn the bright Seven
  Bowed till its wearer was dead on the strand.
Closer and closer the death circle growing,
  Ever the leader's voice, clarion clear,
Rang out his words of encouragement glowing,   15
  "We can but die once, boys, — we'll sell our lives dear!"

Dearly they sold them like Berserkers raging,
  Facing the death that encircled them round;
Death's bitter pangs by their vengeance assuaging,
  Marking their tracks by their dead on the ground.   20
Comrades, our children shall yet tell their story, —
  Custer's last charge on the old Sitting Bull;
And ages shall swear that the cup of his glory
  Needed but that death to render it full.

1. Who was in command of the Indians? How was Custer trapped? Describe the battle. What weapons were used? Explain the reference to the " seven," line 11, page 80.

2. What other famous fighters of Indians do you know? Tell a story of their struggles with the Red Men.

AT THE HELM

By James Fenimore Cooper

During the Revolutionary War, an American frigate was sent to a wild stretch of British coast. There, at the beginning of a storm, it took aboard a mysterious pilot, Mr. Gray.

D URING this time the sea was becoming more agitated and the violence of the wind was gradually increasing. Still the hardy and experienced mariners who directed the movements of the frigate held her to the course that 5 was necessary to their preservation, and still Griffith gave forth, when directed by their unknown pilot, those orders that turned her in the narrow channel where safety was alone to be found.

"Now is the time to watch her closely, Mr. Griffith," 10 cried the pilot. "Here we get the true tide and the real danger. Place the best quartermaster of your ship in those chains and let an officer stand by him and see that he gives us the right water."

"I will take that office on myself," said the captain. 15 "Pass a light into the weather main chains."

"Stand by your braces!" exclaimed the pilot, with startling quickness. "Heave away that lead!" While deep expectation pervaded the frigate, the piercing cry of the leadsman as he called, "By the mark seven" rose above 20 the tempest, crossed over the decks, and appeared to pass away to leeward, borne on the blast like the warnings of some water spirit.

"'Tis well," returned the pilot calmly; "try it again."

The short pause was succeeded by another cry, "And a half five."

"She shoals! she shoals!" exclaimed Griffith. "Keep her a good full!"   5

"Aye, you must hold the vessel in command now," said the pilot, with those cool tones that are most appalling in critical moments because they seem to denote most preparation and care.

The third call, "By the deep four," was followed by a 10 prompt direction from the stranger to tack.

Griffith seemed to emulate the coolness of the pilot in issuing the necessary orders to execute this maneuver.

The vessel rose slowly from the inclined position into which she had been forced by the tempest, and the sails 15 were shaking violently as if to release themselves from their confinement while the ship stemmed the billows, when the well-known voice of the sailing master was heard shouting from the forecastle:

"Breakers! breakers! dead ahead!"   20

This appalling sound seemed yet to be lingering about the ship when a second voice cried:

"Breakers on our lee bow!"

"We are in the bite of the shoals, Mr. Gray," cried the commander. "She loses her way; perhaps an anchor 25 might hold her."

"Clear away the best bower!" shouted Griffith through his trumpet.

"Hold on!" cried the pilot in a voice that reached the very heart of all who heard him. "Hold on everything!" 30

The young man turned fiercely to the daring stranger who thus defied the discipline of his vessel and demanded:

"Who is that dares to countermand my orders? Is it not enough that you run the ship into danger but you must interfere to keep her there? If another word —"

"Peace, Mr. Griffith," interrupted the captain, bending from the rigging, his gray locks blowing about in the wind and adding a look of wildness to the haggard care that he exhibited by the light of his lantern; "yield the trumpet to Mr. Gray; he alone can save us."

Griffith threw his speaking trumpet on the deck and as he walked proudly away muttered in bitterness of feeling:

"Then all is lost, indeed; and among the rest the foolish hopes with which I visited this coast."

There was, however, no time for reply; the ship had been rapidly running into the wind, and as the efforts of the crew were paralyzed by the contradictory orders they had heard, she gradually lost her way and in a few seconds all her sails were taken aback.

Before the crew understood their situation the pilot had applied the trumpet to his mouth, and in a voice that rose above the tempest he thundered forth his orders. Each command was given distinctly, and with a precision that showed him to be a master of his profession. The helm was kept fast and the head yards swung up heavily against the wind, and the vessel was soon whirling round on her heel with a retrograde movement.

Griffith was too much of a seaman not to perceive that the pilot had seized with a perception almost intuitive the only method that promised to extricate the vessel from her situation.

He was young, impetuous, and proud, but he was generous. Forgetting his resentment and his mortification he rushed forward among the men and by his presence and example added certainty to the experiment. The ship fell off slowly before the gale and bowed her yards nearly to the water as she felt the blast pouring its fury on her broadside, while the surly waves beat violently against her stern as if to reproach her at departing from her usual manner of moving.

When the ship had fallen off dead before the wind, her headsails were shaken, her after yards trimmed, and her helm shifted before she had time to run upon the danger that had threatened as well to leeward as to windward. The beautiful fabric, obedient to her government, threw her bows up gracefully toward the wind again, and as her sails were trimmed, moved out from among the dangerous shoals on which she had been embayed, as steadily and swiftly as she had approached them.

A moment of breathless astonishment succeeded the accomplishment of this nice maneuver, but there was no time for the usual expressions of surprise. The stranger still held the trumpet and continued to lift his voice amid the howlings of the blast, whenever prudence or skill required any change in the management of the ship. For an hour longer there was a fearful struggle for their preservation, the channel becoming at each step more complicated, and the shoals thickening around the mariners on every side. The lead was cast rapidly, and the quick eye of the pilot seemed to pierce the darkness with a keenness of vision that exceeded human power. It was apparent to all in the vessel that they were under the guidance of one who understood navigation thoroughly, and their exertions kept pace with their reviving confidence. Again and again the frigate appeared to be rushing blindly on the shoals, where the sea was covered with foam and where destruction would have been as sudden as it was certain, when the clear voice of the stranger was heard warning them of the danger and inciting them to their duty. "Now is the pinch," said the pilot, "and if the ship behaves well we are safe; but if otherwise, all we have done will be useless."

The veteran seaman whom he addressed left the chains at this portentous notice, and calling to his first lieutenant required of the stranger an explanation of his warning.

"See you yon light on the southern headland?" returned the pilot. "You may know it from a star near it by its sinking at times in the ocean. Now observe the hummock a little north of it, looking like a sea fog on the horizon; 'tis a hill far inland. If we keep that light open from the hill we shall do well; but if not we shall go to pieces."

"And gentlemen," he continued, "we must be prompt! We have but a mile to go and the ship appears to fly. That topsail is not enough to keep her up to the wind; we want both jib and mainsail."

"'Tis a perilous thing to loosen canvas in such a tempest," observed the doubtful captain.

"It must be done," returned the collected stranger; "we perish without it. See, the light already touches the edges of the hummock. The sea casts to leeward."

"It shall be done," cried Griffith, seizing the trumpet from the hand of the pilot.

The orders of the lieutenant were executed as soon as issued, and everything being ready, the enormous folds of the mainsail were trusted to the blast.

"She feels it! She springs her luff! Observe," cried the pilot, "the light opens from the hummock already. If she will only bear her canvas, we shall go clear."

A report like that of a cannon interrupted his exclamation and something resembling a white cloud was seen drifting before the wind from the head of the ship, till it was driven into the gloom far to leeward.

"'Tis the jib, blown from the boltropes," said the com- 5 mander of the frigate. "This is no time to spread light duck, but the mainsail may stand it yet."

"The sail would laugh at a tornado," returned the lieutenant, "but the mast springs like a piece of steel."

"Silence, all!" cried the pilot. "Now, gentlemen, we 10 shall know our fate. Let her luff — luff you can."

This warning effectually closed all discourse; and the hardy mariners, knowing that they had done all in the power of man to insure their safety, stood in breathless anxiety awaiting the result. The pilot silently proceeded 15 to the wheel, and with his own hands he undertook the steerage of the ship. Occasionally the fluttering of the sails would be heard, and when the looks of the startled seamen were turned to the wheel they beheld the stranger grasping the spokes, with his quick eye glancing from the 20 water to the canvas. At length the ship reached a point where she appeared to be rushing directly into the jaws of destruction, when suddenly her course was changed and her head receded rapidly from the wind. At the same in- stant the voice of the pilot was heard shouting: — 25

"Square away the yards! In mainsail!"

A general burst from the crew echoed, "Square away the yards!" and quick as thought the frigate was seen gliding along the channel before the wind. The eye had hardly time to dwell on the foam, which seemed like clouds 30 driving in the heavens, and directly the gallant vessel issued from her perils and rose and fell on the heavy sea.

The seamen were yet drawing long breaths and gazing about them like men recovering from a trance, when Griffith approached the man who had so successfully conducted them through their perils. The lieutenant grasped the hand of the other as he said:

"You have this night proved yourself a faithful pilot and such a seaman as the world cannot equal."

The pressure of the hand was warmly returned by the unknown mariner, who replied:

"I am no stranger to the seas, and I may yet find my grave in them. But you, too, have deceived me; you have acted nobly, young man." Saying this, he walked away toward the commander.

Griffith gazed after him a moment in surprise; but as his duty required his attention, other thoughts soon engaged his mind.

— *The Pilot*.

1. An adventure on the sea has a thrill lacking in an adventure on land. Why?

2. What is the situation of the ship when the unknown pilot takes command? What does he do that wins the confidence of the sailors? Was Griffith justified in getting angry at the changed command?

3. James Fenimore Cooper (1789-1851) is best known by his *Leatherstocking Tales* — stories of encounters with the Indians. But in *The Pilot* Cooper displays the knowledge of the sea which he got in the navy, and tells a good story besides. The book was written to prove that the author could write a sea story more accurate than Scott's *The Pirate*. The Mr. Gray is really Paul Jones of historic fame.

WANDERLUST

By Gerald Gould

BEYOND the East the sunrise, beyond the West the
    sea,
And East and West the wanderlust that will not let me be;
It works in me like madness, dear, to bid me say good-by!
For the seas call and the stars call, and oh, the call of the 5
    sky!

I know not where the white road runs, nor what the blue
    hills are,
But man can have the sun for friend, and for his guide a
    star; 10
And there's no end of voyaging when once the voice is heard,
For the river calls and the road calls, and oh, the call of a
    bird!

Yonder the long horizon lies, and there by night and day
The old ships draw to home again, the young ships sail 15
    away;
And come I may, but go I must, and if men ask you why,
You may put the blame on the stars and the sun and the
    white road and the sky!

BALLADS OLD AND NEW

This is a group of poems that tell a story. Some are fashioned in the true-ballad form; but most are merely stirring narrative verse such as all of us like to read.

THE BARON'S LAST BANQUET
(*See page opposite*)

THE BARON'S LAST BANQUET

By Albert Gorton Greene

O'ER a low couch the setting sun had thrown its latest
ray,
Where in his last strong agony a dying warrior lay,
The stern old Baron Rudiger, whose frame had ne'er been
5   bent
By wasting pain, till time and toil its iron strength had
spent.

"They come around me here, and say my days of life are
o'er,
10 That I shall mount my noble steed and lead my band no
more;
They come, and to my beard they dare to tell me now that I,
Their own liege lord and master born — that I, ha! ha!
must die.

15 "And what is death?   I've dared him oft before the Paynim
spear —
Think ye he's entered at my gate, has come to seek me here?
I've met him, faced him, scorned him, when the fight was
raging hot —
20 I'll try his might — I'll brave his power; defy, and fear him
not.

"Ho! sound the tocsin from my tower and fire the cul-
verin —

Bid each retainer arm with speed — call every vassal in —
Up with my banner on the wall — the banquet board
  prepare;
Throw wide the portal of my hall, and bring my armor
  there!"   5

An hundred hands were busy then — the banquet forth was
  spread —
And rung the heavy oaken floor with many a martial tread,
While from the rich, dark tracery along the vaulted wall,
Lights gleamed on harness, plume, and spear, o'er the 10
  proud old Gothic hall.

Fast hurrying through the outer gate, the mailed retainers
  poured
On through the portal's frowning arch and thronged around
  the board.   15
While at its head, within his dark, carved oaken chair of
  state,
Armed cap-à-pie, stern Rudiger with girded falchion sate.

"You're there, but yet I see ye not. Draw forth each
  trusty sword   20
And let me hear your faithful steel clash once around my
  board;
I hear it faintly. — Louder yet! — What clogs my heavy
  breath?
Up all, and shout for Rudiger, 'Defiance unto Death!'"   25

Bowl rang to bowl — steel clanged to steel — and rose a
  deafening cry
That made the torches flare around and shook the flags on
  high:

"Ho! cravens, do ye fear him? — Slaves, traitors! have
    ye flown?
Ho! cowards, have ye left me to meet him here alone?

"But I defy him! — Let him come!" Down rang the
5   massy cup,
While from its sheath the ready blade came flashing half-
    way up;
And with the black and heavy plumes scarce trembling on
    his head,
10 There in his dark, carved oaken chair old Rudiger sat —
    dead!

    1. What kind of man do you think Baron Rudiger was? Make
a list of a half dozen adjectives that describe him.
    2. Describe the picture the poet paints. Compare your descrip-
tion with the illustration on page 90.

THE CHARGE OF THE LIGHT BRIGADE

By Alfred Tennyson

At Balaklava, during the Crimean War, 600 English cavalrymen
were by mistake hurled against Russian artillery.

HALF a league, half a league,
        Half a league onward,
All in the valley of Death
        Rode the six hundred.
5   "Forward, the Light Brigade!
Charge for the guns!" he said:
Into the valley of Death
        Rode the six hundred.

"Forward, the Light Brigade!"
Was there a man dismayed?
Not though the soldier knew
 Some one had blundered:
Theirs not to make reply,
Theirs not to reason why,
Theirs but to do and die:
Into the valley of Death
 Rode the six hundred.

Cannon to right of them,
Cannon to left of them,
Cannon in front of them
 Volleyed and thundered;
Stormed at with shot and shell,
Boldly they rode and well,
Into the jaws of Death,
Into the mouth of Hell
 Rode the six hundred.

Flashed all their sabers bare,
Flashed as they turned in air,
Sab'ring the gunners there,
Charging an army, while
 All the world wondered:
Plunged in the battery smoke
Right through the line they broke;
Cossack and Russian
Reeled from the saber stroke
 Shattered and sundered.
Then they rode back, but not,
 Not the six hundred.

Cannon to right of them,
Cannon to left of them,
Cannon behind them
  Volleyed and thundered;
Stormed at with shot and shell,
While horse and hero fell,
They that had fought so well
Came through the jaws of Death,
Back from the mouth of Hell,
All that was left of them,
  Left of six hundred.

When can their glory fade?
Oh, the wild charge they made!
  All the world wondered.
Honor the charge they made!
Honor the Light Brigade,
  Noble six hundred!

1. This is one of the famous war poems in our language. Compare this ride with "Custer's Last Charge." What other war poems can you find to compare with it?

2. How had somebody blundered in the orders? Was the charge successful?

3. Among the peculiarities of this poem is the omission of all names; also the repetition of several lines or phrases: what are they? You will also observe the irregular number of lines in the various stanzas. Compare it with other poems in this regard.

4. Memorize the poem. It is easy to do. Why?

YANKS

By James W. Foley

O'LEARY, from Chicago, and a first-class fightin' man,
  Born in County Clare or Kerry, where the gentle art
    began;
Sergeant Dennis P. O'Leary, from somewhere on Archie
    road;   5
Dodgin' shells and smellin' powder while the battle ebbed
    and flowed.

And the captain says: "O'Leary, from your fightin'
    company
Pick a dozen fightin' Yankees and come skirmishin' with 10
    me;
Pick a dozen fightin' devils, and I know it's you who can."
And O'Leary, he saluted like a first-class fightin' man.

O'Leary's eye was piercin' and O'Leary's voice was clear:
"Dimitri Georgenopulos!" and Dimitri answered "Here!" 15
Then "Vladimir Slaminsky! Step three paces to the
    front,
For we're wantin' you to join us in a little Heinie hunt!"
"Garibaldi Ravioli!" Garibaldi was to share;
And "Ole Axel Kettleson!" and "Thomas Scalp-the-Bear!" 20
Who was Choctaw by inheritance, bred in the blood and
    bones,
But set down in army records by the name of Thomas
    Jones.

"Van Winkle Schuyler Stuyvesant!"   Van Winkle was a
    bud
From the ancient tree of Stuyvesant and had it in his
    blood;
5 "Don Miguel de Colombo!"   Don Miguel's next kin
Were across the Rio Grande when Don Miguel went in.
"Ulysses Grant O'Sheridan!"   Ulysses' sire, you see,
Had been at Appomattox near the famous apple tree;
And "Patrick Michael Casey!"   Patrick Michael, you can
10   tell,
Was a fightin' man by nature with three fightin' names as
    well.

"Joe Wheeler Lee!"   And Joseph had a pair of fightin'
    eyes;
15 And his granddad was a Johnny, as perhaps you might
    surmise;
Then "Robert Bruce MacPherson!"   And the Yankee
    squad was done
With "Isaac Abie Cohen!" once a light-weight champion.

20 Then O'Leary paced 'em forward and, says he, "You
    Yanks, fall in!"
And he marched 'em to the captain; "Let the skirmishin'
    begin,"
Says he, "the Yanks are comin', and you beat 'em if you
25   can!"
And saluted like a soldier and a first-class fightin' man!

1. This is a ballad of the World War. It is intended to show
that all nationalities are American, and all helped make up our army.
How many nationalities are represented?   List them.

(Used by permission of James W. Foley and *The Saturday Evening Post*.)

IN SCHOOL DAYS

By John Greenleaf Whittier

STILL sits the schoolhouse by the road,
  A ragged beggar sleeping;
Around it still the sumacs grow,
  And blackberry vines are creeping.

Within, the master's desk is seen,   5
  Deep scarred by raps official;
The warping floor, the battered seats,
  The jackknife's carved initial;

The charcoal frescoes on its wall;
  Its door's worn sill, betraying   10
The feet that, creeping slow to school,
  Went storming out to playing!

Long years ago a winter sun
  Shone over it at setting;
Lit up its western windowpanes,   15
  And low eaves' icy fretting.

It touched the tangled golden curls,
  And brown eyes full of grieving,
Of one who still her steps delayed
  When all the school were leaving.   20

For near her stood the little boy
  Her childish favor singled,

His cap pulled low upon a face
　　Where pride and shame were mingled.

Pushing with restless feet the snow
　　To right and left, he lingered;
As restlessly her tiny hands
　　The blue-checked apron fingered.

He saw her lift her eyes; he felt
　　The soft hand's light caressing;
And heard the tremble of her voice,
　　As if a fault confessing.

"I'm sorry that I spelt the word:
　　I hate to go above you,
Because," — the brown eyes lower fell, —
　　"Because, you see, I love you!"

Still memory to a gray-haired man
　　That sweet child face is showing.
Dear girl! the grasses on her grave
　　Have forty years been growing!

He lives to learn, in life's hard school,
　　How few who pass above him
Lament their triumph and his loss,
　　Like her — because they love him.

1. What is the story related? How long before the poem was written had the events happened? Prove your answer.

2. Read aloud the stanzas that describe the schoolhouse. Sketch the boy and the girl.

'TIS THE LAST ROSE OF SUMMER

By Thomas Moore

'TIS the last rose of summer,
　　Left blooming alone;
All her lovely companions
　　Are faded and gone;
No flower of her kindred,　　　　　　5
　　No rosebud is nigh,
To reflect back her blushes
　　Or give sigh for sigh.

I'll not leave thee, thou lone one,
　　To pine on the stem;　　　　　　10
Since the lovely are sleeping,
　　Go, sleep thou with them.
Thus kindly I scatter
　　Thy leaves o'er the bed
Where thy mates of the garden　　　15
　　Lie scentless and dead.

So soon may I follow
　　When friendships decay,
And from Love's shining circle
　　The gems drop away.　　　　　　20
When true hearts lie withered,
　　And fond ones are flown,
O who would inhabit
　　This bleak world alone?

THE WRECK OF THE *HESPERUS*

By Henry W. Longfellow

IT WAS the schooner *Hesperus*
 That sailed the wintry sea;
And the skipper had taken his little daughter,
 To bear him company.

5 Blue were her eyes as the fairy flax,
 Her cheeks like the dawn of day,
And her bosom white as the hawthorn buds,
 That ope in the month of May.

The skipper he stood beside the helm,
10 His pipe was in his mouth,
And he watched how the veering flaw did blow
 The smoke now west, now south.

Then up and spake an old sailor,
 Had sailed the Spanish Main,
15 "I pray thee, put into yonder port,
 For I fear a hurricane.

"Last night the moon had a golden ring,
 And to-night no moon we see!"
The skipper he blew a whiff from his pipe,
20 And a scornful laugh laughed he.

Colder and louder blew the wind,
   A gale from the northeast,
The snow fell hissing in the brine,
   And the billows frothed like yeast.

Down came the storm and smote amain
   The vessel in its strength;
She shuddered and paused, like a frighted steed,
   Then leaped her cable's length.

"Come hither! come hither! my little daughter,
   And do not tremble so;
For I can weather the roughest gale
   That ever wind did blow."

He wrapped her warm in his seaman's coat
   Against the stinging blast;
He cut a rope from a broken spar,
   And bound her to the mast.

"O father! I hear the church bells ring!
   O say, what may it be?"
"'Tis a fog bell on a rock-bound coast."
   And he steered for the open sea.

"O father! I hear the sound of guns!
   O say, what may it be?"
"Some ship in distress, that cannot live
   In such an angry sea."

"O father! I see a gleaming light!
   O say, what may it be?"

But the father answered never a word,
   A frozen corpse was he.

Lashed to the helm, all stiff and stark,
   With his face turned to the skies,
5   The lantern gleamed through the gleaming snow
   On his fixed and glassy eyes.

Then the maiden clasped her hands and prayed
   That savèd she might be;
And she thought of Christ who stilled the wave
10   On the Lake of Galilee.

And fast through the midnight, dark and drear,
   Through the whistling sleet and snow,
Like a sheeted ghost, the vessel swept
   Towards the reef of Norman's Woe.

15   And ever the fitful gusts between,
   A sound came from the land;
It was the sound of the trampling surf
   On the rocks and the hard sea sand.

The breakers were right beneath her bows,
20   She drifted a dreary wreck,
And a whooping billow swept the crew
   Like icicles from her deck.

She struck where the white and fleecy waves
   Looked soft as carded wool;
25   But the cruel rocks, they gored her side
   Like the horns of an angry bull.

Her rattling shrouds, all sheathed in ice,
    With the masts went by the board;
Like a vessel of glass, she stove and sank.
    "Ho! ho!" the breakers roared.

At daybreak, on the bleak seabeach,   5
    A fisherman stood aghast,
To see the form of a maiden fair,
    Lashed close to a drifting mast.

The salt sea was frozen on her breast,
    The salt tears in her eyes;   10
And he saw her hair, like the brown seaweed,
    On the billows fall and rise.

Such was the wreck of the *Hesperus*,
    In the midnight and the snow!
Christ save us all from a death like this,   15
    On the reef of Norman's Woe!

1. This ballad is written in the usual stanza form of the old ballads, such as the songs about Robin Hood. A great many of the old ballads, too, treat of disaster and death, just as this one does.

2. The reef of Norman's Woe is off the coast of Massachusetts. Upon its rocks many a brave ship has gone to pieces in northeasterly gales. This poem is based on an actual occurrence. What parts of it were imagined by the author?

3. Why did disaster befall the ship? When did the skipper give up hope? Why did he lash the little girl to the mast? What happened to the crew?

KING CANUTE

By Bernard Barton

UPON his royal throne he sate
  In a monarch's thoughtful mood;
Attendants on his regal state,
  His servile courtiers stood,
With foolish flatteries, false and vain,
To win his smile, his favor gain.

They told him e'en the mighty deep
  His kingly sway confessed;
That he could bid its billows leap,
  Or still its stormy breast!
He smiled contemptuously and cried,
"Be then my boasted empire tried!"

Down to the ocean's sounding shore
  The proud procession came,
To see its billows' wild uproar
  King Canute's power proclaim,
Or, at his high and dread command,
In gentle murmurs kiss the strand.

Not so thought he, their noble king,
  As his course he seaward sped;
And each base slave, like a guilty thing,
  Hung down his conscious head:

He knew the ocean's Lord on high;
They, that he scorned their senseless lie.

His throne was placed by ocean's side,
   He lifted his scepter there,
Bidding, with tones of kingly pride,   5
   The waves their strife forbear;
And while he spoke his royal will,
All but the winds and waves were still.

Louder the stormy blast swept by,
   In scorn of idle word;   10
The briny deep its waves tossed high,
   By his mandate undeterred;
As threatening, in their angry play,
To sweep both king and court away.

The monarch, with upbraiding look,   15
   Turned to the courtly ring:
But none the kindling eye could brook
   Even of his earthly king;
For in that wrathful glance they see
A mightier monarch wronged than he!   20

Canute, thy regal race is run;
   Thy name had passed away,
But for the meed this tale hath won,
   Which never shall decay:
Its meek, unperishing renown   25
Outlasts thy scepter and thy crown.

The Persian, in his mighty pride,
   Forged fetters for the main,
And when its floods his power defied,
   Inflicted stripes as vain;
But it was worthier far of thee
To know thyself than rule the sea!

1. This poem requires a careful reading to get its full meaning. Make sure you know the meanings of all the words.

2. Did Canute know he could not still the waves? Give proof of your answer. If he knew, why did he make the trial? Explain line 20, page 106.

3. How did the Persian king try to chastise the sea? What is meant by the last two lines of the poem?

THE BATTLE OF BLENHEIM

By Robert Southey

IT WAS a summer evening;
   Old Kaspar's work was done,
And he before his cottage door
   Was sitting in the sun;
And by him sported on the green
His little grandchild, Wilhelmine.

She saw her brother Peterkin
   Roll something large and round,
That he beside the rivulet,
   In playing there, had found:
She ran to ask what he had found,
That was so large and smooth and round.

Old Kaspar took it from the boy,
　　Who stood expectant by ;
And then the old man shook his head,
　　And with a natural sigh,
"'Tis some poor fellow's skull," said he,   5
"Who fell in the great victory."

"Now tell us what 'twas all about,"
　　Young Peterkin, he cries ;
And little Wilhelmine looks up
　　With wonder-waiting eyes ;   10
"Now tell us all about the war,
And what they fought each other for."

"It was the English," Kaspar cried,
　　"Who put the French to rout ;
But what they fought each other for   15
　　I could not well make out ;
But everybody said," quoth he,
"That 'twas a famous victory.

"My father lived at Blenheim then,
　　Yon little stream hard by ;   20
They burned his dwelling to the ground,
　　And he was forced to fly ;
So with his wife and child he fled,
Nor had he where to rest his head.

"With fire and sword the country round   25
　　Was wasted far and wide,
And many a childing mother, then,
　　And new-born baby died ;

But things like that, you know, must be
At every famous victory.

"They say it was a shocking sight
   After the field was won ;
For many thousand bodies here
   Lay rotting in the sun :
But things like that, you know, must be
After a famous victory.

"Great praise the duke of Marlborough won
   And our good Prince Eugene."
"Why, 'twas a very wicked thing !"
   Said little Wilhelmine.
"Nay, nay, my little girl," quoth he,
"It was a famous victory.

"And everybody praised the duke,
   Who this great fight did win."
"But what good came of it at last?"
   Quoth little Peterkin.
"Why, that I cannot tell," said he ;
"But 'twas a famous victory."

1. On what battle ground did this conversation take place? The battle had been fought between what peoples? Who were some of the leaders? Who won?

2. Old Kaspar keeps referring to the battle as "a famous victory." Does he really believe that?

3. What do you think the poem teaches us? What do you think of war? Is it ever justified? Is there any better way to settle quarrels between nations? Discuss.

THE FOX HUNT

By Henry Fielding

THE dusky night rides down the sky,
    And ushers in the morn;
The hounds all join in glorious cry,
    The huntsman winds his horn.

Away they fly to 'scape the rout,   5
    Their steeds they soundly switch;
Some are thrown in, and some thrown out,
    And some thrown in the ditch.

Sir Reynard now like lightning flies,
    And sweeps across the vale;   10
And when the hounds too near he spies,
    He drops his bushy tail.

Fond Echo seems to like the sport,
    And joins the jovial cry;
The woods, the hills, the sound retort,   15
    And music fills the sky.

At last his strength to faintness worn,
    Poor Reynard ceases flight;
Then hungry, homeward we return,
    To feast away the night.   20
                    — *Don Quixote in England.*

THE WORLD OF WORK

The world is a big workshop in which each of us labors for himself and so helps others. In the home, the school, or the factory; at the busy counter or the throttle of the great engine — somewhere your job awaits you. Do well today the tasks that belong to this day, and so fit yourself for your place in the world of work.

THE RAILWAY IS THE BACKBONE OF INDUSTRY
(*See page opposite*)

THE STORY OF THE RAILROAD

A LL great inventions have small beginnings, and this is very strikingly the case with that marvelous contrivance, the railroad. We find the first hint of the railroad in the tramway — that is, a road for trams, or wagons —
5 used two or three hundred years ago for the transportation of coal from English coal mines.

In this primitive railway wooden rails were fastened lengthwise on half-buried timbers, for the purpose of keeping the cart wheels on the track. A little later the
10 carts or cars were wheeled along on the rails themselves; then, to prevent the wooden rails from wearing out, they were covered with iron, and at last the rails were wholly made of that material.

After Watt had perfected the steam engine, the idea of a
15 locomotive, or engine that could move from place to place, began to be thought of. Several ingenious men put their wits to work to contrive a steam carriage; and among these was Oliver Evans, an American. People thought Evans must be insane when he talked of steam carriages,
20 and made merry at his expense; but he said, "Wait and see! The time will come when passengers and goods will travel fifteen miles an hour in them."

Curiously enough, in all these early experiments the steam carriage was made to move on common roads. The
25 hint given by the old tramway was not taken by the first experimenters, none of whom thought of putting his steam carriage on a track.

The first trial of steam on a railroad was made on a tramway in Wales. But all kinds of difficulties were met with, and the locomotive was but a rude machine. It moved slowly and burned a great deal of coal, hardly anyone had thought of using it for passenger travel, and the track was 5 rough and very costly. What the locomotive needed was a master to make it really useful and to bring it to perfection. Such a master was George Stephenson. This great engineer was born in 1781, at a coal village near Newcastle, in England. 10

As a lad George was set to work in a small way about the engine at one of the mines; and as he was not only very industrious but very ingenious and useful, he was finally promoted to be engineer at a place called Newburn. Although now eighteen years of age, young Stephenson was 15 still ignorant of the alphabet. He made up his mind to learn to read, and in less than a year he could not only read very well but write a fair hand and solve some problems in arithmetic. During the night watches and between mealtimes, young Stephenson would scrawl his letters and 20 figures with a bit of chalk on the sides of the coal wagons of the mine.

As soon as he had mastered the art of reading he eagerly devoured all the books on engineering and mechanics that he could find. He began to see how the steam engine 25 could be improved; he made models of new engines in clay; and people soon began to speak of him as a skillful and inventive engineer.

It was in the year 1815 that Stephenson devised and built the first locomotive, and in 1821 he was appointed 30 engineer to one of the first English railroads. Soon after this the Liverpool and Manchester Railway Company

offered a prize of five hundred pounds for the best locomotive that could be built by a certain day. When Stephenson proposed to make an engine that would go twelve
miles an hour, everyone said that this was absurd — that it
5 could not be done. "Twelve miles an hour!" said the
critics; "as well trust one's self to be fired off on a rocket."
But when the appointed day came and the different locomotives were offered and tested, Stephenson easily carried
off the prize.

10 From that day forward his right to be considered the
foremost of railroad inventors was never disputed, and the
myriad locomotives of the present day are in the main
identical with the Stephenson locomotive of almost a
century ago.

15 What magical changes have resulted from the genius
and labors of this man! The locomotive engine has
changed the character of human life. It has made the
globe smaller for us, and our knowledge of its countries
and people and products vastly greater. Surely the man
20 who perfected it, George Stephenson, deserves to be
called one of the great teachers and benefactors of mankind.

1. To get the full sense of this article you must know its three
main points. The first and second paragraphs treat the first main
topic; the third, fourth, and fifth paragraphs treat the second
topic; and the remainder of the selection deals with the third.
Express each topic in a single sentence.

2. The third topic is the main one. Break it up into three or
four lesser topics, and state each in a sentence.

3. Elect committees from your class to report on the following
subjects: life of Evans; life of Stephenson; first railway in America;
railroads of to-day. Get your facts from encyclopedias and library
books.

THE STEAMBOAT

BEFORE the invention of the steam engine there were only two methods of driving vessels through the water — the one by sails and the other by oars. Men had only sailboats and rowboats, as we may say; the steamboat — that is, the boat driven by steam power — had not yet been thought of. Sailing vessels, subject to the changing winds and helpless in a calm, are loiterers at the best, and the fleetest of them lag far astern of any modern steamer. The same ocean that Columbus was so long in crossing is but a week's journey for the voyager of to-day.

Soon after Watt had perfected the steam engine — that is, about one hundred years ago — two Americans, John Fitch and James Rumsey, devised machinery for applying the power of the steam engine to the movement of boats. Fitch's boat moved by means of a row of paddles arranged along its sides. Rumsey's plan was to take in water through an opening in the bow of his boat and then drive it out at the stern with so much force as to push the boat forward. Both Rumsey and Fitch made steamboats that would travel four or five miles an hour, and both sent models and descriptions to Watt. These early steamers were never put to practical use, for to neither Fitch nor Rumsey had occurred the thought of propelling his boat by means of a revolving paddle wheel, the device later employed by Fulton.

A few years after this time a Scotchman, named William

Symington, succeeded in constructing a side-wheel steamboat with a speed of five miles an hour. This boat of Symington's, with the improvements that have since been made upon it, is the river steamboat of the present day.

The two men who were mainly instrumental in improving Symington's steamer and bringing it into actual use were Robert Fulton and Robert Livingston, both Americans, and both for many years close students of the whole subject of steam navigation. About the beginning of the present century these two men made a series of experiments on the river Seine, at Paris, Fulton having made a special journey to Europe to see and examine Symington's boat. In the first of these experiments their boat broke through in the middle and sank when the engines were placed on board; but a later trial was more successful. It was of this boat that Napoleon exclaimed, "It is capable of changing the face of the world."

Shortly after this Fulton returned to this country and built at New York the first American side-wheel steamboat. In this boat, which he had named the *Clermont* ("Fulton's Folly" as scoffers called her), he made a successful trip up the Hudson River to Albany, in 1807.

Fulton's own account of this first trip is very interesting. In it he says: "To me it was a most trying occasion. The moment arrived when word was to be given for the vessel to move. My friends were in groups on the deck. I read nothing in their looks but disaster, and almost repented my efforts. The signal was given; the boat moved on a short distance, then stopped and became immovable. I could hear whispers of 'I told you so; it is a foolish scheme.' I hurried below and discovered the cause of the delay. It was quickly obviated; the boat went on."

Within a few years of this trial trip on the Hudson, thousands of steamboats had been built in this country alone, while to-day they are numbered by tens of thousands. Just such a change as the railway locomotive has made in overland travel and trade, the steamboat has wrought 5 in the commerce of the world's great waterways.

It is common to speak of Robert Fulton as the inventor of the steamboat, but we should rather think of him as one of its inventors, and, in particular, as that one of them who first in our own country brought navigation by steam 10 power to a practical success.

1. Who were the early experimenters with steam-driven vessels? What was Rumsey's plan? Symington's?

2. Report on the first trip of the *Clermont*. Find pictures of the *Clermont* and later ships and compare them.

THE CORN SONG

By J. G. WHITTIER

HEAP high the farmer's wintry hoard!
　　Heap high the golden corn!
No richer gift has Autumn poured
　　From out her lavish horn!

Let other lands, exulting, glean   5
　　The apple from the pine,
The orange from its glossy green,
　　The cluster from the vine;

We better love the hardy gift
    Our rugged vales bestow,
To cheer us when the storm shall drift
    Our harvest fields with snow.

5   Through vales of grass and meads of flowers,
    Our plows their furrows made,
While on the hills the sun and showers
    Of changeful April played.

We dropped the seed o'er hill and plain,
10   Beneath the sun of May,
And frightened from our sprouting grain
    The robber crows away.

All through the long, bright days of June
    Its leaves grew green and fair,
15   And waved in hot midsummer's noon
    Its soft and yellow hair.

And now, with autumn's moonlit eves,
    Its harvest time has come,
We pluck away the frosted leaves,
20   And bear the treasure home.

                — The Huskers.

    1. Explain how the ground is prepared for planting corn. When is the grain planted? When is it harvested?

    2. What are our great corn-growing states? Find them on the map. What is corn used for? In what shape do you eat it?

    3. What is meant by the following lines: 5–6, page 118; 11–12, 19–20, page 119?

A WORD ABOUT COTTON

By Fanny E. Coe

HAVE you ever considered how important the cotton plant is? About its little black seeds, no bigger than the seeds of a lemon, is wrapped the clothing of half the world. Furthermore, three fourths of all the cotton in the world is raised in the United States. This is because 5 in the South we have almost perfect conditions for growth. Cotton needs great heat and abundant rainfall. Consequently it flourishes in the Carolinas, Georgia, Florida, Alabama, Mississippi, and other Southern states. Texas produces an enormous crop each year. 10

As soon as the frost is out of the ground in early spring, the plows are at work turning up the soil. Then in March the planting occurs. The brownish-black seeds are dropped into the fine mellow earth in rows about four feet apart.

In a short time the tiny plants appear, making bright 15 green stripes across the dark plowed fields. By midsummer the upland cotton stands about three feet high. Its leaves look like those of the maple, and its flowers resemble the wild rose in shape and color. While the bushes are loaded with the exquisite blossoms the plan- 20 tations are most beautiful sights. On the first day the flower petals are white; on the second day they change to a lovely pink. Soon the petals fall, leaving a tiny green pod which later develops into the cotton boll.

When the pod, or cotton boll, has matured, it bursts 25 open, revealing within it a mass of cotton — white as snow, soft as silk, light as thistledown. Buried in the midst of the cotton fibers are the small dark seeds.

On looking more closely, however, you will discover that each white fiber is fastened to a seed. It clings so strongly
5 that quite a little effort is required to separate the two.

The cotton is usually gathered by hand. Negro men, women, and children toil day after day in the fields, filling bags that are hung around their necks or waists. When the bags are filled they are emptied into huge baskets
10 standing at the ends of the rows. Carts drawn by mules or horses carry the cotton to the building where the ginning and baling are done.

Before the cotton fiber can be spun into thread, it has to be freed from those clinging black seeds. This was
15 once a very slow process. A century ago a negro, working diligently all day, could gin but one pound of cotton. This step in preparing cotton for the market was so slow and so expensive that there was little profit in raising and manufacturing cotton. Comparatively few acres were
20 then given over to its culture. But Eli Whitney's cotton gin changed all this. To-day the steam gin seeds fifteen bales of cotton or more in one day. A single gin thus does as much work as several thousand men used to do in the olden days.

25 Baling is the pressing of the cotton into a solid mass, or bale, weighing about five hundred pounds. In the same factory the bale is covered with coarse bagging and bound with iron bands, so that it is about as compact as a block of wood four feet square and five feet high.

30 And now its travels begin. Either by train or boat it is sent north to the great cotton mills of New England. Perhaps it may even cross the ocean to England. There,

in Lancashire, more cotton is made into cloth than in any other place in the world.

Of late years, mills have been built at the headwaters of the rivers in the Southern States, so that the cotton may now become cloth close to its own home fields.

About three fourths of the cotton manufactured in the United States is turned out by the manufactories in New England. In Fall River alone, the cotton mills weave two miles of cloth a minute during every working day throughout the year.

In colonial times the spinning and the weaving were done in the homes. During the long winter evenings or in the afternoons, when the cleaning and cooking were over for the time, the mother brought out her wheel or loom and with deft fingers spun the thread or wove the cloth for the family.

To-day all this laborious work is done by swift machinery. When the cotton bale is torn open, machines begin at once to free the fiber from all clinging leaves, twigs, or dust. It is blown upon and beaten by powerful engines until it is clean and fair as the driven snow. The next step is the carding. The fibers of the cotton come from the bale much tangled, and need to be straightened. Great rollers studded with close, fine wire teeth gnash and gnaw at the mass of cotton until all the fibers lie smooth and straight in a soft, white, thick rope.

This rope is then passed through several machines. At length it appears as a fine cotton thread, ready to be used in the making of cloth.

In the great cotton mills the process of weaving cotton thread into cloth is accomplished by hundreds of power looms run by steam and electricity. These giant world

forces have taken the place of frail human hands.   Thunder go the wheels and cogs and bands, and the millions of threads dart in and out and to and fro, and the yards of beautiful firm cotton whirl out from what seems to visitors
5 a bewildering tangle of machinery.

Calicoes, cambrics, ginghams, muslins, laces, embroideries, towels, sheetings, cotton batting, and spool cotton — all these are made from the contents of the cotton boll. Who can tell where any particular yard of cloth will go?
10 About one half the people of the world wear cotton now, and the number is growing every year.   As has been said, "We are tied with cotton thread to almost every nation, people, and tribe upon this big round earth."

— Makers of the Nation.

1. The following topics set forth in their proper order the points treated in this article :

a. Importance of cotton to the world and to the United States.

b. Different stages of the growing cotton plant.

c. Gathering, ginning, and baling.

d. Weaving cotton cloth.

2. Tell which paragraphs come under each of the above topics.

3. Which of the above topics should be broken up into smaller topics?   Make these subdivisions.

4. In what states is cotton grown?   Find these on your map.

5. How was cotton formerly ginned?   Who invented the cotton gin?

6. How was cotton cloth formerly woven?   How is it now woven?

7. What sections of our country make cotton cloth?   What other country weaves cotton goods?

8. Write a list of articles in your own home that are made of cotton.

THE STORY OF THE REAPER

By Frank P. Bachman

THE chief occupation the world over is farming. This will always be true, because our food comes from the farm. The most important article of food is bread, and the best bread is made from wheat. The amount of wheat raised depends largely on the amount that can be ⁵ harvested. The farmer, as a rule, has ample time to prepare the ground and sow the wheat, but the time within which he can harvest the golden grain is limited to from four to ten days. Very soon after the wheat is ripe the stalks begin to break and fall down, and the grain begins ¹⁰ to shatter. Unless cut very soon after it is ripe, the crop is lost. The harvesting of wheat is, then, most important. Each improvement in methods of harvesting has increased the amount of wheat raised and has decreased the amount of hunger in the world.   ¹⁵

In the very earliest times the harvester walked along and pulled the heads off by hand, leaving the stalks to stand in the field. The first improvement over this primitive method was the use of a long-bladed knife. By grasping a bunch of stalks with one hand and using the ²⁰ knife with the other, a number of heads could be cut off at one stroke. A knife that was slightly curved answered better than one with a straight blade, and this led to the making of the sickle.

In the days when the sickle was king, the whole family ²⁵ turned out to help gather in the harvest. The women could reap quite as well as the men. It was a good day's work for one person to cut and bind into sheaves or bundles a half acre of wheat, which would yield anywhere from five to twenty bushels of grain.

The sickle gave way to the cradle, which first came into use about the time of the Revolutionary War. The cradle is merely a scythe furnished with wooden fingers running parallel with the blade. These wooden fingers hold the stalks of grain, after they have been cut off, in an upright position and enable the cradler to lay the grain down in a neat row with the stalks parallel, ready to be gathered into bunches and bound into sheaves.

A strong man could cut with a cradle from two to two and a half acres of wheat in a day, and a second man following along could gather it up and bind it into sheaves. The cradle was thus a great improvement over the sickle or reap hook, for it increased two to three times the amount of wheat one man could harvest. But cradling and binding grain was the very hardest work on the farm. In hot weather even the strongest men could keep at work only part of the time. So long, then, as the cradle was the best means of harvesting, the amount of wheat that could be raised on a single farm was small. Still, the cradle continued to be the king of harvesters until almost the middle of the last century. Even to-day, wheat raised in stumpy ground, in small fields, and in orchards, is cut with a cradle.

The success of men like Watt with the steam engine, and Arkwright with the water frame, set many a man in England working on labor-saving machines. One of these, Patrick Bell, of Scotland, came near making a practical reaper.

But though it soon worked its way to a considerable success, the cutting part of Bell's machine, as in all the early reapers, was not satisfactory. If the grain was ripe, stood up well, and was free from grass and weeds, it went satisfactorily. But if the grain was down and there was an abundance of weeds and grass, the machine choked, running over the wheat without cutting it. As a rule only about four fifths of a field could be harvested with this machine; the remainder had to be cut with the cradle.

Not long afterwards, however, a reaper was invented which, when perfected, was used in all parts of the world. This reaper took the place of the sickle and the cradle, it increased many times the amount of wheat raised, and it relieved the farmers of the back-breaking work of cutting and binding grain by hand. The man who took the chief part in the invention and improvement of this reaper was an American, Cyrus H. McCormick, born in 1809, near Midvale, Virginia. He was the oldest of a family of eight children and grew up like many another country boy, familiar from childhood with farm life. He prided himself on knowing how to do every kind of farm work and how to run and repair every bit of machinery in use. The winter months he spent in the near-by "Field School," studying reading, writing, and arithmetic, and the rest of the year was given to work, either on the farm, in the mills, or in the shop. By the time he was twenty-one, Cyrus was as big and strong as any man in all the region round about; he was a good farmer and was skilled in the use of blacksmith tools.

A reaping machine had been his father's hobby, and one day in the early harvest of 1831, it was decided to make a trial of the invention on which he had spent fifteen years.

Cyrus, you may be sure, was more than an onlooker. He had doubtless had a considerable part in the making of the machine. So when it choked down and would not cut, he was probably even more disappointed than his father. But when the disappointed father said, "I am through with it; it is impossible to make a practical reaping machine," not so with Cyrus. The surrender of the father was the call of the son to battle. Then and there Cyrus resolved to make a successful reaper. The machine was pulled back to the blacksmith shop, and Cyrus took up the work where his father left off.

By the harvest of 1832, the improved machine probably looked very much like the one patented in 1834. At all events, Cyrus felt ready to take his machine out into the "wide, wide world." A public exhibition was given near Lexington, which was attended by the farmers and laborers for miles around. The field in which the trial was to be made was very rough. The machine did not work well, and it looked for a time as if it also were a failure.

"Here," shouted the owner of the field, "stop your horses. That won't do; you are ruining my wheat."

This delighted the laborers, who feared that the machine would take work away from them.

"It's a humbug," shouted one.

"Give me the old cradle yet," cried another.

All this, you may be sure, was discouraging enough to the farmer-inventor. But farmers like fair play.

"I'll see that you have a fair chance, young man," said a farmer. "That field of wheat on the other side of the fence belongs to me. Pull down the fence and cross over."

Cyrus pulled down the fence and crossed over. The

field was level, and before sundown he had laid low a full six acres of grain.

With this unheard-of feat accomplished, the machine was driven into Lexington and exhibited at the courthouse square. One spectator, after looking it over carefully, said, "This machine is worth a hundred thousand dollars."

Probably quite as agreeable to Cyrus were the words of his father: "It makes me feel proud, to have a son do what I could not do."

McCormick advertised in the local newspaper reapers for sale, as early as 1833. But it was seven years before he sold his first machine. To the farmers of that time the machine was not only costly — the price was fifty dollars — but it was also very complex. "It can be run," said the farmers, "right well, by one who knows all its cogs and levers, but we are running farms and not circuses."

Most persons would have been discouraged, would have given up. McCormick was not that kind of man; he worked even harder than before. He succeeded in selling seven machines in 1842, twenty-nine in 1843, and fifty in 1844. This was big business.

Best of all, seven reapers were ordered from the West. These seven orders gave great joy to the McCormick brothers, who were now all busy at the old blacksmith shop, turning out a reaper a week. But when the question how to get reapers out to Ohio, Missouri, Iowa, Illinois, and Wisconsin arose, Cyrus saw that the old "home farm" was no place to make reapers, if these were to be sent to the West.

About this time a friend remarked, "Cyrus, why don't you go West with your reaper, where the fields are large and level and where labor is scarce?"

McCormick decided that this was the best thing for him to do. He located in Chicago, built a factory, and five hundred reapers were manufactured for the harvest of 1848 and fifteen hundred for the harvest of the next year. The making of reapers on a large scale in the West was thus a success from the first.

The reaper did away with the hard work of cutting grain with the sickle or cradle. Farmers soon began to ask, "Why cannot a device be invented to do away with the even harder work of the raker?" In answer, a self-rake was invented in 1852, by Jearum Atkins, an invalid. Atkins had a McCormick reaper placed outside his window. Day after day he sat in his chair and worked on an attachment which would of itself rake from the platform the cut grain. Success finally crowned his efforts, and McCormick, always anxious to meet the demands of the farmer, bought this invention.

The farmers nicknamed the contrivance the "Iron Man." It was surely a spectacle to see its long rake-fingered arm, whirling up through the air and then descending to the platform, rake off the cut grain in great bunches ready to be bound. The self-rake saved the labor of from one to two men, and after 1860 farmers scarcely bought any other kind of machine.

The reaper by this time had taken away fully half the hard work of the harvest. There remained only the binding of the bunches of cut grain about the middle with a straw rope, so that the grain could be easily handled. This, to be sure, was back-breaking toil, but most of the farmers thought it would always have to be done by hand. "How can a machine ever gather the grain into bundles and tie bands about them?" they would ask.

In 1849, an inventor by the name of Mann fitted a McCormick reaper with a canvas elevator to carry the cut grain into a wagon moving along beside the machine. Nine years later, two brothers by the name of Marsh were using a machine of this kind, when one asked the other, "Why 5 should the grain be carried up to the wagon? Why can't we put a platform on the side of the machine to stand on, make a table all round to work on, and bind the grain as fast as it comes up?" By the next harvest the Marsh boys had their new rigging arranged. As they expected, 10 they could bind grain nearly three times as fast as before.

The Marsh harvester cut the cost of binding grain in two. The binders had no longer to walk from bundle to bundle, nor were they compelled to stoop over each time they bound a sheaf. They could stand still and straight 15 at their work. Two men could do what before it took five or six to do. Besides reducing the cost and the drudgery of binding grain, the Marsh harvester was a long step towards what the farmers said could never be done. All that was now needed to do "the impossible" was to teach 20 the Marsh harvester to twist a wire or to tie a knot.

In the winter of 1874, Charles Withington, of Janesville, Wisconsin, carried to McCormick at Chicago a new invention. It was a remarkable device. Two steel arms caught a bundle of grain between them, put a wire tightly 25 around the bundle, and fastened the two ends of the wire together by a twist. This was the long-sought self-binder, the very thing the farmer said could never be made. A wire self-binder was built and tested in the following July. It cut fifty acres of wheat and bound almost every bundle 30 without a slip. Within the next five years, McCormick alone made and sold fifty thousand of these machines.

This was the end of harvest drudgery. Sickles, cradles, rakers, binders, each in turn was set free. From this time on, all that was needed was a man or a good-sized boy to drive the team and to manage the machine. The machine cut the grain, bound it into sheaves, collected these on a carrier, and dropped them to the ground ready to be placed in shocks — all without the aid of the human hand.

There was one defect in the wire binder, which proved to be its undoing. The wire mixed with the straw got into the mouths of the cattle and at times killed them. Pieces of wire mixed in the grain cut the hands of those handling it. So, while the farmers were delighted with the self-binder, they disliked the wire.

At the very time the wire binder seemed to be most secure in its position in the harvester world, John Appleby, of Wisconsin, took to William Deering, the chief maker of the Marsh harvester, an invention which he claimed could tie a knot more quickly and more securely than was ever done by a sailor.

Deering knew the dislike of the farmers for wire.

"Here," he said to himself, "is the device to make the perfect binder, a binder that will use twine." And he forthwith accepted the new device without the slightest hesitation.

During the winter of 1880, word went about among the makers of binders that "Deering is crazy over a twine binder. Why, he is making three thousand of them." Before the harvest of 1880 was over, the shoe was on the other foot; for Deering not only made three thousand twine binders, but he sold them at a profit of one hundred thousand dollars.

With one of these machines, having almost human skill, a sixteen-year-old boy can harvest as much grain as a dozen strong men could harvest with the cradle or even forty with the sickle.

The final step in the improvement of the reaper was the invention of the complete harvester, which is really a harvester and thrasher in one machine. The complete harvesters are used, in our own country, chiefly on the Pacific Coast. They are great machines drawn by thirty to forty horses or by an engine. They cut a swath from twenty to twenty-five feet wide, and a single machine will cut, thrash, clean, and sack from seventy-five to a hundred acres of grain in a day, all at a cost of not more than forty cents an acre.

Chiefly because of the reaper, the amount of wheat produced in the world has increased by leaps and bounds, until it now amounts to about four billions of bushels a year.

— *Great Inventors and Their Inventions.*

1. Outline this article under topics like those of the preceding story of cotton. (See page 123.)

2. Name in order the various machines used to harvest wheat.

3. Bring to class any pictures you can find of any of the kinds of machines described.

4. If you have seen wheat harvested, tell how it is done.

5. What are the wheat-producing states of our country?

6. What foods do you eat that are made from wheat?

THE FISHERMEN

By John Greenleaf Whittier

HURRAH! the seaward breezes
   Sweep down the bay amain;
Heave up, my lads, the anchor!
   Run up the sail again!
Leave to the lubber landsmen
   The rail car and the steed;
The stars of heaven shall guide us,
   The breath of heaven shall speed.

From the hilltop looks the steeple,
   And the lighthouse from the sand;
And the scattered pines are waving
   Their farewell from the land.
One glance, my lads, behind us,
   For the homes we leave, one sigh,
Ere we take the change and chances
   Of the ocean and the sky.

Now, brothers, for the icebergs
   Of frozen Labrador,
Floating spectral in the moonshine,
   Along the low, black shore!
Where like snow the gannet's feathers
   On Brador's rocks are shed,
And the noisy murre are flying,
   Like black scuds, overhead;

Where in mist the rock is hiding,
　And the sharp reef lurks below,
And the white squall smites in summer,
　And the autumn tempests blow;
Where, through gray and rolling vapor,　　5
　From evening unto morn,
A thousand boats are hailing,
　Horn answering unto horn.

There we'll drop our lines and gather
　Old Ocean's treasures in,　　10
Where'er the mottled mackerel
　Turns up a steel-dark fin.
The sea's our field of harvest,
　Its scaly tribes our grain;
We'll reap the teeming waters　　15
　As at home they reap the plain!

In the darkness as in daylight,
　On the water as on land,
God's eye is looking on us,
　And beneath us is His hand!　　20
Death will find us soon or later,
　On the deck or in the cot;
And we cannot meet him better
　Than in working out our lot.

1. Where are these fishermen bound for? What kind of ships have they? What are some of the perils they may meet?

2. Where are some famous fishing grounds near the United States? What kinds of fish are caught?

3. Select from the poem a list of words that have to do with the sea.

MAPLE SUGAR

By J. G. Dorrance

A S the first hunters, the first woodsmen, and the first
builders in the American wilderness were Indians,
so also were the first sugar makers. The Indian went
about his sugar making in ways quite different from those
5 we see and know to-day. With the coming of the first
thaws in March, when the nights were still frosty and cold
but the days were warm and the snow beginning to melt
slowly away from beneath the trees, the red man began to
make ready for gathering the sap.

10 Then, as now, there were several kinds of maples in the
forests — the hard, or sugar, maple; the red and silver
maples; and one or two others of less importance. All of
these have sweet sap, but only that of the hard maple
contains enough sugar to be of any practical value. So
15 the trees which the Indian selected for his use were large,
full-crowned sugar maples, trees that had been growing
for many years and were full of sap.

On the sunny side of each tree he made a deep, slanting
cut with his hatchet or tomahawk, and into the lower end
20 of this he drove a curved piece of bark or a hollow reed.
This carried the slowly running sap to a small dish of clay
or birch bark placed on a stone at the foot of the tree.
As the dishes became full, the sap was emptied into large
troughs of elm bark, troughs which were sometimes large
25 enough to hold fifty or a hundred gallons of this sweet
stuff.

The sap was changed to sirup, then to sugar, in one of two ways. Sometimes it was made thicker and sweeter by being allowed to freeze in shallow bark vessels. The ice, as it formed on the surface, was thrown out until enough water had been removed to give a thick sirup or a sirup 5 which would crystallize into sugar. This was a slow process, and its employment depended entirely upon the condition of the weather. A better way to evaporate the sap was by boiling, but this also was slow and troublesome. For the Indian, having no iron pots, could boil the sugar water 10 only by dropping hot stones into it.

From the days when maple sugar was a necessity down to the time when its making became a business and its use a luxury, many changes and improvements have been made in the methods of its manufacture. This industry 15 is one peculiarly American, and one that is to-day, as it has been in fact for many years, largely conducted by American farmers.

The early settlers, also, sometimes tapped their trees by means of deep ax cuts. The sap was stored in great 20 tree trunks hollowed into rough troughs. It was afterwards boiled down in large kettles in the open woods. Green timber, as well as wood already dead and down, supplied all the fuel that was needed. The old-fashioned iron kettle was hung over the fire from the end of a long, 25 stout pole, which was weighted at the other end so that the kettle might easily be swung on or off the fire. Sometimes a number of kettles were hung from a single horizontal pole or were set into a rude furnace constructed of clay and stones. The sap was kept from boiling over by 30 dashing cold water into the kettle or by reducing the fire, and the pieces of bark or leaves and other impurities were skimmed off while the kettle was over the fire. The sirup thus produced, if removed from the fire at the proper time, formed a molasses, pleasant to the taste but dark in color and not always of good quality.

5 With the increase of population the demand for good sirup and sugar grew. This induced better methods and the result was less waste and purer products. Sugar is seldom made now in the open woods, and in nearly every sugar bush is a small house, or sugar shanty, used in each 10 spring's sugar making.

The old ax cut was replaced by an auger hole, which did not injure the tree. At first this was a large opening, made to hold the wooden spout, or "spile," then used. Gradually it was made smaller, until now the small metal spouts used 15 fill holes only an inch deep and less than half an inch in diameter. Wooden pails took the place of bark dishes for catching the sap, and they in turn have now given way to vessels of galvanized iron. Years ago the men who went from tree to tree gathering sap wore over their shoulders 20 wooden yokes for carrying two pails of sap. Most farmers now have a wooden sledge in the camp. Barrels are placed on this, and the sledge is drawn from tree to tree by horses or oxen.

In some camps iron kettles are still used, and the sap 25 is boiled down until thick enough for good sirup, or until it will crystallize and make sugar. The old way of finding this out was to dip into the boiling sirup a small twig bent into a loop or to drop some of it on snow. If it formed a little film over the loop or made taffy on the snow, it was 30 taken from the fire and poured into molds where it soon turned into sugar. About four gallons of sap are needed to make a single pound of sugar. Usually the sap runs for three or four weeks, good trees giving as much as fifteen or twenty gallons of sap in that time.

In some of the larger groves the sap is now brought to the camp by pipe lines running in from the woods. In such groves the camp has become a roomy house for sugar making. It is kept with much cleanliness and care. In it the old iron kettle is no longer found. Instead, a long, shallow pan over an iron fire box, or arch, is used. The pan is only a few inches deep, but made so that almost all of it is directly over the fire. The sap enters, from a large storage tank, at the upper end of this pan, or "evaporator," and partitions in the pan cause it to flow slowly from side to side. The water in it rapidly evaporates. It is sirup when it reaches the other end, and is strained through flannel. Some of it may be reboiled in a sugaring-off arch until it crystallizes into sugar.

— The Story of the Forest.

1. From what plants do we now get most of our sweets? In what forms do we get these sweets?

2. How did the Indians make sugar? Do we use the same source of supply?

3. Describe the processes of making maple sirup in former times. Describe present methods.

4. If you have seen a sugar bush or a sugar camp in the spring, report what was taking place there.

BROTHERS OF THE WORLD

By Frank G. Carpenter

FOOD, clothing, and shelter are man's three great necessities. They are common to all races and tribes, to all
localities, and to all times. The desire for them has
formed the basis of civilization, and how far that desire
5 has been satisfied is the chief criterion of the civilization
which each people possesses.

Our food now comes from all parts of the world and our
dinner tables have articles upon them which were brought
thousands of miles for our use. The tea we drank to-day
10 may have been picked by a Chinese boy or girl last year,
and the sugar in it may have come from cane raised in Cuba.
The coffee was grown on bushes in southern Brazil, and
if we could follow the pepper back to its home, we might
find half-naked little brown boys of Java or Sumatra play-
15 ing among the vines on which it grew. If the loaf of bread
could tell its story, it might speak of vast fields of golden
wheat beyond the Great Lakes; and the roast beef, only a
few weeks ago, was part of an animal which galloped over
the Texas prairies with a cowboy behind it.

20 Every meal we eat, in fact, has been brought to us from
many parts of the earth, and the people who furnished it
are probably eating some things supplied by us. In this
way the whole world is working for you and me, and we
in turn are working for every nation which buys the things
25 we make or raise to sell.

The felt of that boy's hat contains fur which last year

was warming a beaver, building his dam in the wilds of northern Canada. His shoes came from the sides of a cow that was then grazing upon the plains of Argentina, and his woolen suit from the back of a sheep that very likely fed along the edges of the Australian Desert. Those pearl 5 buttons on his shirt were once parts of the houses of oysters in the waters off the Philippine Islands, and the buttons upon his coat were kernels of vegetable-ivory nuts on a South American palm tree. The cotton of his shirt came from cotton plants grown in our Southern States; 10 and the linen of its collar was once in a flax field in Belgium or Ireland.

And then the clothes which the girls are wearing! We shall have to travel halfway around the world to reach the places whence they came. If those gay silk 15 hair ribbons could speak, they might say that their lives began in the bodies of silkworms, tended by yellow-skinned women and children on the other side of the globe. If the hats knew our language, they might tell how the straw in them grew on the shores of Japan and was gathered by other 20 cream-colored mortals; and at the same time the bright feathers that decorate them might whisper that they formed the tails of birds which the brown Papuans chased through the wilds of New Guinea.

The alpaca of Lucy's fine gown could give us stories of the 25 high plateau of the Andes, and the mohair of Susie's dress might tell us tales of the goats of Angora, in Turkey, south of the Black Sea. The leather in her shoes might speak of its life on the back of a kid on the edge of the Desert of Sahara; and the rubbers that keep the leather dry could 30 tell of the Indians who gathered it as the sap of trees on the banks of the Amazon River. Every girl has articles upon her which began their existence far, far away; and if one of our boys were to travel back to all the places from which the things he is now wearing came, he would be many, many months on the road.

5 If we should start out to follow these materials on their wanderings to us, our travels would be much greater still. We should have to trail the Indian who trapped the beaver to the trader who bought its skin and sent it to the great hat factory; and we should have to go there to 10 see the fur felted and molded into shape. Supposing our shoes came from South American hides, we might go beyond the equator and follow them on their long sea trip along the Atlantic coast to our tanneries, where they are made into leather; and thence to our shoe factories, 15 where the leather is cut, sewed, and nailed into footgear. For our jackets, if the wool came from Australia, we should journey with it upon wagons or cars to the sea-ports, and thence over the oceans to the great weaving mills and on to the shops where the goods are sewed into 20 clothing.

— *Industrial Readers* (*adapted*).

1. Trace one of your articles of clothing back to its source. Do the same with an article of food.

2. Be able to locate all the places named in this selection.

3. Why is this selection called "Brothers of the World"? Find another suitable name for it.

4. What do you hope your part of the work of the world will be?

THE PLOW

By R. H. Horne

ABOVE yon somber swell of land
   Thou seest the dawn's grave orange hue,
With one pale streak like yellow sand,
   And over that a vein of blue.

The air is cold above the woods;   5
   All silent is the earth and sky,
Except with his own lonely moods
   The blackbird holds a colloquy.

Over the broad hills creeps a beam,
   Like hope that gilds a good man's brow;   10
And now ascends the nostril steam
   Of stalwart horses come to plow.

Ye rigid plowmen, bear in mind
   Your labor is for future hours!
Advance — spare not — nor look behind —   15
   Plow deep and straight with all your powers!

1. The first two stanzas draw a picture. Describe it in your own words. What time of year is it?
2. The third stanza introduces the workers. What are they? What is meant by "nostril steam"? What does the term tell you about the weather?
3. What does the fourth stanza do?

EARLY DAYS IN AMERICA

Most of us were born in this country. The parents of many of us were born in Europe. All of us should know the hardships the American pioneers underwent in first helping to make our great country what it is. To know this will help us all to be better citizens. Let us resolve, like the American pioneers, to make our country even greater and better than it now is.

THE INDIAN MAID WARNS GLADWYN
(*See page opposite*)

A STORY OF DETROIT

The following incident took place after the French and Indian War. That war was won by the American colonists and the British. It decided that the English-speaking people, not the French, should rule America.

THE early history of Detroit is highly romantic. It was founded by the French in 1700 as a military colony. It soon became one of the most important of the western outposts of Canada, and as the French and Indians were usually on the most friendly terms the colony for a long time existed in a state of happiness and contentment.

At the close of the French War, Detroit contained over two thousand inhabitants. Canadian dwellings with their lovely gardens lined the banks of the river for miles. Within the limits of the settlement were several Indian villages. Here the light-hearted French Canadian smoked his pipe and told his story and the friendly Indian supplied him with game and joined in his merrymaking.

In the year 1760 Detroit was taken possession of by the English. The Indians hated the English as much as they had loved the French. Pontiac, the ruling spirit of the forests at this time, was a most powerful and statesmanlike chief. When he found that his friends, the French, had lost their power, he sought to unite the Indian tribes against the English colonies and to destroy the English garrison at Detroit by strategy.

He was chief of the Ottawas but possessed great influence over several other tribes. Pontiac believed, and rightly,

that the establishment of English colonies would be fatal
to the interests of the Indian race. He strode through the
forests like a giant, inciting the tribes to war. He urged
a union of all the Indian nations from the Lakes to the
Mississippi for the common defense of the race. 5

There lived near Detroit a beautiful Indian girl called
Catherine. The English commander, Gladwyn, was
pleased with her and showed her many favors, and she
formed a warm friendship for him.

One lovely day in May this girl came to the fort 10
and brought Gladwyn a pair of elkskin moccasins. She
appeared very sad.

"Catherine," said Gladwyn, "what troubles you?"

She did not answer at once. There was a silent struggle
going on in her heart. She had formed a strong attachment 15
for the white people and she was also devoted to her own
race.

"To-morrow," she said at length, "Pontiac will come to
the fort with sixty of his chiefs. Each will be armed
with a gun, which will be cut short and hidden under his 20
blanket. The chief will ask to hold a council. He will
then make a speech and offer a belt of wampum as a peace
offering. As soon as he holds up the belt, the chiefs will
spring up and shoot the officers and the Indians outside will
attack the English. Every Englishman will be killed. 25
The French inhabitants will be spared."

Gladwyn made immediate preparations to avoid the
danger which threatened them. The soldiers were put
under arms. Orders were given to have them drawn up
in line on the arrival of the Indians the following day. 30

The next morning Indian canoes approached the fort
from the eastern shores. They contained Pontiac and his

sixty chiefs. At ten o'clock the chiefs marched to the fort in fantastic procession. Each wore a colored blanket and was painted, plumed, or in some way gayly ornamented. As Pontiac entered the fort a glance showed him that his plot was discovered. He passed in amazement through glittering rows of steel. He made a speech expressing friendship; but he did not dare to lift the wampum belt which was to have been the signal for attack. He was allowed to depart peaceably.

When he found that his plot had been discovered his anger knew no bounds. He gathered his warriors from every hand and laid siege to Detroit. He was defeated, and with his defeat ended the power of the Indian tribes in the region of the Upper Lakes.

1. In what state is Detroit? Locate it on the map. What about its location made Pontiac wish to seize it?

2. Give the reasons for Pontiac's making war on the English.

3. What was his plan for seizing Detroit? How was it defeated?

4. Did Catherine do right in betraying the plans of her own people? Give reasons for your answer.

5. How large is Detroit now? How many other cities in the United States are larger? What is its leading industry?

6. If your own community has had an exciting experience in times of war, find out about it and report it to the class. Your teacher will suggest local people (such as the librarian, town or city officials) who can give you help.

PIONEER HOUSES

By Frank G. Carpenter

OUR homes are far different from those of our forefathers. When the Puritans and Cavaliers crossed
the Atlantic to settle in the New World they had to cut
their dwellings out of the woods. There were no sawmills
and planing mills where shingles and boards, window sashes [5]
and doors, and all sorts of wood ready-made to be fitted
into a house, could be bought. There were no hardware
establishments with great stores of nails, screws, hinges,
and locks of all kinds. There were no brickyards or stone
quarries or places where one could buy lime, cement, and [10]
plaster. The whole country was a wilderness and the most
of it covered with trees which had to be chopped down.

Suppose you were one of a family just landed on the
shore of a land of this kind, with little more than an ax, a
saw, and a hatchet or so; how would you begin to build [15]
a home? You would first look about for some kind of
shelter in which to stay while you could cut down the great
trees and erect a log cabin.

That is what many of our great-great-grandparents did.
They huddled together in caves when they could find them; [20]
or dug holes into the sides of the hills and made shelters
there by driving in poles which they supported by crotched
sticks sunken into the ground at right angles. Upon these
as a framework branches and leaves and grass were fastened,
making rude walls and a roof, which, added to the earth [25]
at the back and sides, formed their first homes.

In many parts of the colonies, and especially in the south, they built wigwams like those of the Indians, using mats, grass, or deerskins to cover the poles. Farther north they had wigwams and houses of bark. Within six years after the Pilgrims first landed on Plymouth Rock and began to erect their log huts, there were only thirty dwellings on the island of Manhattan, and all but one were of bark. These rude little shelters were situated on the lower part of the island. They stood on the very places which are now covered with steel-and-brick office buildings, some of which are thirty, forty, and even more than fifty stories high.

It was not long after the settlers came before they had their log houses under roof. Every man was his own carpenter, builder, and furniture maker. He chopped down the trees and hewed the logs into lumber. He then called upon his neighbors to aid him in putting the structure together and in raising the framework for the roof. In some places the walls were made of logs from fourteen to eighteen feet long, set perpendicularly side by side in deep trenches running around a square which formed the floor of the dwelling. The earth was then pounded down and the logs fastened together with wooden pins and crosspieces, after which the spaces between were chinked with mud. Then a roof of hewn boards or bark shingles, or of a framework covered with thatch, was put on and the main part of the house was complete.

In such cabins the logs were so cut as to leave openings for the windows and doors. The windows had wooden shutters with hinges of withes or leather and sometimes a sash with panes of greased paper. The doors were of boards hewn from logs, fastened to crosspieces with wrought-iron nails or wooden pins. They were hung upon hinges of vines or of leather. Sometimes bark doors and shutters were used.

The furniture consisted of a rude bed, a table, and some stools or chairs of rough wood, cut out of the trees. The huts made of fourteen-foot logs had but one story. Those of logs eighteen feet long had usually a loft in addition.

Many of the cabins of that time were of logs notched near the ends and laid horizontally one upon the others, crossing at right angles and forming an oblong or square room. Such logs were added, layer by layer, until the house was of the desired height, when the framework for the roof was raised into place. This was then covered with thatch, clapboards, or split shingles. Some of the logs were cut shorter to fit into the places where the openings for such windows and doors as have been already described were to be.

The house was then made tight by chinking, or filling in, all the holes and spaces between the logs with mud and broken stones and by plastering the spaces with clay. The floor was the earth, well pounded down; or in the better cabins it was of split or hewed logs, called "puncheons." A large fireplace was built in one end of the cabin and this formed a part of the great chimney of earth and sticks, or of earth and stones, laid up on the outside of the wall.

Such houses seem rude to us now, but they were the first permanent dwellings of thousands in colonial times. They were the homes of the earliest settlers, and as the pioneers chopped their way through the woods towards the Mississippi Valley, each settler erected his log home and cutting down the forest about it broke the land for his farm. Many such cabins are still to be found in the mountains and in the wilder woodlands of our country.

It was in houses like these that some of the most eminent men of our country were born, and to-day we have people living in palaces whose fathers or grandfathers were born in log cabins and as babies were rocked in sugar troughs. The sugar trough was a short section of a big log, split in two and so hollowed out that it could be used to catch the sap from the maple trees. In those days cans and buckets were scarce and such troughs took their places. A trough was just about big enough to hold the baby and it often formed the rocking and sleeping place instead of a cradle.

Captain Miles Standish lived in a log house and the same is true of Captain John Smith and the other colonists who founded Jamestown. Not far from Berryville, Virginia, I was once shown a log hut in which George Washington dwelt when a boy of sixteen. He was then employed in surveying a great tract of land belonging to Lord Fairfax, who paid him five dollars a day, and he used this hut as his home. It was not more than twelve feet square and of about the same height, having a ridge roof covered with clapboards. The logs which formed the walls had been chopped square and their ends so dovetailed into the corners that but few nails were needed. The cabin had two rooms, one above the other. It was entered by a door of hewed planks. There were no stairs, and the young surveyor who afterwards became the great general and president had to stand upon a stool or climb a ladder to reach his rude sleeping apartment.

Presidents Lincoln and Garfield were born in log cabins. When Abraham Lincoln was eight years old his father moved from Kentucky to Indiana. The family traveled on horseback, sleeping at night under the trees. When they reached the site of their future home, they put up a shed of logs and branches, inclosed on three sides, the fourth being open; and in this they lived for a year. By that time Abraham's father had built a log house about eighteen 5 feet square. The rude structure had but one room, and little Abe's sleeping place was made by fitting some slabs into the logs overhead, making a half loft which was reached by a ladder. The floor was the hard-beaten ground; and a bedstead, a table, and four stools, all 10 hewed out of trees, formed the only furniture. There was a wide fireplace, and by the light of this, little Abraham Lincoln studied his lessons at night.

Garfield's log-cabin home, built by his father, Abram Garfield, was in northern Ohio, near a tract of forest not far 15 from Lake Erie. The nearest house was seven miles away. It was built of rough logs to which the bark and moss still clung. The roof was of pine slabs and the walls were of logs so notched at the corners that they fitted quite close together, the spaces between them being filled up, or 20 chinked, with clay. The house had a floor made of split logs hewn smooth with an ax, and its doors were of planks hung upon wrought-iron hinges. The lock was a wooden bar which rose and fell in a wooden socket as a leather string which ran through a hole in the door was pulled or 25 let go. At night the string was drawn into the house and only those within could open the door. This string was called the latchstring, and from this custom has come the expression denoting hospitality, "The latchstring is always out for you." 30

In colonial times many of the schoolhouses were made of logs and in some the only desks were boards resting on pegs driven at the right height into the logs of the walls, with benches before them. The teacher's seat was in the center of the room and the older scholars sat at these desks, facing the walls with their backs to the teacher. The younger scholars sat on blocks or benches of logs between the desks and the teacher. Such schoolrooms were frequently lighted by panes of white paper greased with lard and fastened to sashes which fitted into the walls. The heat came from great fireplaces, the fuel being sent in by the parents as part pay for the teaching. It is said that the child whose parent did not send his wood in on time was often forced to sit in the coldest part of the schoolroom.

As our country developed, the homes of the colonists began to improve. The cabins became larger. The logs were more smoothly hewed and there were many two-story dwellings. By and by buildings of clapboards or hewn slabs were constructed. Then sawmills were erected and boards came into use. In Virginia, Pennsylvania, New York, and New England, the people soon began to build dwellings of stone. The first bricks were sent across the Atlantic Ocean from Europe. They were burned bricks of red and black, and were laid in a checkerboard fashion. The windows were made of tiny glass panes, which were also imported. Many of these houses still stand.

— How the World is Housed.

1. Imagine that you are an American pioneer. Explain to the class how your first house in the wilderness was built.

2. Make a sketch of the schoolhouse described in this selection. Bring to class all the pictures of log houses you can find.

3. Interview some old citizen in your community and report what he or she tells you about the homes of the pioneers.

A TRUE HERO

By James Baldwin

JOHN STIRLING was a typical pioneer of the class who may be called the Makers of the Northwest. He was one of those who came from the South for conscience' sake; he could not bear to see human beings in bondage; he wanted to bring up his children in a land 5 dedicated to freedom. He could trace his ancestry for four centuries through a long line of English gentry, and every one of his forefathers had been a champion of liberty. The story of his life in the Northwest is but the story of a thousand others as brave, as self-sacrificing, as ingenious, 10 as industrious, as he.

In a single small wagon drawn by two horses, John Stirling brought his family and his household goods across the mountains by way of Cumberland Gap and through the half-settled districts of Kentucky. He crossed the 15 Ohio near the mouth of the Great Miami, and then made his way northwestwardly into the almost unbroken wilderness, looking for a suitable place to make his home. The roads for hundreds of miles were little better than wood paths; over a part of the course he was obliged to cut his 20 own way among the fallen trees and through thick underwoods. The journey from beginning to end occupied nearly six weeks, and yet John Stirling and his family were thankful that it had been so short.

Having selected the spot for his farm, the pioneer's 25 next care was to become its possessor. He bought it from the Government at a dollar and a quarter an acre, and when this was paid he had scarcely a cent left. But of what use would money be in a place where there was nothing to buy?

5 With the help of his two boys he felled trees and cleared a small place for the homestead. He cut the logs into proper lengths and with them built the walls of a rude cabin. He hewed rough puncheons for the floor, rived long boards for the roof, made a great fireplace of flat 10 stones, built a chimney of sticks and clay, and within five days had finished a habitation that was to be the shelter and home of the family for twice that many years. Not a nail or a brick was used in the construction of that house — nails and bricks were luxuries which the onward 15 march of civilization would by and by bring into that region, but the time for such luxuries was not yet.

For weeks, during that first spring in the forest, the doorway of the cabin was closed simply by hanging a bedquilt loosely from the top, like a kind of curtain. The wolves 20 howled around the cabin at night; the pioneer was not disturbed by such sounds — the hunger wolf was more to be dreaded than the gray beast that skulked in the thickets. Until his first small crop of corn had ripened he was by no means sure of food for the winter. He carried his grain 25 fifteen miles to mill and waited for it to be ground in order not to disappoint the expectant family, hungry for bread and eagerly waiting for the grist of meal.

The first twelve months were months of sore trial; but the end of the year found John Stirling firmly established 30 in his new home and beyond the reach of want. Even in the very darkest moments, he saw in imagination the wilderness giving place to fields of yellow grain and orchards of overladen trees; and these thoughts gave him fresh courage and strength for further conquests.

Little by little the great trees and the thick underwoods gave way before the three sharp axes of the Stirlings. Every year new deadenings were made in the woods and broader patches of corn and wheat and flax were planted in the openings. Herds and flocks increased and flourished in the woodland pastures, without expense and without special care. And sooner than he had dared hope, the pioneer began to see the realization of his dreams.

The comforts of civilized life, however, were long wanting. For several years all the clothing of the family was home-spun; tow cloth and linen from flax raised on the farm, jeans and linsey-woolsey of flax threads interwoven with wool from the farmer's own sheep. Nobody was idle. Wife and daughters were busy from daylight till dark: caring for the cows and the poultry, digging in the garden, carding the wool, turning the spinning wheel, mending garments, knitting, sewing, churning; and if need be, they were neither afraid nor ashamed to do a day's work in the field — it was all a part of the family economy.

The farmer himself was a jack-at-all-trades and good at more than one. He manufactured his own chairs and tables; he tanned the hides of his beeves into fairly good leather; he made his children's shoes and hats; he wove jeans and tow cloth for his own clothing and that of the boys; he knew something about coopering and harness making; he could make a spinning wheel or a turning lathe; he repaired the clocks as well as the wagons of his less skillful neighbors, and even built barns and houses for them; and in the long winter evenings, he tied brooms and taught his boys and girls how to read and write.

When, in time, the farm produced more grain than the
family and the livestock needed for food, Mr. Stirling began
to think how he might dispose of the surplus. During
the first few years the nearest market was on the Ohio,
more than fifty miles distant; but that was only a trifle
of three days' journey and the entire trip going and coming
could be made in a week. Over roads of the worst sort a
few bushels of wheat and perhaps some vegetables or a
pail of butter were hauled to that distant market. It was
rather a holiday than anything more serious; for the
farmers of the neighborhood usually went together in caravan style, camping by the roadside at night and withal
making a right merry time of it. The produce was bartered
for salt and such other necessary things as could not be
made at home. Now and then a few yards of calico or
some ribbons or some bits of queen's ware were carried
home to rejoice the goodwife and the grown-up daughters.
There was no hardship in all this. The long journey
once or twice a year relieved the monotony of pioneer
life — the markets would certainly be nearer some time.

And little by little the markets did come nearer, and
not only were there larger crops but the price of grain was
higher, and the farmer began to know by actually seeing
it the color and shape of money. One comfort after another came to lighten the labors of the household. The
buzz of the steam sawmill and after a while the whistle
of the locomotive became familiar sounds. The boys
and girls gradually laid aside their homespun and put on,
especially on Sundays, clothing made of "boughten goods";
and the farmer himself indulged now and then in some in-
expensive luxury which he had hitherto denied himself.
One after another he put aside his weaving and tanning and

shoemaking and carpentering, and finally he had nothing to do but give his whole attention to his farm and stock. A neat "frame house" was built nearer the roadside, and the old log cabin, the scene of many joys as well as sorrows, was deserted.   Comfort and plenty abounded.   The bless- 5 ings of civilization, following in the wake of honest labor, had come at last.

— The Conquest of the Old Northwest.

1. Make a list of household conveniences that you have which the Stirling family never heard of.
2. Select the words in the selection that belong peculiarly to pioneer times.   List opposite these, words of present-day times, unheard of by the pioneers.

A TEA PARTY

By Samuel Adams Drake

THERE is a dense crowd of men, with a sprinkling of women, arguing and gesticulating about the door of the brick church, and the interior is so choked up with people that we can scarcely elbow our way in.   The men's faces, we notice, are flushed and excited, and there is an 5 angry buzz of half-suppressed voices.   Evidently something uncommon has brought these people here.   What can it be?

Ah! they are all talking about tea.

"You can lead a horse to water but you can't make him drink," says one, very significantly, to his neighbor.   10

"Aye; and they can send us tea but they can't make us drink it," responded his neighbor.

"Let them take it back to England then, and peddle it out there," ejaculates a third. "We will not have it 5 forced down our throats," he adds.

"What sort of drink would tea and salt water make?" suggests a man who is evidently losing patience; for it has grown dark and the lamps shed a dim light throughout the unquiet crowd.

10 "Good for John Rowe!" shout the bystanders approvingly, and as his words pass from mouth to mouth the people laugh and clap.

Presently a man of middle age speaks. At his first words every voice is hushed; every eye is turned upon him. 15 In a grave and steady voice he tells the people that their purpose to send the tea ships home to England with their cargoes untouched has been thwarted by Governor Hutchinson, who refuses to give the vessels a pass, without which they cannot sail. "And now," concludes this same grave 20 and earnest voice, to which all eagerly listen, "this meeting can do nothing more to save the country."

There is a moment's silence — a moment of keen disappointment, an ominous silence. Then some one in the gallery cries out in a ringing voice, "Boston Harbor a 25 teapot to-night! Hurrah for Griffin's Wharf!"

Instantly, before the people are aware what is intended, an Indian war whoop pierces the air; and at that signal, half a hundred men, disguised as Indians, brandishing hatchets and shouting as they run, pour through Milk 30 Street followed by the crowd.

They turn down to Griffin's Wharf, where the tea ships are lying, clamber on board, take off the hatches in a hurry, and while some pass up the chests from the hold others smash them and pitch them overboard. Crash go the hatchets, splash goes the tea. Crash, crash! Splash, splash! Everyone works with a will.

Never were ships more quickly unloaded. The frightened 5 captains and crews were told to go below and stay there, and they should not be harmed. They obeyed. No one but the fishes drank that tea.

After finishing their work, the lads who have been making a teapot of Boston Harbor march gayly back to town to 10 the music of a fife. While on their way they pass by the residence of Mad Montagu, the British admiral and commander of the fleet of warships then lying at anchor within gunshot of the town.

The admiral threw up his window, thrust out his head, 15 and hallooed, "Well, boys, you have had a fine, pleasant evening for your Indian caper, haven't you? But mind, you've got to pay the fiddler yet!"

"Oh, never mind, Squire," shouted the leader. "Just come out here, if you please, and we'll settle the bill in 20 two minutes."

The admiral shut his window in a hurry, and the tea party, with a laugh for the admiral, marched on. He was fond of a fight but thought it best to decline this invitation.

1. When and where did the events of this story take place? Prove your answer from the selection.

2. Why was the tea thrown overboard? The answer to this question may require some reading in your history.

3. What war was fought soon after the tea party?

4. Name some of the leaders of the New England colonists who probably knew of the tea-party plan.

THE AMERICAN PIONEER

By Franklin K. Lane

This is one of the finest tributes ever paid to the pioneers of any country. It was given as a speech at the Panama-Pacific International Exposition at San Francisco, in 1915. If you remember as you read it that it was spoken to a great exposition crowd, on grounds decorated with fine buildings and magically lighted by electricity, many of the references explain themselves.

THE sculptors who have ennobled these buildings with their work have surely given full wing to their fancy in seeking to symbolize the tale which this exposition tells. Among these figures I have sought for one which
5 would represent to me the significance of this great enterprise.

Prophets, priests, and kings are here, conquerors and mystical figures of ancient legend; but these do not speak the word I hear.

10 My eye is drawn to the least conspicuous of all — the modest figure of a man standing beside two oxen, which look down upon the court of the nations, where east and west come face to face.

Towering above his gaunt figure is the canopy of his
15 prairie schooner.

Gay conquistadores ride beside him, and one must look hard to see this simple, plodding figure.

Yet that man is to me the one hero of this day.

Without him we should not be here.

20 Without him banners would not fly nor bands play.

Without him San Francisco would not be to-day the gayest city of the globe.

Shall I tell you who he is, this key figure in the arch of our enterprise?

That slender, dauntless, plodding, modest figure is the American pioneer.

To me, indeed, he is far more; he is the adventurous spirit of our restless race.

Long ago he set sail with Ulysses. But Ulysses turned back.

He sailed again with Columbus for the Indies and heard with joy the quick command, "Sail on, sail on and on." But the westward way was barred.

He landed at Plymouth Rock and with his dull-eyed oxen has made the long, long journey across our continent.

His way has been hard, slow, momentous.

He made his path through soggy, sodden forests where the storms of a thousand years conspired to block his way.

He drank with delight of the brackish water where the wild beasts wallowed. He trekked through the yielding, treacherous snows; forded swift-running waters; crept painfully through rocky gorges, where Titans had been at play; clambered up mountain sides, the sport of avalanche and of slide; dared the limitless land without horizon; ground his teeth upon the bitter dust of the desert; fainted beneath the flail of the raw and ruthless sun; starved, thirsted, fought; was cast down but never broken; and he never turned back.

Here he stands at last beside this western sea, the incarnate soul of his insatiable race — the American pioneer.

Pity? He scorns it.

Glory? He does not ask it.

His sons and his daughters are scattered along the path he has come.

Each fence post tells where some one fell.

Each farm, brightening now with the first smile of spring, was once a battlefield, where men and women fought the choking horrors of starvation and isolation.

His is this one glory — he found the way; his the adventure.

It is life that he felt, life that compelled him.

That strange, mysterious thing that lifted him out of the primeval muck and sent him climbing upward — that same strange thing has pressed him onward, held out new visions to his wondering eyes, and sung new songs into his welcoming ears.

And why?

In his long wandering he has had time to think.

He has talked with the stars, and they have taught him not to ask why.

He is here.

He has seated himself upon the golden sand of this distant shore and has said to himself that it is time for him to gather his sons about him and talk of things done.

Here on this stretch of shore he has built the outermost camp fire of his race and he has gathered his sons that they may tell each other of the progress they have made — utter man's prayers, things done for man.

His sons are they who have cut these continents in twain, who have slashed God's world as with a knife, who have gleefully made the rebellious seas to lift man's ships across the barrier mountains of Panama.

This thing the sons of the pioneer have done — it is their prayer, a thing done for man.

And here, too, these sons of the pioneer will tell of other things they do — how they have filled the night with jeweled light conjured from the melting snows of the far-off mountains; how they talk together across the world in their own voices; how they baffle the eagles in their flight 5 through the air and make their way within the spectral gloom of the soundless sea; how they reach into the heavens and draw down food out of the air to replenish the wasted earth.

These things and more have they done in these latter 10 days, these sons of the pioneer.

And in their honor he has fashioned this beautiful city of dreams come true.

In their honor has he hung the heavens with flowers and added new stars to the night.   15

In blue and gold, in scarlet and purple, in the green of the shallow sea and the burnt brown of the summer hill-side, he has made the architecture of the centuries to march before their eyes in column, colonnade, and court.

We have but to anchor his quaint covered wagon to the 20 soil and soon it rises transformed into the nave of some mighty cathedral.

For after all Rome and Rheims, Salisbury and Seville, are not far memories to the pioneer.

Here, too, in this city of the new nation the pioneer has 25 called together all his neighbors that we may learn one of the other.

We are to live together side by side for all time.

The seas are but a highway between the doors of the nations.   30

We are to know each other and to grow in mutual under-standing.

Perhaps strained nerves may sometimes fancy the gesture of the pioneer to be abrupt, and his voice we know has been hardened by the winter winds.

But his neighbors will soon come to know that he has no hatred in his heart, for he is without fear; that he is without envy, for none can add to his wealth.

The long journey of this slight, modest figure that stands beside the oxen is at an end.

The waste places of the earth have been found.

But adventure is not to end.

Here in his house will be taught the gospel of an advancing democracy — strong, valiant, confident, conquering — upborne and typified by the independent, venturesome spirit of that mystic materialist, the American pioneer.

1. What suggested the subject to the speaker? Describe the sculpture as he has pictured it.

2. Read the lines that refer to the completion of the Panama Canal; to the wanderings of a Greek hero; to the voyages of a famous Italian; to airplanes; to the making of nitrogen for fertilizer; to submarines; to electric lighting.

3. What do the items named above have to do with American pioneering?

4. Lines 5–30, page 162, suggest the history of the pioneer from the time of ancient Greece to his stopping on the Pacific coast. Read the section aloud and explain what is meant by each sentence or phrase.

5. There are many words in this reading which you should add to your vocabulary. Learn their pronunciation, their spelling, and their meaning. Then see if you cannot use them properly in the class recitation on this lesson. Try these: trekked; incarnate; insatiable; significance; limitless; rebellious; replenish; transformed; symbolize.

TRAVELING

By Eva Wilkins

This is an account of the migration of a family of cloth weavers — a "mill family" — in the thirties or forties, via the Erie Canal.

IN THE old days three sorts of boats traversed the Erie Canal. The freight boat, drawn by two horses driven tandem, as all canal horses were, and which took over a week to cross the state of New York; the swift packets, drawn by three horses and carrying passengers only, and 5 which made the distance in four days; and the line boats, so named because several of them made the trip together. The line boats were constructed to carry freight, and passengers who were accompanied by their household goods. 10

In the middle of a line boat, under the deck, freight was stowed, and at the bow was a cabin for passengers, and the dining room was in the stern. The little cabin, reached by a narrow, steep staircase, was arranged with red-cushioned lockers at each side, seats by day and beds by 15 night. Pretty red curtains hung at the windows, and red curtains hung before an alcove at the end of the cabin, which contained two large lower berths and two narrow shelflike berths above. A mirror with a gilt frame fitted into the end of the alcove and when the curtains were 20 drawn back it reflected the length of the pretty cabin. A trip from the cabin to the dining room, across the deck strewn with light local freight, compelled a discreet picking of one's steps. It was well when thus progressing that the steersman's warning cry, "Bridge!" did not call for a sudden seating of one's self on almost anything, or that "Low Bridge!" did not demand that the deck be cleared of passengers.

The captain of any boat carrying passengers presided at the table and was expected to play the gracious host, with due regard for his personal appearance; and on the packets, a diamond ring and pin might adorn his person.

As has been said, two horses drew the line boat, and it should be mentioned that while the two horses on duty were urged forward for a stretch of three miles by a boy who usually rode the foremost horse, two others munched in their stalls below deck or poked a nose out of the tiny window that opened before each patient, hollow-templed face.

The boy drivers seemed always a jolly set, whistling and singing the latest popular tunes. "Ha, Jim along, Jim along, Josey" was a roaring song, but "A Life on the Ocean Wave" was thought to show a higher musical taste. Then soon a hard-working little chap started up with the parody :

" A life on the raging canawl,
A home on the heelpath side."

The heelpath side is the side opposite the towpath — a proper and safe place for a humble cot.

The horses drawing the packet were stabled ashore, and it was a matter of pride to the drivers to hitch on fresh horses without slackening the speed of the boat. But the line-boat boy and the freight-boat boy must each lead his fresh horses over the gangplank, and wait for the relieved team to get into the boat. This, and the fact that the packet had the right of way, were most exasperating to the boy of the slower boat, but it greatly stimulated his ambition to rise in the business and some day drive packet horses, and pass everything on the canal, and compel some one else to "slack rope" while he trotted over the low towline.

Some of the line boats were also six-day boats and tied up on Sunday that the crew might rest and both crew and passengers attend church. Some line boats even advertised a Christian captain and, what was more remarkable, a nonswearing crew.

Speaking of attending church brings to one's mind the chambermaid on a six-day boat. She was usually a young person of consequence along the "heelpath side," and her appearance of a Sunday when she was ready for church was such that on Monday ladies often asked her for the pattern of some garment of the latest cut.

The cook, a colored man in white cap and apron, seemed always a good-tempered person. When the larger towns were entered he stood at the stern of the boat and shouted orders for provisions to a person on shore who represented some favored grocer.

Besides enjoying the services of such worthy persons as have been mentioned, a family traveling on a six-day boat was sure of very proper company. When, therefore, an eastward moving came at length to the Jennings family, Uncle Fitch, after bringing the family and household goods in two great wagons to Buffalo, saw to it that his sister and nieces took passage in a particularly respectable six-day boat.

"My position in Clayville is to be permanent if all goes well — and go well it must." So wrote Mr. Jennings from

Clayville, a little factory village a few miles south of Utica, New York. The valley of the swift Sanquoit was attracting many sorts of mills, and a prosperity equal to that enjoyed by the people in like New England valleys was expected in this new industrial center.

It was but three weeks after the reception of the letter quoted above that Julia and Lucy were looking across at each other from the narrow upper berths in the alcove of the *Mary Ann*, the carefully selected six-day boat which was to be their home for a long delightful week.

It was their first night on the boat, and their mother had said, "Keep quiet and you will soon go to sleep," as she went into the cabin to chat with some new acquaintances.

"Of course we cannot sleep until we get used to the tramping over our heads," said Julia as her mother dropped the curtain shutting off the alcove.

"No, of course not; let's peep into the cabin. Don't you think that a whale-oil lamp is chokier than candles? See how this one has blackened the ceiling. Arrange your peek hole like this, just a little wave in the edge of the curtain."

"I thought of that. There comes the chambermaid down the stairs. People will have to get off the lockers; she is going to make them into beds."

"Yes, isn't her little black-silk apron pretty? I think that things are as nice here as on a packet. See how polite she is! She is telling the married ladies to have their husbands go forward beyond the curtains and then all the other gentlemen will see it's time to go."

"Mother looks tired, but she has to wait to hear the stout lady in brown tell how sick her husband was. We had better lie down and begin to get sleepy."

"Yes, my neck just aches."

The girls were silent for a few minutes, and then Lucy whispered across, "Julia, can you see the girls in our school — and Sarah? Do you have a queer feeling in your throat?"

"Yes," choked Julia, "I wish —"

At that moment Mrs. Jennings came quickly into the alcove, and slipping off her cloth dress, put on a white sack and began brushing her long, wavy hair. The children lay quiet, feeling that they were very wakeful and sad, but when the lamp was blown out and the little window opened they —

> "Knew nothing more until it was day."

The next morning the children found that even eating one's breakfast was interesting under such unusual conditions. The captain, while serving the thin and overdone steak, remarked on the fresh and charming looks the night's rest had given the ladies.

"Don't you think the gentlemen look rested, too?" Lucy whispered to her sister.

"Of course. You are the goosiest! The captain is being complimentary," Julia whispered back.

After this Lucy was silent until she felt quite certain that she had gathered some valuable information from the talk about her. "We are the only ones going through. That means to Schenectady," she ventured.

"Yes, I heard too," Julia replied.

"How is it then, about your goods? I understand that you are moving to Clayville, but you will first make a visit in Schenectady?" the large woman in brown asked Mrs. Jennings.

"The goods are to be taken off at Utica and sent on by

wagon. We are to return to Utica by the steam cars,"
Mrs. Jennings replied; and the girls felt that this statement threw distinction upon their party.

"I still consider it a most dangerous mode of travel, but
5 perhaps less so than it looks," Mr. Jennings had written.

Indeed, later, when at night a whistle and a roar and a
glare of light heralded a monster that seemed about to
rush into the canal, the children believed in the danger
themselves. Still in the daytime there was only the
10 frightful speed to alarm, and they determined to hold their
father to his promise.

The early darkness of a fall day had prevented the children
from seeing just how the canal and broad Niagara River
kept company for a time. They learned from the chamber-
15 maid, however, that they were not to miss the locks at
Lockport and were too "shivery" to eat much dinner.

"I'd sit flat on deck if I were not so old," said Julia as
the *Mary Ann* approached the locks.

"Our boat will have to give the right of way to that
20 packet, so we can see just how bad it will be," Lucy said,
as she bravely placed her chair close to her sister's. "Oh,
see that little girl!" she added, as with a frightful roar of
falling water the lock filled, and a child on the deck of the
packet seized her mother and with tight-shut eyes and
25 wide-open mouth made herself stiff with shrieks that were
seen but not heard. The Jennings children resolved to
maintain a quiet dignity when their turn came.

The packet "made" the lock, and then the water roared,
and the lock filled for the *Mary Ann*. She glided forward
30 and the upper gates closed behind her. The lower gates
slowly opened and down, down she sank. The stone sides
of the lock dripped and shone; active men with long poles

kept the boat free and steady; and after a few anxious
moments the *Mary Ann* glided out of the lock, and then
other locks were "made."   At last, when everybody had
had quite enough, the *Mary Ann* entered a great pond or
basin.   5

"Let's fish in this quiet place.   There are boats and
boats to get out of here before our turn comes," suggested
Lucy, who was somewhat shaken by her lock experience.

"Yes, and I will find the twine, and pins for hooks,"
Julia kindly responded.   Soon the girls were fishing from 10
neighboring windows of the cabin, and with this calming
pastime they finished the afternoon.

That evening when the girls were getting ready for bed,
Julia said, "Tell us, mother, what the people on deck were
saying about Lafayette — we had to fish just then."   15

"Well, if you do not stop undressing —" assented the
mother.

"We won't," said both girls.

"His blue landing is on our large blue platter," murmured
Lucy parenthetically.   20

"There, don't stir up Julia," said Mrs. Jennings with a
warning pause.   Then she continued, "When Lafayette
visited America, long years after he had helped us in the
Revolutionary War, they gave him a rather unusual reception at Lockport.   The canal was finished as far as 25
Lockport, and they were blasting out the rocks for the
locks.   So they had a number of blasts all ready to touch
off, and the sound of a great explosion and the sight of
flying rocks greeted the general as he drove into the new
settlement.   Of course Lafayette was pleased, but I think 30
the Rochester surprise was more interesting."

"What was that?" asked Julia from above, for now the

children were sitting on their shelves, wrapped in their
long white gowns.

"At Rochester the canal is carried in an aqueduct over
the Genesee River, just above the falls. Lafayette, coming
from the West, had taken the canal at Lockport. They
reached Rochester early on the second morning, and when
the general was escorted on the deck there they were, boat,
canal, and all, over the roaring water. That was something
to show a stranger!" the mother finished proudly.

"Oh, my, the same thing will happen to us! But it will
be so early — will you wake us, mother?" Julia begged.

"I cannot promise, but perhaps the roaring of the water
will wake us all. There, cover up; I am going to put out
the lamp — ugh, how it smokes!" and Mrs. Jennings
opened the little window and waved a towel to hasten the
airing of the alcove. The children were soon asleep, and
great was their disappointment on waking to find that
Rochester had been passed and the roaring of the water had
not wakened even their mother. Perhaps this was as well,
for on the next night their dreams were much disturbed.

It was expected that Mosquito Swamp would be reached
at early evening.

"Hartshorn wafted about will keep the mosquitoes
away," said the large lady in brown very decidedly, as the
ladies seated themselves in the cabin after dinner.

"I think you are quite mistaken. Camphor is far
better," spoke up a lady in a checked traveling dress.
The discussion that followed soon became so animated
that Julia called the groups of ladies the "Hartshorns"
and the "Camphors."

Soon after sunset the cabin windows were closed and the
curtains closely drawn, and the *Mary Ann* entered the

swamp. The mosquitoes arrived and settled the hartshorn-camphor question at once. Neither of these remedies was of the slightest use.

For three long hours the passengers battled in the hot little cabin. At the end of that time the mosquitoes left 5 as suddenly as they had come, and merry was the laughter of everybody over everybody else, for not a passenger could boast of two open eyes and a nose unmarred.

"The 'Hartshorns' were right and the 'Camphors' were right — about each other," remarked Julia to her sister, 10 and they had a little laugh all to themselves in the alcove.

"Quickly into your gowns; they will feel cool, and I'll hand up wet towels," said Mrs. Jennings as she followed her daughters into the alcove, carrying a bowl of soda and water.

"They are some good," the sufferers reported after 15 shifting the cloths about, and soon, with the burning somewhat lessened, they fell asleep.

After Mosquito Swamp was passed, towns became more frequent — towns that were seen in the distance and hours afterward were entered in triumph, the horses often trotting 20 several rods. When the platform where the passengers were waiting was reached, a man with a coil of rope leaped ashore and wound the rope several times around a post to ease up the speed of the boat.

— The Weaver's Children.

1. How many people were traveling in the party to which the girls belonged? Where were they going?

2. Where is the Erie Canal? When was it opened to commerce? (See any encyclopedia or United States History.)

3. Describe a canal boat. Find a picture of one, if you can, and bring it to class. How were canal boats propelled?

4. Who were some of the interesting people on the boat? How did the girls amuse themselves?

DAYS WE HONOR

Gladly do we look forward to a special holiday; but do we always appreciate the meaning of the day so honored? Holidays stand on the calendars as reminders to us of what we owe to some person or group of persons or to our country. If they come to mean to us only a day's escape from work, we are the losers: we then fail to give honor where honor is due, and lose just so much honor ourselves by our failure.

"VIVE LA FRANCE! VIVE L'AMERIQUE!"
(*See page 179*)

COLUMBUS

By Joaquin Miller

BEHIND him lay the gray Azores;
  Behind, the Gates of Hercules;
Before him not the ghost of shores,
  Before him only shoreless seas.
The good mate said: "Now we must pray,
  For lo, the very stars are gone.
Brave Admiral, speak; what shall I say?"
  "Why, say, 'Sail on! sail on! and on!'"

"My men grow mutinous day by day;
  My men grow ghastly wan and weak."
The stout mate thought of home; a spray
  Of salt wave washed his swarthy cheek.
"What shall I say, brave Admiral, say,
  If we sight naught but seas at dawn?"
"Why, you shall say at break of day,
  'Sail on! sail on! sail on! and on!'"

They sailed and sailed, as winds might blow,
  Until at last the blanched mate said:
"Why, now not even God would know
  Should I and all my men fall dead.
These very winds forget their way,
  For God from these dread seas is gone.
Now speak, brave Admiral; speak and say" —
  He said: "Sail on! sail on! and on!"

They sailed.   They sailed.   Then spake the mate:
  "This mad sea shows its teeth to-night.
He curls his lips, he lies in wait
  With lifted teeth, as if to bite!
Brave Admiral, say but one good word;   5
  What shall we do when hope is gone?"
The words leapt as a leaping sword:
  "Sail on! sail on! sail on! and on!"

Then, pale and worn, he kept his deck,
  And peered through darkness. Ah, that night   10
Of all dark nights! And then a speck —
  A light! A light! A light! A light!
It grew, a starlit flag unfurled!
  It grew to be Time's burst of dawn.
He gained a world; he gave that world   15
  Its grandest lesson: "On! sail on!"

  1. What are the Azores?   The Gates of Hercules?
  2. Why did the mate come to the Admiral?   Is it a fact in history that Columbus's men mutinied?   What were the mate and the
men afraid of?
  3. Explain the reference in lines 13 and 14, page 178.
  4. When is Columbus Day?   Why is it on that date?   What
would be a good motto to adopt for Columbus Day?
  5. The author of this poem, Joaquin Miller (1841–1912), was
himself a pioneer; hence his admiration for Columbus. Miller
belongs to the days of overland voyaging across our country; to
the days of gold rushes in the West and Northwest.

  (Permission granted to use "Columbus" by the Harr Wagner Publishing Co., publishers
of Joaquin Miller's *Complete Poems*.)

ARMISTICE DAY

This is an actual occurrence, related by American soldiers on their return from the World War. First read the selection through rapidly to sense the spirit of the occasion.

IT WAS early on an autumn morning — November 11, 1918. The right wing of a division of American soldiers was resting upon a little French village just back of the line of battle. The thunder of distant German "heavies" and the nearer, sharper detonation of the 75's shook the stone houses along the three streets of the old town; but the villagers had become used to the bombardment and were not disturbed in the least by it. It was only the usual morning fusillade.

Nor did it worry the fine young fellows in khaki who were lounging about the benches in the little green at the convergence of the three highways or sitting on the steps of the stone church that held the place of honor in the green itself. The storm of big guns and the crackle of small arms had come to be a routine part of their lives — terrible at first but now only annoying.

But on this particular morning both citizens and soldiers were more keenly conscious than usual of the background of roaring guns. Since the afternoon before, the rumor had persistently gone round that this day was to be one of moment. Speculation on what was meant by the tale drew the soldiers and townspeople into little groups of expectant talkers. Was the drive on Metz to begin? Were the combined forces of the Allies about to start a still heavier drive against the Germans? Or — had the Germans had enough at last?

Breakfast passed, and still no news. The morning wore away, and the great guns were roaring at each other more savagely than ever. A relief of front-trench soldiers marched stolidly away down one of the roads. War had apparently become the established order; peace was nowhere in sight.

Suddenly across the little green hobbled the one-legged sexton of the church, a white-haired veteran of the '70's. He hammered his crutch furiously on the cobblestone walk in his endeavor to reach the church steps in a hurry. Up the steps he pounded, and disappeared behind the doors. A violent fusillade of heavy cannon shook the very foundation stones. Then silence — dead, vacant, oppressive silence. Soldiers half leaped up and looked at each other in amazement. *What had happened to the guns?*

From the belfry came the sharp peal of the bell — seven magic strokes that brought from all directions a green full of citizens and soldiers, eyes askance upon the church. As the last echo died out, the church doors opened, and out strode the priest, followed by the sexton.

Slowly the priest turned to the expectant crowd. He extended his uplifted hand and knelt. Impelled by the strong feeling of the situation, the crowd followed his example until the entire green was filled by kneeling people. Men knelt then and there who had never before knelt to pray. Slowly and distinctly the priest returned thanks for the victory that had come; the horrors of war were ended at last.

He rose. The crowd rose also, but a deathlike silence of awe was upon them. The shift from war to peace was too rapid even for the irrepressible American soldiers to grasp at once, and they looked at each other in blank astonishment.

Not so with the ancient sexton. The pronouncement of victory over the Germans was too strong for his sense of veneration. Up flew his crutch into the air, and from his pair of husky lungs he emitted a yell that brought the crowd back again to a matter-of-fact world. "Vive la France!" he cried. "Vive la France!"

Villagers took up the cry; Americans repeated it. Around a corner swept an American band flying the French colors and playing the *Marseillaise*. Dozens of tricolors, long concealed, swept out upon the highways, and twined with them were the Stars and Stripes. Another band followed. It, too, was American and it was playing the *Star-Spangled Banner*.

"Vive l'Amerique!" shouted the sexton.

"Vive l'armistice!" echoed the crowd.

1. Re-read the story to pick up broken threads of your hurried reading. To do so will require an understanding of such words as: "heavies," 75's, fusillade, convergence, Metz, askance, irrepressible, vive.

2. Find out how the first armistice day (November 11, 1918) was celebrated in America. What was the World War? Name the chief combatants. How did the United States come to be a participant?

MRS. NOVEMBER'S DINNER PARTY

By Agnes Carr

THE Widow November was very busy indeed this
year. What with elections and harvest homes, her
hands were full to overflowing; for she takes great interest
in politics, besides being a social body, without whom no
apple bee or corn husking is complete.

Still, worn out as she was, when her thirty sons and
daughters clustered round and begged that they might
have their usual family dinner on Thanksgiving Day, she
could not find it in her hospitable heart to refuse, and immediately invitations were sent to her eleven brothers and
sisters, old Father Time, and Mother Year, to come with
all their families and celebrate the great American holiday.

Then what a busy time ensued! What a slaughter of
unhappy barnyard families — turkeys, ducks, and chickens!
What a chopping of apples and boiling of doughnuts!
What a picking of raisins and rolling of pie crust, until
every nook and corner of the immense storeroom was
stocked with "savory mince and toothsome pumpkin
pies," while so great was the confusion that even the stolid
red-hued servant, Indian Summer, lost his head and
smoked so continually he always appeared surrounded by
a blue mist, as he piled logs upon the great bonfires in the
yard until they lighted up the country for miles around.

But at length all was ready; the happy day had come,
and all the little Novembers, in their best "bib and tucker,"

were seated in a row awaiting the arrival of their uncles, aunts, and cousins, while their mother, in russet-brown silk trimmed with misty lace, looked them over, straightening Guy Fawkes's collar, tying Thanksgiving's neck ribbon, and settling a dispute between two little presidential candidates as to which should sit at the head of the table.

Soon a merry clashing of bells, blowing of horns, and mingling of voices were heard outside, sleighs and carriages dashed up to the door, and in came, "just in season," Grandpa Time with Grandma Year leaning on his arm, followed by all their children and grandchildren, and were warmly welcomed by the hostess and her family.

"Oh, how glad I am we could all come to-day," said Mr. January in his crisp, clear tones, throwing off his great fur coat and rushing to the blazing fire. "There is nothing like the happy returns of these days."

"Nothing, indeed," simpered Mrs. February, the poetess. "If I had had time I should have composed some verses for the occasion; but my son Valentine has brought a sugar heart with a sweet sentiment on it to his cousin Thanksgiving. I, too, have taken the liberty of bringing a sort of adopted child of mine, young Leap Year, who makes us a visit every four years."

"He is very welcome, I am sure," said Mrs. November, patting Leap Year kindly on the head. "And, Sister March, how have you been since we last met?"

"Oh! we have had the North, South, East, and West Winds all at our house, and they have kept things breezy, I assure you. But I really feared we should not get here to-day; for when we came to dress I found nearly everything we had was Lent; so that must account for our shabby appearance."

"He! he! he!" tittered little April Fool.   "What a sell!"
And he shook until the bells on his cap rang; at which his
father ceased for a moment showering kisses on his nieces
and nephews, and boxed his ears for his rudeness.

"Oh, Aunt May! do tell us a story," clamored the younger
children, and dragging her into a corner she was soon deep
in such a moving tale that they were all melted to tears,
especially the little Aprils, who cry very easily.

Meanwhile, Mrs. June, assisted by her youngest daughter, a "sweet girl graduate," just from school, was engaged
in decking the apartment with roses and lilies and other
fragrant flowers that she had brought from her extensive
gardens and conservatories, until the room was a perfect
bower of sweetness and beauty; while Mr. July draped
the walls with flags and banners, lighted the candles, and
showed off the tricks of his pet eagle, Yankee Doodle,
to the great delight of the little ones.

Madam August, who suffers a great deal with the heat,
found a seat on a comfortable sofa as far from the fire as
possible and waved a huge feather fan back and forth, while
her thirty-one boys and girls, led by the two oldest, Holiday
and Vacation, ran riot through the long rooms.   They
picked at their Aunt June's flowers and played all sorts of
pranks, regardless of tumbled hair and torn clothes, while
they shouted, "Hurrah for fun!" and behaved like a pack
of wild colts let loose in a green pasture.   Finally Uncle
September called them, together with his own children,
into the library and persuaded them to read some of the
books with which the shelves were filled or play quietly
with the game of Authors and the Dissected Maps.

"For," said Mr. September to Mrs. October, "I think
Sister August lets her children romp too much.   I always

like improving games for mine, although I have great trouble in making Equinox toe the line as he should."

"That is because you are a schoolmaster," laughed Mrs. October shaking her head, adorned with a wreath of gayly tinted leaves; "but where is my baby?"

At that moment a cry was heard without, and Indian Summer came running in to say that little All Hallows had fallen into a tub of water while trying to catch an apple that was floating on top. Mrs. October rushed off to the kitchen, and returned with her youngest in a very wet and dripping condition and screaming at the top of his lusty little lungs. He could only be consoled by a handful of chestnuts, which his nurse, Miss Frost, cracked open for him.

The little Novembers, meanwhile, were having a charming time with their favorite cousins, the Decembers, who were always so gay and jolly and had such a delightful papa. He came with his pockets stuffed full of toys and sugarplums, which he drew out from time to time and gave to his best-loved child, Merry Christmas, to distribute amongst the children, who gathered eagerly around their little cousin, saying:

" Christmas comes but once a year
   But when she comes she brings good cheer."

At which Merry laughed gayly and tossed her golden curls, in which were twined sprays of holly and clusters of brilliant scarlet berries.

At last the great folding doors were thrown open. Indian Summer announced that dinner was served, and a long procession of old and young was quickly formed, and led by Mrs. November and her daughter Thanksgiving, whose birthday it was. They filed into the spacious dining

room, where stood the long table, groaning beneath its
weight of good things; while four servants ran continually
in and out, bringing more substantials and delicacies to
grace the board and please the appetite. Winter staggered
beneath great trenchers of meat and poultry, pies and 5
puddings; Spring brought the earliest and freshest vegetables; Summer, the richest creams and ices; while
Autumn served the guests with fruit.

All were gay and jolly and many a joke was cracked as
the contents of each plate and dish melted away like snow 10
before the sun and the great fires roared in the wide chim-
neys as though singing a glad Thanksgiving song.

New Year drank everybody's health and wished them
"many returns of the day," while Twelfth Night ate so
much cake he made himself quite ill and had to be put 15
to bed.

Valentine sent mottoes to all the little girls and praised
their bright eyes and glossy curls. "For," said his mother,
"he is a sad flatterer and not nearly so truthful, I am sorry
to say, as his brother, George Washington, who never told 20
a lie."

At which Grandfather Time gave George a quarter and
said he should always remember what a good boy he was.

After dinner the fun increased, all trying to do something
for the general amusement. Mrs. March persuaded her 25
son, St. Patrick, to dance an Irish jig, which he did to
the tune of the *Wearing of the Green*, which his brothers,
Windy and Gusty, blew and whistled on their fingers.

Easter sang a beautiful song, the little Mays "tripped the
light fantastic toe" in a pretty fancy dance, while the 30
Junes sat by, so smiling and sweet it was a pleasure to look
at them.

Independence, the fourth child of Mr. July, who is a bold little fellow and a fine speaker, gave them an oration he had learned at school; and the Augusts suggested games of tag and blindman's buff, which they all enjoyed heartily.

Mr. September tried to read an instructive story aloud, but was interrupted by Equinox, April Fool, and little All Hallows, who pinned streamers to his coat tails, covered him with flour, and would not let him get through a line; at which Mrs. October hugged her tricksy baby and laughed until she cried, and Mr. September retired in disgust.

"That is almost too bad," said Mrs. November, as she shook the popper vigorously, in which the corn was popping and snapping merrily. "But, Thanksgiving, you must not forget to thank your cousins for all they have done to honor your birthday."

At which the demure little maiden went round to each one and returned her thanks in such a charming way it was quite captivating.

Grandmother Year at last began to nod over her teacup in the chimney corner.

"It is growing late," said Grandpa Time.

"But we must have a Virginia Reel before we go," said Mr. December.

"Oh, yes, yes!" cried all the children.

Merry Christmas played a lively air on the piano, and old and young took their positions on the polished floor with grandpa and grandma at the head.

Midsummer danced with Happy New Year, June's Commencement with August's Holiday, Leap Year with May Day, and "all went merry as a marriage bell."

The fun was at its height when suddenly the clock in

the corner struck twelve. Grandma Year motioned to all
to stop, and Grandfather Time, bowing his head, said
softly, "Hark! my children, Thanksgiving Day is ended."

1. Make a list of the people who came to this dinner party. In
whose honor was the party given?

2. What is the significance of the names of the children of the
Months? Explain in each instance.

A THANKSGIVING

By Robert Herrick

LORD, Thou hast given me a cell
    Wherein to dwell —
A little house whose humble roof
    Is weatherproof —
Under the spars of which I lie   5
    Both soft and dry;
Where Thou, my chamber for to ward,
    Hast set a guard
Of harmless thoughts, to watch and keep
    Me while I sleep.   10
Low is my porch as is my fate —
    Both void of state —
And yet the threshold of my door
    Is worn by the poor
Who hither come and freely get   15
    Good words or meat.
Like as my parlor, so my hall
    And kitchen's small.

A little buttery, and therein
   A little bin,
Which keeps my little loaf of bread
   Unchipped, unfled.
Some brittle sticks of thorn or brier
   Make me a fire,
Close by whose living coal I sit,
   And glow like it.
Lord, I confess too, when I dine,
   The pulse is Thine,
And all those other bits that be
   There placed by Thee.
'Tis Thou that crown'st my glittering hearth
   With guiltless mirth,
And giv'st me wassail bowls to drink,
   Spiced to the brink.
Lord, 'tis Thy plenty-dropping hand
   That soils my land,
And giv'st me for my bushel sown
   Twice ten for one.

All these and better Thou dost send
   Me to this end —
That I should render, for my part,
   A thankful heart;
Which, fired with incense, I resign
   As wholly Thine —
But the acceptance, that must be,
   My God, by Thee.

1. In what kind of circumstances is the maker of this prayer?
2. Explain: spars, threshold, pulse, wassail, soils; unfled = Not sliced off.

CHRISTMAS EVE IN NORWAY

IT IS more than nineteen hundred years since there lay in the manger at Bethlehem, the Child whose birthday is the day of days to the children of Christendom. Every year the message flies around the world, "Peace on earth, good will to men." 5

Christmas is a joyous season to children everywhere. Not only in our own land but in lands beyond the sea, little voices swell the chorus until the great round earth seems to be filled with joy and gladness.

The day before Christmas in Norway is a busy one. 10 Out of doors the men are preparing the Yule wood, which must be perfectly dry, cut into even smooth sticks, and placed under the bench that extends the whole length of the living room. After this has been done the men go up on the mountain side and cut down a load of fir trees. The 15 branches, except a tuft of them at the top, are stripped off. These trees are then set up all around the low house. A pretty sight they make, especially if the snow falls upon them in the night.

In the house the women are flying about — scouring 20 and decorating floor, furniture, and walls. They suspend from the ceiling a crown of straw from which dangle shreds of bright-colored cloth of green, red, and blue. The gable end of the room is hung with cloth on which Scriptural scenes are pictured. The floor is covered with wisps of 25 rye straw, in memory of the stable in which Christ was born. Polished copper and pewter vessels are neatly arranged on the shelves and the best clothes hung in regular order on a long pole where the Yule fire may shine upon them. Great oblong loaves of Yule bread are browning in the oven with the round cakes of rye bread.

5 And the children! What are they doing? Oh, they are everywhere, their eyes glistening with excitement, hands and feet not still a moment. They must bring in the straw, help polish the cups, gather up the branches cut off from the trees — help here and help there.

10 Then they have some special work of their own to do. To-morrow every gable and post must bear its Christmas sheaf for the birds that are already chattering about the feast to come. They will be here in large flocks in the morning and will waken these little boys and girls with their 15 Christmas carol.

The children have gleaned the grain from the harvest field long before. How they enjoy climbing about to fasten the sheaves to gable and post! How they laugh to see the eager birds nod from their perches!

20 Now it is growing dark, and the children must go with the women to the cow house. They give the cattle their best forage and say to each one, as they put a new collar on her neck, "This is Christmas Eve, little one."

Then they proceed to the stable where they give the 25 horses their choicest hay. The fowls are remembered with bits of food and the watchdog is set free on this one night of the year. For these good folks say, "All creatures should have cause to rejoice on Christmas Eve."

Soon the fires are lighted, the Bible is read, and the 30 merriment begins. The children keep running to the door as if they expected some one and clap their hands with delight when they hear a bell ring just outside. They spring to throw open the door and welcome an old man and an old woman, a queer-looking couple.

These old people are grotesquely dressed but they are most beautiful to the children, whose great round eyes sparkle with delight. The woman carries a large basket 5 of sealed packages. She hands out each package to the one whose name it bears, and when her basket is empty disappears to return with a new supply. The name of the giver is not attached to the presents and there is great fun guessing and questioning one another. The gifts them- 10 selves are usually very simple.

Music, dancing, and games follow, and supper at ten o'clock. Before supper grace is said and the meal closes with a psalm. All the family must sleep under the same roof, and the children on rye straw. The candles and fire 15 must burn until morning, and the remains be kept until the next Christmas.

1. Where is Norway? What do the people do for a living? Why is mention of the cow house made in this selection?

2. Imagine you are a Norwegian boy or girl dwelling near a fiord. Relate what you do on Christmas Eve. What would be some of the games you could play on Christmas?

3. If you know or can find out any other ways of celebrating Christmas, in any country, report them to the class.

CHRISTMAS IN MERRY ENGLAND

By Sir Walter Scott

HEAP on more wood! — the wind is chill;
But let it whistle as it will,
We'll keep our Christmas merry still.
Each age has deemed the new-born year
5   The fittest time for festal cheer:
Even, heathen yet, the savage Dane
At Iol more deep the mead did drain,
High on the beach his galleys drew,
And feasted all his pirate crew;
10   Then in his low and pine-built hall,
Where shields and axes decked the wall,
They gorged upon the half-dressed steer,
Caroused in seas of sable beer,
While round in brutal jest were thrown
15   The half-gnawed rib and marrowbone.

And well our Christian sires of old
Loved when the year its course had rolled,
And brought blithe Christmas back again
With all his hospitable train.
20   Domestic and religious rite
Gave honor to the holy night;
On Christmas Eve the bells were rung,
On Christmas Eve the Mass was sung;
The damsel donned her kirtle sheen;
25   The hall was dressed with holly green;

Forth to the wood did merrymen go,
To gather in the mistletoe.
Then opened wide the baron's hall
To vassal, tenant, serf, and all;
The heir, with roses in his shoes,   5
That night might village partner choose;
The lord, underogating, share
The vulgar game of "post and pair."
All hailed, with uncontrolled delight
And general voice, the happy night   10
That to the cottage, as the crown,
Brought tidings of salvation down.

The fire, with well-dried logs supplied,
Went roaring up the chimney wide;
The huge hall table's oaken face,   15
Scrubbed till it shone, the day to grace,
Bore then upon its massive board
No mark to part the squire and lord.
Then was brought in the lusty brawn
By old blue-coated serving man;   20
Then the grim boar's head frowned on high,
Crested with bays and rosemary.

Well can the green-garbed ranger tell
How, when, and where the monster fell,
What dogs before his death he tore,   25
And all the baiting of the boar.
The wassail round, in good brown bowls
Garnished with ribbons, blithely trowls.
There the huge sirloin reeked; hard by
Plum porridge stood and Christmas pie;   30

Nor failed old Scotland to produce
At such hightide her savory goose.
Then came the merry maskers in,
And carols roared with blithesome din;
If unmelodious was the song
It was a hearty note and strong.
Who lists may in their mumming see
Traces of ancient mystery;
White shirts supplied the masquerade,
And smutted cheeks the visors made;
But oh! what maskers richly dight
Can boast of bosoms half so light!

England was merry England when
Old Christmas brought his sports again.
'Twas Christmas broached the mightiest ale,
'Twas Christmas told the merriest tale;
A Christmas gambol oft could cheer
The poor man's heart through half the year.

— *Marmion.*

1. Scott pictures two Christmas scenes, the one briefly, the other at length. What people and times are the subject of each?

2. In the days of castles and lords, what was the proper custom at Christmas time for the nobleman of the neighborhood to follow? Where did all the neighborhood expect to gather?

3. Describe one of these gatherings: the people attending, the amusements, the feast.

4. What can you find out about the life of Scott that makes you know he loved medieval times?

THE SILVER SHIP

DANIEL DESMOND, a white-headed mariner who for fifty years had followed the sea, had at last given up the pursuit and moored his old hulk in the place of his birth. He was living in the old house which his father had built and where his childish memories clustered. About this place he had spent the sunny hours of childhood; and here he had cast his last anchor.

That afternoon his shaggy dog, Lion, sole house companion, had strayed away whither he knew not; and Daniel shook his head miserably all the evening as he crouched over his fire, which warmed his old bones, to be sure, but seemed unable to send a particle of warmth into his shivering soul. As he sat rubbing his hands slowly over his head, he began to think of his voyages, of the strange lands he had seen.

Everywhere that he had been, to be sure, he had thought it not half so beautiful as the little home on the mountains; but somehow, now that he was here, the old man was restless to be elsewhere. He went to the window and looked out, shading his face with his hands. Nothing to be seen; it was all black and there was no sign of the faithful Lion.

"Dear, dear," he sighed to himself, "if only I could take one voyage more and sail to some new land, where all this trouble should be gone and things wouldn't be quite so black and dismal! Oh, this is a doleful New Year's Eve. It does not look as if the new year were going to be much better than the old ones." And Daniel fumbled about the room with his tallow candle, putting things to rights before he should go to bed.

Even when he had gathered himself up for a night's sleep, he continued to shake his head and mumble over the forlorn world which he had to live in, when he was sure there was one somewhere which was bright and pure. But where was the bark that would sail to such a world and take in such a weather-beaten, dreary fellow? If Daniel had been asked, he would have shaken his head more dolefully than before; and yet near it was, and now indeed began a wonder.

The mariner had shut his eyes upon the old earth with its leafless trees and dingy ground, its gloomy forest hemming in the open clearing, and the open clearing itself, with its stubble and decayed stumps and rotten fences. All that was out of sight, not to be wished back; something better was to come, and that right soon. For now there came, without sound, but filling the place with light, a ship of silver, shaped like the new moon, without mast or sails or rudder and yet floating on the air close by the white-headed mariner.

"Come! sail with us, Daniel," he heard a voice call, and wondering but nothing loath, old Daniel stepped aboard and away sailed the silver ship through the air. He was not alone; for as he sat, feeling a gentle warmth steal through him, there he saw bright figures all about and one more beautiful than the rest, who had called him to the ship and now stood beside him. It was Neonetta, the fairy of New Year's Night; this was her silver ship, and these were her attendants.

The light grew brighter and Daniel's eyes got more open, for everything now was distinct. They had left the dingy

earth; that and the old year had gone off together; they
were sailing over a sea of cloud which lay in billows beneath, while above the bright stars were shining.   There
was no wind to chill, and yet the ship sped on, cutting her
way over the billowy clouds.   5

But what were all the little attendants doing?   Wonderful works they were at, to be sure, for looking behind, Daniel
saw a bright train of them reaching over the ship's side
and receiving from little hands glittering balls of every hue;
they tossed them as if in merry sport, and a shower of the 10
balls shot across the silver ship.   But beyond in the prow
was another train of bright fairies, leaning over the side
and flinging down the balls into the deep.   Once, looking
at the wake, the clouds parted, and Daniel saw that the
train reached far down in a brilliant flowing line; he could 15
see them flinging up the little balls, which grew brighter
and brighter as they neared the ship; but strange to say,
as they shot along to the fairies at the prow they clung
together, and from glittering balls of every hue they
became starry forms of pure white.   20

"These are the white star-makers," said Neonetta
smiling, as old Daniel looked wonderingly at her.   "They
are busy now, for we are sailing to a new land, in which I
am to be queen, and the white stars are to decorate the
country.   Are you not weary of the old earth and the bare 25
trees and ragged ground?"

Daniel nodded vehemently.   "Yes, yes," he mumbled;
but he could not hear himself speak.

"Well," she continued, "that is gone.   I knew you were
weary of it, and so I am taking you to my home.   Oh, 30
it will be glorious there, so pure and still!"   The little
lady waved her hands and faster flew the bright balls, while

the white stars danced through the air as if they too were glad.

"What house shall we live in, Daniel?" asked Neonetta, dancing about him. "Shall it be one with shining spires and glittering domes, with stars for windows and crystals for doors?"

"Let us have a good fire," mumbled Daniel, who at this moment felt the wind from Neonetta's robe.

"No, no!" she cried, looking faint; "but we will have a soft white carpet, and when we walk abroad, soft white mantles over our shoulders. But what shall we have to eat, Daniel? We will pluck the boughs and shake off the sweet fruit that grows on the evergreens. And then the music and the pictures! Music so sweet that it is like the chiming of distant bells, and such pictures as never were seen on the old, dingy earth."

Again the little lady flung up her tiny arms and danced over the silver ship. Faster flew the white stars, and the long train of fairies ascended and descended in a flowing line of changing light. The silver ship sped on, and now the billowy clouds grew thinner, while above, the stars that had shone, went out one by one before a clearer light which began to spread and spread over the sky.

"The new land!" cried Neonetta, dancing about old Daniel, who was now peering over the ship's side. "Come with me, out of my silver ship," and she reached her hand to him.

He looked around; the shining fairies had vanished, but Neonetta was by him. He looked once more. Neonetta was gone, and at the same moment vanished the silver ship.

Old Daniel sprang up. It was dark about him, but his old legs bore him, half groping, toward an opening of light.

He looked beyond, and there, far away in the distant sky, was sailing the silver ship, now turned to gold. In crescent form it was floating in the air and sailing away, away, growing fainter and fainter.

He looked about him and found himself in the new land; for instead of the old dingy earth, there was a pure-white soil, stretching away in gentle ridges. Instead of the naked trees which he had left in all their dismal barrenness, here were fair trees laden with white foliage, their boughs weighed down with the heavy white fruit.

He turned and looked behind him. There stood a little house all dressed in white, with a white robe flung over it that hung down from the roof and over the window top. He looked above and beyond. A mountain raised itself, like a good old man with splendid brow; while a forest spread around like a great company of beautiful maidens clad in snowy white.

The air was still, when a chickadee set up its little note of cheer and welcome. Far off he heard a wagon with its load of wood. As it moved over the new soil a blissful sound rose in the air as if in this new land all toil was sweet with music. Then, better still, he heard a distant baying. "Ho, ho!" it cried, like a clear bell; "ho, ho!" nearer still, coming through the forest.

Old Daniel looked again for the silver ship turned golden, but it had gone, and in its place bright colors of rose and violet filled the sky, as if no clouds were to hang over this beautiful earth, but glad hues of every kind. He listened still and heard now the voice of Neonetta calling to him in the distance.

"Come," she cried, "ere it is too late!" and the voice, even while she spoke, grew fainter.

"Ho, ho!" sounded the baying, nearer now and nearer.

"Come!" cried Neonetta in faint tones.

"Ho, ho!—ho, ho!"

Only a moment more, Queen Neonetta, for thy enchant-
ment over Daniel! The sun will rise, the cock will crow,
good Lion will bound across the snow-covered clearing.
But we will not stay. Hark! there is Lion again—"Ho,
ho!"

1. Tell who Daniel was, what his past life had been like, and
what he was doing at the time of this story.

2. In reading the story what did you first think had happened
to Daniel when he sailed away with Neonetta? Did he really see
Neonetta? Who is she supposed to be? What was the silver ship?

3. What actually had happened to the world outside while Daniel
slept? Where do you first get an inkling that Neonetta was some
kind of frost spirit?

4. Do you think Daniel was glad to find himself still in his own
cottage at daybreak?

WASHINGTON'S BIRTHDAY

By Margaret E. Sangster

'TIS splendid to live so grandly,
That long after you are gone,
The things you did are remembered,
And recounted under the sun;
To live so bravely and purely,
That a nation stops on its way,
And once a year, with banner and drum,
Takes thought of your natal day.

'Tis splendid to have a record
　　So white and free from stain,
That, held to the light, it shows no blot,
　　Though tested and tried amain;
That age to age forever　　　　　　　　　　5
　　Repeats its story of love,
And your birthday lives in a nation's heart
　　All other days above.

And this is Washington's glory,
　　A steadfast soul and true,　　　　　　　10
Who stood for his country's honor
　　When his country's days were few;
And now, when its days are many,
　　And its flag of stars is flung
To the breeze in defiant challenge,　　　　15
　　His name is on every tongue.

Yes, it's splendid to live so bravely,
　　To be so great and strong,
That your memory is ever a tocsin
　　To rally the foes of the wrong;　　　　20
To live so proudly and purely
　　That your people pause in their way,
And year by year, with banner and drum,
　　Take thought of your natal day.

1. What is the "glory of Washington," according to the poem?
For what does the name of Washington stand, in your mind: is
it love for his mother, military knowledge, political wisdom, common
sense, sacrifice of self for country — or what?

2. We cannot all be Washingtons, but we can be like him in some
ways. How? What can we do on the twenty-second of each
February to be more like Washington?

THE PLANTING OF THE APPLE TREE

By William Cullen Bryant

Bryant (1794–1878) is one of America's great poets. Nature furnished him with a goodly part of the subjects for his poetry. Woods, rivers, flowers, birds — all are treated in the lofty style of verse he made his own. Bryant began his professional life as a lawyer, but soon shifted to literary work. He was editor of *The New York Evening Post* for nearly fifty years.

COME, let us plant the apple tree!
    Cleave the tough greensward with the spade;
Wide let its hollow bed be made;
There gently lay the roots, and there
5 Sift the dark mold with kindly care,
    And press it o'er them tenderly,
As round the sleeping infant's feet
We softly fold the cradle sheet;
  · So plant we the apple tree.

10   What plant we in this apple tree?
Buds which the breath of summer days
Shall lengthen into leafy sprays;
Boughs where the thrush with crimson breast
Shall haunt, and sing, and hide her nest;
15   We plant upon the sunny lea
    A shadow for the noontide hour,
    A shelter from the summer shower,
    When we plant the apple tree.

What plant we in this apple tree?
Sweets for a hundred flowery springs
To load the May wind's restless wings,
When from the orchard row he pours
Its fragrance through our open doors; 5
 A world of blossoms for the bee,
Flowers for the sick girl's silent room,
For the glad infant sprigs of bloom,
 We plant with the apple tree.

What plant we in this apple tree? 10
Fruits that shall swell in sunny June,
And redden in the August noon,
And drop when gentle airs come by,
That fan the blue September sky;
 While children, wild with noisy glee, 15
Shall scent their fragrance as they pass,
And search for them the tufted grass
 At the foot of the apple tree.

And when above this apple tree
The winter stars are quivering bright, 20
And winds go howling through the night,
Girls whose young eyes o'erflow with mirth
Shall peel its fruit by the cottage hearth;
 And guests in prouder homes shall see,
Heaped with the orange and the grape, 25
As fair as they in tint and shape,
 The fruit of the apple tree.

The fruitage of this apple tree,
Winds and our flag of stripe and star
Shall bear to coasts that lie afar,
Where men shall wonder at the view,
And ask in what fair groves they grew;
   And they who roam beyond the sea
Shall think of childhood's careless day,
And long hours passed in summer play
   In the shade of the apple tree.

   Each year shall give this apple tree
A broader flush of roseate bloom,
A deeper maze of verdurous gloom,
And loosen, when the frost clouds lower,
The crisp brown leaves in thicker shower.
   The years shall come and pass — but we
Shall hear no longer, where we lie,
The summer's songs, the autumn's sigh,
   In the boughs of the apple tree.

   But time shall waste this apple tree.
Oh, when its aged branches throw
Thin shadows on the ground below,
Shall fraud and force and iron will
Oppress the weak and helpless still?
   What shall the task of mercy be,
Amid the toils, the strifes, the tears
Of those who live when length of years
   Is wasting this apple tree?

"Who planted this old apple tree?"
The children of that distant day
Thus to some aged man shall say;
And gazing on its mossy stem,
The gray-haired man shall answer them:
"A poet of the land was he,
Born in the rude but good old times;
'Tis said he made some quaint old rimes
On planting the apple tree."

1. Bryant describes the planting, the fruitage, and the later years of the apple tree. What does he say about each? When should apple trees be planted? What kinds do you know?

TREES

By Joyce Kilmer

I THINK that I shall never see
A poem lovely as a tree.

A tree whose hungry mouth is pressed
Against the earth's sweet flowing breast;

A tree that looks at God all day   5
And lifts her leafy arms to pray;

A tree that may in summer wear
A nest of robins in her hair;

Upon whose bosom snow has lain;
Who intimately lives with rain.   10

Poems are made by fools like me,
But only God can make a tree.

THE BLUE AND THE GRAY

BY FRANCIS MILES FINCH

Our Civil War was fought (1861–1865) between the North and the South. The Northern, or Union, soldiers wore blue uniforms; the Southern soldiers, or Confederates, wore gray uniforms.

BY THE flow of the inland river,
   Whence the fleets of iron have fled,
Where the blades of the grave-grass quiver,
   Asleep are the ranks of the dead.
5   Under the sod and the dew,
        Waiting the judgment day;
      Under the one, the Blue;
        Under the other, the Gray.

These, in the robings of glory;
10   Those, in the gloom of defeat;
All, with the battle blood gory,
   In the dusk of eternity meet.
      Under the sod and the dew,
        Waiting the judgment day;
15   Under the laurel, the Blue;
        Under the willow, the Gray.

From the silence of sorrowful hours
   The desolate mourners go,
Lovingly laden with flowers,
20   Alike for the friend and the foe.

Under the sod and the dew,
　　Waiting the judgment day;
Under the roses, the Blue;
　　Under the lilies, the Gray.

So with an equal splendor
　　The morning sun rays fall,
With a touch impartially tender
　　On the blossoms blooming for all.
　　Under the sod and the dew,
　　　　Waiting the judgment day;
　　Broidered with gold, the Blue;
　　　　Mellowed with gold, the Gray.

So when the summer calleth,
　　On forest and field of grain,
With an equal murmur falleth
　　The cooling drip of the rain.
　　Under the sod and the dew,
　　　　Waiting the judgment day;
　　Wet with the rain, the Blue;
　　　　Wet with the rain, the Gray.

Sadly, but not with upbraiding,
　　The generous deed was done;
In the storm of the years that are fading
　　No braver battle was won.
　　Under the sod and the dew,
　　　　Waiting the judgment day;
　　Under the blossoms, the Blue;
　　　　Under the garlands, the Gray.

No more shall the war cry sever,
  Or the winding rivers be red;
They banish our anger forever
  When they laurel the graves of our dead.
5   Under the sod and the dew.
    Waiting the judgment day;
  Love and tears, for the Blue;
    Tears and love, for the Gray.

1. Explain the meaning of the Blue and the Gray.

2. Who were the combatants in the Civil War? Which side was victorious? Who were some of the leaders on each side? Name the greatest man on each side, developed by this war.

3. Read the lines in the second stanza that suggest the victor and the vanquished. Read various lines of the poem that put the Blue and the Gray on an equality.

4. What occasion would this poem fit? When are the memories of our fallen heroes especially honored?

THE FALLEN HEROES

MOLDERING side by side
  Peaceful the heroes rest.
Each bravely fought and died
  For the cause he loved the best.
5 Cast no reflections now,
  Silent lie friend and foe;
Honor the graves of all;
  Ask not who lies below.

DEDICATION OF GETTYSBURG CEMETERY

By Abraham Lincoln

On July 1–3, 1863, the greatest battle ever fought on American soil took place between the Union and the Confederate forces at Gettysburg, Pennsylvania. So many men fell on both sides that the battlefield became a large burying ground. Accordingly, it was decided to make it a National Cemetery. At its dedication, November 19, 1863, President Lincoln made the following address — in some ways the greatest speech in the English language.

It is a model of brevity, containing only 267 words. These words are mostly short, Anglo-Saxon terms, insuring simplicity. And finally, the sincerity of the speaker lifts the address to the high plane of true literature.

FOURSCORE and seven years ago, our fathers brought forth upon this continent a new nation, conceived in liberty and dedicated to the proposition that all men are created equal. Now we are engaged in a great civil war, testing whether that nation — or any nation so con- 5 ceived and so dedicated — can long endure.

We are met on a great battlefield of that war. We have come to dedicate a portion of that field as the final resting place for those who here gave their lives that that nation might live. It is altogether fitting and proper that we 10 should do this.

But, in a larger sense, we cannot dedicate, we cannot consecrate, we cannot hallow, this ground. The brave men, living and dead, who struggled here, have consecrated it, far above our poor power to add or detract. The world 15 will little note nor long remember what we say here; but it can never forget what they did here.

It is for us, the living, rather, to be dedicated here to the unfinished work which they who fought here have thus far so nobly advanced. It is rather for us to be here dedicated to the great task remaining before us; — that from these honored dead we take increased devotion to that cause for which they gave the last full measure of devotion; — that we here highly resolve that these dead shall not have died in vain, that this nation, under God, shall have a new birth of freedom, and that government of the people, by the people, for the people, shall not perish from the earth.

1. Edward Everett was the chief speaker at the dedication. His oration was delivered from an open platform on the battlefield to an audience of tens of thousands. He spoke for two hours. Then the President was called upon to "make a few remarks," and this great little speech followed. One who was present said: "The tall form of the President appeared on the stand, and never before have I seen a crowd so vast and restless, after standing so long, so soon stilled and quieted."

2. You can do nothing more profitable than re-read this speech till you know it by heart. The language is simple and direct. As a political document and as an example of fine English, the speech should become one of the permanent possessions of your memory.

With malice toward none; with charity for all; with firmness in the right, as God gives us to see the right, let us strive on to finish the work we are in; to bind up the nation's wounds; to care for him who shall have borne the battle, and for his widow and his orphan — to do all which may achieve and cherish a just and lasting peace among ourselves, and with all nations.

— *Abraham Lincoln.*

FLAG O' MY LAND

By T. A. Daly

U P TO the breeze of the morning I fling you,
   Blending your folds with the dawn in the sky;
There let the people behold you, and bring you
   Love and devotion that never shall die.
Proudly, agaze at your glory, I stand,   5
   Flag o' my land!   Flag o' my land!

Standard most glorious, banner of beauty,
   Whither you beckon me there will I go,
Only to you, after God, is my duty;
   Unto no other allegiance I owe.   10
Heart of me, soul of me, yours to command,
   Flag o' my land!   Flag o' my land!

Pine to palmetto and ocean to ocean,
   Though of strange nations we get our increase,
Here are your worshipers one in devotion.   15
   Whether the bugles blow battle or peace,
Take us and make us your patriot band,
   Flag o' my land!   Flag o' my land!

1. When do we celebrate Flag Day? What is the purpose of that day? Why is this a good poem to read on a Flag Day occasion?
2. Explain the meaning of lines 2, 10, 13-14.

(Used by special permission of Harcourt, Brace, and Company, publishers of T. A. Daly's *McAroni Ballads*.)

TWICE–TOLD TALES

He cometh unto you with a tale which holdeth children from play, and old men from the chimney corner.

— Sir Philip Sidney.

*I cannot tell how the truth may be;
I say the tale as 'twas said to me.*

— Sir Walter Scott.

SWEN SURPRISES THE PRINCESS
(*See opposite page*)

THE YOUTH WHO COULD NOT LIE

A LONG time ago there was a man who had three sons. When the time came for him to die it was his wish to divide his property equally among them, but being old and weak he had forgotten how to count. After he had given his two elder sons their shares he discovered that nothing was left for the youngest.

"My dear Swen," he said, "this is a nice kettle of fish! I have given your brothers all that I possess and now I have nothing to bestow on you but my blessing and a pair of old woolen gloves."

"Don't worry yourself about that, my dear father," replied Swen. "I am quite content with my share. An old pair of woolen gloves is a good thing to have when the cold nips one's fingers, and your blessing is worth more to me than all the gold in the world."

So Swen received the gloves and the blessing and a little later the father died. Swen slung his bow across his shoulders, hung his sword at his side, and tucked his flute away inside his jacket. Then putting the gloves in a pocket he took leave of his brothers, wishing them the best of luck. He had scarcely turned his back before they began to quarrel over their inheritance. Swen, however, had gone whistling on his way to try his fortune in the great world, of which he had heard so much.

"How easily a fellow can march along when he has no pack and not so much as a penny to weigh him down!" thought Swen.

Springtime was coming. All the frozen rivers and brooks had melted and were flowing swiftly along between their steep, rocky banks. High above the fields the first larks were singing.

"I can trill, too," said Swen; and seating himself upon a stone in the middle of the brook he played his flute. So near did the birds come flying that they brushed his cap with their wings and the small trout in the stream danced to the tune he played.

And so the days passed happily. Whenever he was hungry Swen would shoot a hare and roast it. If he lost his way in the forest he would make a path with his sword. In the evening he would play for the dance in the peasants' cottages and get in return a supper and a corner of the barn to sleep in. Wherever Swen wandered he hastened along with so quick a step and so bright a face that the folk who met him would turn round to look at him. "That's a merry youngster for you!" they would say.

At last Swen came to the garden of the king's palace, and there on all sides placards were posted bearing the word "Notice" in large letters. The placards stated that the Lord Chamberlain was dead and that anyone who wished might apply for the place.

"Best is good enough," thought Swen. "I must try my luck here."

With this he walked straight into the royal audience chamber. There sat the king on his throne, hot and perspiring and thoroughly worn out from hearing the many applicants for the position. Beside him, on a high narrow throne, sat his daughter, the princess, swinging her feet and eating cherries out of a silver basket.

"Good day, your majesty," said Swen.

"Good day," replied the king. "Pray, what is your errand?"

"I have come to apply for the place of Lord Chamberlain," answered Swen. "I suppose that anyone who wishes has a right to apply."

"Do you think you are fit for such a post?" asked the king, stroking his long beard.

"I will tell you that when I have had a try at it," said Swen.

The king looked at the princess and the princess looked at the king. The princess was throwing cherry stones on the carpet.

"You shouldn't do that," said Swen. "They might leave stains."

"That's none of your business," replied the princess and went on eating.

"I see you are an archer," said the king, noticing the bow Swen carried. "Can you always hit the bull's-eye?"

"I am not sure of that," answered Swen. "No man can be sure until he tries. At any rate I will shoot a cherry stone out of the princess' hand."

Then he told the princess to stretch out her hand and put a cherry stone on it. She would have been glad to escape from this but the king said, "No, you must do it."

Thereupon she held out her hand and Swen bent his bow. Away flew the arrow and knocked the cherry stone from her hand.

"Ugh!" said the princess, who had become quite red in the face; "that was horrid!"

The king only sat there and smiled. Presently he said, "Well, Swen, what about your sword? You can wield that too, I suppose, better than any other fighter."

"Who can make that boast?" answered Swen. "Any man may meet his master."

"You are an odd fellow," said the king. "All the others who have been in here have said they could do anything, while you make no boast at all."

"That is nearly true," answered Swen; "but there is one thing of which I do boast. I cannot lie."

"There you lie already," said the king. "Every man lies in a hasty moment."

"Well, that is your opinion," replied Swen. "Stick to it if you like, only let me stick to mine."

After a while the king caught sight of the flute in Swen's coat.

"You play the flute, I see," said he. "You are master of that instrument, I dare say."

"Larks and finches trill better than I," answered Swen. "I can, however, play a bit of a tune."

Swen began to play and the birds flew in through the open window and perched around to listen. The cat blinked her eyes as much as to say, "Not so bad, not so bad for a needy-looking wretch like that!"

Even the flies on the windowpane buzzed softly in order to hear him. The princess sat with a cherry in her hand and her mouth open, forgetting to pop the fruit in, so charmed was she with the music. When Swen had come to the end of his last trill the princess said, "It was just like the ice melting, the finches twittering, and the trout dancing in the brook."

"Yes, that was just what I meant it to be," said Swen.

The princess sat there with eyes tender and wistful and the king asked, "What do you think of the princess, Swen? Is she not a beautiful young maiden?"

"Yes," answered Swen, "but I have seen handsomer girls."

This made the princess angry. She got up so hastily that she upset the basket of cherries and then left the great hall as fast as her small feet could carry her.

"You may remain in my service," said the king to Swen. "To-night you shall keep your first watch. Now let us go and eat our supper. All this business makes me hungry."

Swen ate and drank to his heart's content. Afterward he went to the king's bedchamber to keep watch outside the door till daybreak.

"Be sure to stay awake," said the king; "for he who sleeps at his post is a dead man."

The great door leading into the garden was locked. The king took off his crown and gold chains and laid them side by side on the table before Swen. Then he went into his own apartments and it was not long before the young guard heard the royal snores disturbing the quiet of the night.

Swen stood like a statue. He feared to sit down lest he should fall asleep. He thought of all sorts of things while the shadows stole across the sky and the stars began to twinkle. As he stood there he was overcome with a drowsiness the like of which he had never felt before. Sparks danced before his eyes, his head became as heavy as a cannon ball, he found it quite impossible to keep on his legs. The youth tried hard to fix his eyes on the king's crown but could not. Once he thought he saw the princess eating cherries and throwing the stones in his eyes.

"Stop that," he cried aloud and the next moment he was fast asleep.

When he awoke it was early morning. He felt that he had been asleep and looked around in terror. The king's crown and chains had vanished and what was more the great door leading into the garden stood wide open.

When Swen saw that the thieves had left the great door open, he knew that he could save his life if he wished. Nevertheless he stuck to his post, that he might be able to tell what had happened.

Presently the king came out and said, "Good morning, Swen; my crown, please."

"The crown is gone," Swen answered.

"Gone!" shouted the king. "Give me my gold chains, then."

"The chains are gone, too," replied Swen. "I slept like a dog at my post."

"Don't you know that means you are a dead man?" asked the king. "Why did you not escape when the door was open?"

"How could you have got hold of me then, to chop off my head?" answered Swen. "As it is, I can die at once."

At that moment the princess appeared, ready for her morning walk. When she saw the king's angry face she asked what was the matter.

"Oh, it is only Swen, who has slept at his post. Now we must go and chop off his head," said the king.

Thereupon the princess began to sob and cry and wring her hands. She told the king that it must have happened through some mean trick, for she was ready to swear that Swen could never have slept at his post.

"You mustn't swear to anything of the kind," said Swen, "for if you do you swear falsely. I slept — there is nothing more to be said."

But just then the king stopped him.

"You are an honest fellow, Swen," he said, "and now I know you cannot tell a lie. I myself put a sleeping draught in your drink last night and opened the great door to give you a chance to escape."

"It was a shabby trick of yours, your majesty," said Swen. "You ought by rights to pay me damages for this." He was really very angry by this time.

"Will you marry my daughter?" asked the king.

"Thank you, your majesty, I am greatly obliged!" answered Swen, taking the princess' hand in his.

"You would marry her just as quickly, I suppose, if she were a beggar maid?" asked the king.

"Well, I am not so sure of that," answered Swen, scratching his head. "It is a fine thing to marry a real, live princess."

So the king had a most gorgeous wedding for Swen and his daughter and they were all as happy as could be.

"Yet here am I without a thing to give you for a wedding present," said Swen to his bride. "I received only two things from my father. The first was his blessing; that was for me alone, so I cannot give it away. Here is the other — a pair of woolen gloves. These you may have, but you will have to darn them for there are holes in all the fingers."

1. You will agree that this is an unusual story. How is it different from the usual fairy tale of the hero and the princess?

2. Why did everybody like Swen? Why do you like him? Why was the princess attracted by him? What do you think of the princess? The king?

THE ARAB AND HIS HORSE

A CARAVAN on its way to Damascus was once attacked and captured by a party of Arabs. While the robbers were dividing their spoils they were assailed by a troop of Turkish horsemen that had gone out from Acre to escort the caravan.

The scales of fortune were at once turned. The robbers were overpowered. Many of them were killed and the rest were taken prisoners. Among the wounded Arabs was a man named Hassan, who had a very fine horse which also fell into the hands of his captors.

As Hassan lay at night by the side of one of the tents, his feet bound together by a leathern thong, he heard the neighing of his horse. As is the custom in the East, it passed the night in the open air near the tents; but its legs were fastened together so that it could not move. Hassan knew its voice, and wishing to see his favorite horse once more, he crawled along upon his hands and knees till he reached the spot where the horse stood.

"My poor friend," said he, "what will become of you in the hands of the Turks? They will shut you up in close and unwholesome stables with the horses of a pasha. Go back to the tent of your master. Tell my wife that she will never see her husband more, and lick the hands of my children with your tongue, in token of a father's love."

While thus speaking Hassan had gnawed away the thong of goatskin with which the legs of his horse had been fastened together, and the noble animal stood free. But when the horse saw his wounded master at his feet, he stooped his head, and grasping with his teeth the leathern girdle round his waist, he ran off with him in his mouth at full gallop. He thus bore him over many a weary mile of mountain and plain until his desert home was reached. Then, having gently laid him by the side of his wondering wife and children, he fell down dead from exhaustion!

All the tribe to which Hassan belonged wept over the body of the faithful steed, and more than one poet has commemorated in song his sagacity and devotion.

1. This is an old tale of the East. Whether the incident is true or not, the story does not overstate the love of the Arab for his horse, or the devotion of the horse to his master. Some of the finest blood in our race horses comes from the Arabian steeds.

2. For other stories about horses, you will be interested in reading Baldwin's *Fifty Famous Rides and Riders*.

THE PRINCESS' ESCAPE FROM THE GOBLINS

By George Macdonald

THERE was once a little princess whose father was king over a great country full of mountains and valleys. His palace was built upon one of the mountains, and was very grand and beautiful. The princess, whose name was Irene, was born there.

Because her mother was not very strong, the princess was sent soon after her birth to be brought up by country people in a large house. This house, which was half castle, half farmhouse, stood on the side of another mountain, about halfway between its base and its peak.

The princess was a sweet little creature and at the time my story begins was about eight years old, I think; but she got older very fast. Her face was fair and pretty, with eyes like two bits of night sky, each with a star dissolved in the blue. Those eyes! you would have thought they came from there, so often were they turned up in that direction.

The ceiling of her nursery was blue, with stars in it, as like the sky as they could make it. But I doubt if ever she saw the real sky with the stars in it, for a reason which I had better mention at once.

These mountains were full of hollow places underneath; huge caverns and winding ways, some with water running through them and some shining with all colors of the rainbow when a light was taken in. There would not have been much known about them had there not been mines there — great deep pits with long galleries and passages running off from them, which had been dug to get at the ore of which the mountains were full. In the course of digging, the miners came upon many of these natural caverns. A few of them had far-off openings, out on the side of a mountain or into a ravine.

Now in these caverns lived a strange race of beings, called by some gnomes, by some kobolds, by some goblins.

There was a legend current in the country that at one time they lived above the ground and were very like other people. But for some reason the king had laid what they thought too heavy taxes upon them or had required observances of them they did not like or had begun to treat them with more severity, and so they had all disappeared from the face of the country.

According to the legend, however, instead of going to

some other country they had all taken refuge in the mountain caverns, whence they never came out but at night, and then seldom showed themselves in any numbers and never to many people at once. It was only in the least 5 frequented and most difficult parts of the mountains that they were said to gather, even at night, in the open air.

Those who had caught sight of any of them said that they had greatly altered in the course of generations; and no wonder, seeing they lived away from the sun, in cold and 10 wet and dark places. They were now absolutely hideous, both in face and form. And as they grew misshapen in body they had grown in knowledge and cleverness and now were able to do things no mortal could do. But as they grew in cunning they grew in mischief, and their great 15 delight was to annoy the people who lived in the open-air story above them. Although dwarfed and misshapen they had strength equal to their cunning.

In the process of time they had got a king and a government of their own, whose chief business beyond their own 20 simple affairs was to devise trouble for their neighbors.

It will be pretty evident why the little princess never saw the sky at night. Her guardians were much too afraid of the goblins to let her out of the house then, even in company with ever so many attendants; and they had good 25 reason as we shall see by and by.

The princess was very fond of being out of doors, and one morning she nearly cried when she saw that the weather was rainy. But as the hours went on it grew brighter and brighter, and late in the afternoon the sun broke out so 30 gloriously that Irene clapped her hands and called to her nurse: "See, see, Lootie! The sun has had his face washed. Look how bright he is! Do get my hat, and let us go out for a walk. Oh, dear! Oh, dear! how happy I am!"

Lootie was very glad to please the princess. She got her hat and cloak and they set out together for a walk up the mountain, for the road was so hard and steep that the water could not rest upon it and it was always dry enough for walking a few minutes after the rain had ceased.

The clouds were rolling away in broken pieces like great, overwoolly sheep whose wool the sun had bleached till it was almost too white for the eyes to bear. Between them the sky shone with a deeper and purer blue, because of the rain. The trees on the roadside were hung all over with drops which sparkled in the sun like jewels.

The only things that were no brighter for the rain were the brooks that ran down the mountain; they had changed from the clearness of crystal to a muddy brown; but what they lost in color they gained in sound — or at least in noise, for a brook when it is swollen is not so musical as before.

Irene was in raptures with the great brown streams tumbling down everywhere. Lootie shared in her delight, for she too had been confined to the house for three rainy days.

At length Lootie observed that the sun was getting low and said it was time to be going back. She made the remark again and again, but every time the princess begged her to go on just a little farther and a little farther, reminding her that it was much easier to go downhill and saying that when they did turn they would be at home in a moment. So on and on they went, now to look at a group of ferns over whose tops a stream was pouring in a watery arch, now to prick a shining stone from a rock by the wayside, now to watch the flight of some bird.

Suddenly the shadow of a great mountain peak came up from behind and shot in front of them. When the nurse saw it she started and shook, and catching hold of the princess' hand turned and began to run down the hill.

"What's all the haste, nursie?" asked Irene, running alongside of her.

"We must not be out a moment longer."

It was too true. The nurse almost cried. They were much too far from home. It was against orders to be out with the princess one moment after the sun was down, and they were nearly a mile up the mountain! If His Majesty, Irene's papa, were to hear of it Lootie would certainly be dismissed; and to leave the princess would break her heart. It was no wonder she ran.

But Irene was not in the least frightened, not knowing anything to be frightened at. She kept on chattering as well as she could, but it was not easy.

"Lootie! Lootie! why do you run so fast? It shakes my teeth when I talk."

"Then don't talk," said Lootie.

But the princess went on talking. She was always saying, "Look, look, Lootie!" but Lootie paid no more heed to anything she said, only ran on.

"Look, look, Lootie! Don't you see the funny man peeping over the rock?"

Lootie only ran the faster. They had to pass the rock, and when they came nearer saw it was only a lump of the rock itself that she had taken for a man.

"Look, look, Lootie! There's such a curious creature at the foot of that old tree. Look at it, Lootie! It's making faces at us, I think."

Lootie gave a stifled cry and ran faster still — so fast that Irene's little legs could not keep up with her and she fell with a crash. It was a hard, downhill road and she had been running very fast — so it was no wonder she began to cry. This put the nurse nearly beside herself, but all she could do was to run on, the moment she got the princess on her feet again.

"Who's that laughing at me?" said the princess.

"Nobody, child," said the nurse almost angrily.

But that instant there came a burst of coarse tittering from somewhere near, and a hoarse, indistinct voice that seemed to say, "Lies! lies! lies!"

"Oh!" cried the nurse with a sigh that was almost a scream, and ran on faster than ever.

"Nursie! Lootie! I can't run any more. Do let us walk a bit."

"What am I to do?" said the nurse. "Here, I will carry you."

She caught her up, but found her much too heavy to run with and had to set her down again. Then she looked wildly about her, gave a great cry, and said:

"We've taken the wrong turning somewhere, and I don't know where we are. We are lost, lost!"

The terror she was in had quite bewildered her. It was true enough they had lost their way. They had been running down into a little valley in which there was no house to be seen.

Now Irene did not know what good reason there was for her nurse's terror, for the servants all had strict orders never to mention the goblins to her. Before she had time to grow thoroughly alarmed like her nurse, however, she heard the sound of whistling and that revived her.

Presently she saw a boy coming up the road from the valley to meet them. He was the whistler, but before they met, his whistling changed to singing. And this is something like what he sang:

"Ring! dod! bang!
Go the hammers clang!
Hit and turn and bore!
Whizz and puff and roar!
Thus we rive the rocks,
Force the goblin locks,
See the shining ore!
One, two, three —
Bright as gold can be!
Four, five, six —
Shovels, mattocks, picks!
Seven, eight, nine —
Light your lamp at mine.
Ten, eleven, twelve —
Loosely hold the helve.
We're the merry miner boys,
Make the goblins hold their noise."

"I wish you would hold your noise," said the nurse rudely, for the very word "goblin" at such a time and in such a place made her tremble. But whether the boy heard her or not, he did not stop singing:

"Thirteen, fourteen, fifteen —
This is worth the siftin';
Sixteen, seventeen, eighteen —
There's the match, and lay't in.
Nineteen, twenty —
Goblins in a plenty."

"Do be quiet," cried the nurse in a whispered shriek of horror.

But the boy, who was now close at hand, still went on :

> "Hush ! scush ! scurry !
> There you go in a hurry !
> Gobble ! gobble ! goblin !
> There you go a-wobblin' ;   5
> Hobble ! hobble ! hobblin' ;
> Cobble ! cobble ! cobblin' !
> Hob-bob-goblin ! — Huuuuuh !"

"There !" said the boy, as he stood still opposite them. "There ! that'll do for them.   They can't bear singing and 10 they can't stand that song.   They can't sing themselves, for they have no more voice than a crow ; and they don't like other people to sing."

The boy was dressed in a miner's dress, with a curious cap on his head.   He was a very nice-looking boy, with eyes 15 as dark as the mines in which he worked and as sparkling as the crystals in their rocks.   He was about twelve years old.   His face was almost too pale for beauty, which came of his being so little in the open air and the sunlight — for even vegetables grown in the dark are white ; but he 20 looked happy — merry, indeed — perhaps at the thought of having routed the goblins ; and his bearing, as he stood before them, had nothing clownish or rude about it.

"I saw them," he went on, "as I came up ; and I'm very glad I did.   I knew they were after somebody but I 25 couldn't see who it was.   They won't touch you so long as I'm with you."

"Why, who are you ?" asked the nurse, offended at the freedom with which he spoke to them.

"I'm Peter's son."   30

"Who's Peter ?"

"Peter the miner."

"I don't know him."

"I'm his son, though."

"And why should the goblins mind you, pray?"

"Because I don't mind them. I'm used to them."

5 "What difference does that make?"

"If you're not afraid of them, they're afraid of you. I'm not afraid of them. That's all. But it's all that's wanted — up here, that is. It's a different thing down in the mines. They won't always mind that song even, down 10 there. And if anyone sings it they stand grinning at him awfully; and if he gets frightened and misses a word or says a wrong one, they — oh! don't they give it to him!"

"What do they do to him?" asked Irene with a trembling voice.

15 "Don't go frightening the princess," said the nurse.

"The princess!" repeated the little miner, taking off his curious cap. "I beg your pardon, but you oughtn't to be out so late. Everybody knows that's against the law."

"Yes, indeed it is!" said the nurse, beginning to cry 20 again. "And I shall have to suffer for it."

"What does that matter?" said the boy. "It must be your fault. It is the princess who will suffer for it. I hope they didn't hear you call her the princess. If they did they're sure to know her again; they're awfully sharp."

25 "Lootie! Lootie!" cried the princess. "Take me home."

"Don't go on like that," said the nurse to the boy, almost fiercely. "How could I help it? I lost my way."

"You shouldn't have been out so late. You wouldn't have lost your way if you hadn't been frightened," said 30 the boy. "Come along. I'll soon set you right again. Shall I carry your little Highness?"

"Impertinence!" murmured the nurse; but she did not

say it aloud, for she thought if she made him angry he might take his revenge by telling some one in the house and then it would be sure to come to the king's ears.

"No, thank you," said Irene. "I can walk very well, though I can't run so fast as nursie. If you will give me one hand Lootie will give me another, and then I shall get on famously."

They soon had her between them, holding a hand of each.

"Now let's run," said the nurse.

"No, no," said the little miner. "That's the worst thing you can do. If you hadn't run before, you would not have lost your way. And if you run now, they will be after you in a moment."

"I don't want to run," said Irene.

"You don't think of me," said the nurse.

"Yes, I do, Lootie. The boy says they won't touch us if we don't run."

"Yes, but if they know at the house that I've kept you out so late, I shall be turned away and that would break my heart."

"Turned away, Lootie! Who would turn you away?"

"Your papa, child."

"But I'll tell him it was all my fault. And you know it was, Lootie."

"He won't mind that. I'm sure he won't."

"Then I'll cry and go down on my knees to him and beg him not to take away my own dear Lootie."

The nurse was comforted at hearing this and said no more. They went on, walking pretty fast but taking care not to run a step.

"I want to talk to you," said Irene to the little miner; "but it's so awkward. I don't know what your name is."

"My name's Curdie, little princess."

"What a funny name! Curdie! What more?"

"Curdie Peterson. What's your name, please?"

"Irene."

"What more?"

"I don't know what more. What more is it, Lootie?"

"Princesses haven't more than one name. They don't want more."

"Then, Curdie, you must call me Irene and no more."

"No, indeed," said the nurse indignantly. "He shall do no such thing."

"What shall he call me, then, Lootie?"

"Your Royal Highness."

"My Royal Highness! What's that? No, no, Lootie. I won't be called names. You told me once yourself it's only rude children that call names and I'm sure Curdie wouldn't be rude. Curdie, my name's Irene."

"Well, Irene," said Curdie, with a glance at the nurse, "it is very kind of you to let me call you anything. I like your name very much."

He expected the nurse to interfere again, but she was too frightened to speak. She was staring at something a few yards before them, where the path narrowed between rocks so that only one could pass at a time.

"It is very much kinder of you to go out of your way to take us home," said Irene.

"I'm not going out of my way yet," said Curdie. "It's on the other side of those rocks the path turns off to my father's."

"You wouldn't think of leaving us till we're safe home, I'm sure," gasped the nurse.

"Of course not," said Curdie.

At that instant the something in the middle of the way, which had looked like a great lump of earth brought down by the rain, began to move. One after another it shot out four long things like two arms and two legs, but it was now too dark to tell what they were. The nurse began to tremble from head to foot. Irene clasped Curdie's hand yet faster and Curdie began to sing again:

"One, two —
Hit and hew!
Three, four —
Blast and bore!
Five, six —
There's a fix!
Seven, eight —
Hold it straight.
Nine, ten —
Hit again!
Hurry! scurry!
Bother! smother!
There's a toad
In the road!
Smash it!
Squash it!
Fry it!
Dry it!
You're another!
Up and off!
There's enough! — Huuuuuuh!"

As he uttered the last words, Curdie let go his hold of his companion and rushed at the thing in the road as if he would trample it under his feet. It gave a great spring and ran straight up one of the rocks like a huge spider. Curdie turned back laughing and took Irene's hand again. She grasped him very tight but said nothing till they had passed the rocks. A few yards more and she found herself on a part of the road she knew, and was able to speak again.

"Do you know, Curdie, I don't quite like your song; it sounds to me rather rude," she said.

"Well, perhaps it is," answered Curdie. "I never thought of that; it's a way we have. We do it because they don't like it."

"Who don't like it?"

"The cobs, as we call them."

"Don't," said the nurse.

"Why not?" said Curdie.

"I beg you won't. Please don't."

"Oh, if you ask me that way, of course I won't, though I don't know a bit why. Look! there are the lights of your great house down below. You'll be at home in five minutes now."

Nothing more happened. They reached home in safety. Nobody had missed them or even known they had gone out; and they arrived at the door belonging to their part of the house without anyone seeing them.

— *The Light Princess*.

1. All sorts of stories of goblins have long been told in northern Europe. In some of the stories a princess is made captive by the fairies. Why could they not get the princess in this tale?

2. Why were the goblins afraid of Curdie? Do you think his queer songs had anything to do with his chasing the goblins?

3. Why did the king object to having the princess know about the goblins? Would it have been better for her had she known?

THE SPIDER AND THE FLY

By Mary Howitt

"WILL you walk into my parlor?" said the Spider to
the Fly.

"'Tis the prettiest little parlor that ever you did spy;

The way into my parlor is up a winding stair,

And I have many curious things to show when you are 5
there."

"Oh, no, no," said the little Fly, "to ask me is in vain,

For who goes up your winding stair can ne'er come down
again!"

"I'm sure you must be weary, dear, with soaring up so 10
high;

Will you rest upon my little bed?" said the Spider to the
Fly.

"There are pretty curtains drawn around, the sheets are
fine and thin,   15

And if you like to rest awhile I'll snugly tuck you in."

"Oh, no, no," said the little Fly, "for I've often heard it
said,

They never, never wake again, who sleep upon your bed!"

Said the cunning Spider to the Fly, "Dear friend, what can 20
I do

To prove the warm affection I've always felt for you?

I have within my pantry good store of all that's nice;

I'm sure you're very welcome; will you please to take a
slice?"   25

"Oh, no, no," said the little Fly, "kind sir, that cannot be;
I've heard what's in your pantry and I do not wish to see."

"Sweet creature!" said the Spider, "you're witty and you're
wise!
5 How handsome are your gauzy wings, how brilliant are
your eyes!
I have a little looking-glass upon my parlor shelf,
If you'll step in one moment, dear, you shall behold yourself."
10 "I thank you, gentle sir," she said, "for what you're
pleased to say,
And bidding you good morning now, I'll call another day."

The Spider turned him round about and went into his den,
For well he knew the silly Fly would soon be back again;
15 So he wove a subtle web in a little corner sly,
And set his table ready to dine upon the Fly.
Then he went out to his door again and merrily did sing,
"Come hither, hither, pretty Fly, with the pearl-and-silver
wing;
20 Your robes are green and purple, there's a crest upon your
head,
Your eyes are like the diamond bright but mine are dull as
lead."

Alas, alas! how very soon this silly little Fly,
25 Hearing his wily, flattering words came slowly flitting by;
With buzzing wings she hung aloft, then near and nearer
drew,
Thinking only of her brilliant eyes and green and purple
hue,

Thinking only of her crested head — poor foolish thing!
    At last
Up jumped the cunning Spider and fiercely held her fast.

He dragged her up his winding stair into his dismal den,
Within his little parlor — but she ne'er came out again!   5
And now, my dear young friends, who may this story read,
To idle, silly, flattering words, I pray you, ne'er give heed;
Unto an evil counselor, close heart, and ear, and eye,
And take a lesson from this tale of the Spider and the Fly.

    1. In how many different ways did the spider try to tempt the fly?
How did he finally get her into his web?
    2. What is meant by the saying, "Remember the spider and the fly"?

THE IMAGINARY BANQUET

IT IS related that one Schacabac was reduced by reverses
of fortune to the necessity of begging his bread. In
this occupation he acquitted himself with great address;
his chief aim being to procure admission, by bribing the
officers and domestics, into the houses of the great and, by 5
having access to their persons, excite their compassion.

By this means he one day gained admission to a magnificent building, in which, luxuriously reclining on a sofa
in a room richly furnished, he found the master, a Barmecide, who in the most obliging manner thus addressed him: 10

"Welcome to my house. What dost thou wish, my
friend?"

Schacabac. I am in great want. I suffer from hunger and have nothing to eat.

The Barmecide was much astonished at this answer. "What!" he cried. "What! Nothing to eat! Am I in the city and thou in it hungry? It is a thing I cannot endure. Thou shalt be happy as heart can wish. Thou must stay and partake of my salt. Whatever I have is thine."

Schac. O my master! I have not patience to wait, for I am in a state of extreme hunger. I have eaten nothing this day.

Barm. What! is it true that even at this late hour thou hast not broken thy fast? Alas! poor man, he will die with hunger. Halloo, there, boy! bring us instantly a basin of water that we may wash our hands.

Although no boy appeared and Schacabac observed neither basin nor water, the Barmecide nevertheless began to rub his hands as if some one held the water for him; and while he was doing this he urged Schacabac to do the same. Schacabac by this supposed that the Barmecide was fond of fun, and as he liked a jest himself he approached and pretended to wash his hands and afterwards to wipe them with a napkin held by the attendant.

Barm. Now bring us something to eat and take care not to keep us waiting. Set the table here. Now lay the dishes on it. Come, friend, sit down at the table here. Eat and be not ashamed, for thou art hungry and I know how thou art suffering from the violence of thy hunger.

Saying these words, although nothing had been brought to eat, he began as if he had taken something on his plate and pretended to put it in his mouth and chew it, adding, "Eat, I beg of thee; for a hungry man, thou seemest to have but a poor appetite. What thinkest thou of this bread?"

Schac. (*to himself*). Verily this is a man that loveth to jest with others. (*To the Barmecide*) O my master, never in my life have I seen bread more beautifully white than 5 this or of a sweeter taste. Where didst thou procure it?

Barm. This was made by a slave of mine whom I purchased for five hundred pieces of gold. (*Calling aloud*) Boy! bring to us the dish the like of which is not found among the viands of kings. Eat, O my guest! for thou art 10 hungry — violently so — and in absolute want of food.

Schac. (*twisting his mouth about as if eating heartily*). Verily this is a dish worthy the table of the great Solomon.

Barm. Eat on, my friend. Boy! place before us the lamb fattened with almonds. Now this is a dish never 15 found but at my table and I wish thee to eat thy fill of it.

As he said this the Barmecide pretended to take a piece in his hand and put it to Schacabac's mouth. Schacabac held his head forward, opened his mouth, and pretended to take the piece, and to chew and swallow it with the 20 greatest delight.

Schac. O my master! verily this dish hath not its equal in sweetness of flavor.

Barm. Do justice to it, I pray, and eat more of it. The goose, too, is very fat. Try only a leg and a wing. 25 Ho, there, boy! bring us a fresh supply.

Schac. Oh, no, my lord! for in truth, I cannot eat any more.

Barm. Let the dessert, then, be served, and the fruit brought. Taste these dates; they are just gathered and 30 very good. Here, too, are some fine walnuts and here some delicious raisins. Eat and be not ashamed.

Schacabac's jaws were by this time weary of chewing nothing. "I assure thee," said he, "I am so full that I cannot eat another morsel of this cheer."

He had hardly finished this speech before the Barmecide 5 burst into laughter. "Come," said he, "I have long been looking for a man of thy character. Let us be friends. Thou has kept up the jest in pretending to eat; now thou shalt make my house thy home, and eat in earnest."

Having said this he clapped his hands. Several slaves 10 instantly appeared, whom he ordered to set out the table and serve the dinner. His commands were quickly obeyed and Schacabac now enjoyed in reality the good things of which he had before partaken only in dumb show.

— Arabian Nights.

1. This tale is from one of the oldest books of stories we know — the *Arabian Nights.* Some think this book was compiled for the daughter of Queen Esther, of Old Testament history. Is it still interesting? How is it different from modern stories you have read?

THE PINE–TREE SHILLINGS

By Nathaniel Hawthorne

CAPTAIN JOHN HULL was the mintmaster of Massachusetts and coined all the money that was made there. This was a new line of business, for in the earlier days of the colony the current coinage consisted of gold 5 and silver money of England, Portugal, and Spain. These coins being scarce, the people were often forced to barter their commodities instead of selling them.

For instance, if a man wanted to buy a coat he perhaps exchanged a bearskin for it. If he wished for a barrel of molasses he might purchase it with a pile of pine boards. Musket bullets were used instead of farthings. The Indians had a sort of money, called wampum, which was made of clamshells; and this strange sort of specie was likewise taken in payment of debts by the English settlers. Bank bills had never been heard of. There was not money enough of any kind, in many parts of the country, to pay the salaries of the ministers; so that they sometimes had to take quintals of fish, bushels of corn, or cords of wood, instead of silver or gold.

As the people grew more numerous and their trade one with another increased, the want of current money was still more sensibly felt. To supply the demand the General Court passed a law for establishing a coinage of shillings, sixpences, and threepences. Captain John Hull was appointed to manufacture this money and was to have about one shilling out of every twenty to pay him for the trouble of making them.

Hereupon all the old silver in the colony was handed over to Captain John Hull. The battered silver cans and tankards, I suppose, and silver buttons of worn-out coats, and silver hilts of swords that had figured at court — all such curious old articles were doubtless thrown into the melting pot together. But by far the greater part of the silver consisted of bullion from the mines of South America, which the English buccaneers — who were little better than pirates — had taken from the Spaniards and brought to Massachusetts.

All this old and new silver being melted down and coined, the result was an immense amount of splendid shillings, sixpences, and threepences. Each had the date, 1652, on the one side and the figure of a pine tree on the other. Hence they were called pine-tree shillings. And for every twenty shillings that he coined, you will remember, Captain John Hull was entitled to put one shilling into his own pocket.

The magistrates soon began to suspect that the mint-master would have the best of the bargain. They offered him a large sum of money if he would but give up that twentieth shilling which he was continually dropping into his own pocket. But Captain Hull declared himself perfectly satisfied with the shilling. And well he might be; for so diligently did he labor that in a few years his pockets, his moneybags, and his strong box were overflowing with pine-tree shillings.

When the mintmaster had grown very rich, a young man, Samuel Sewall by name, came a-courting to his only daughter. His daughter — whose name I do not know, but we will call her Betsey — was a fine, hearty damsel, by no means so slender as some young ladies of our own days. On the contrary, having always fed heartily on pumpkin pies, doughnuts, Indian puddings, and other Puritan dainties, she was as round and plump as a pudding herself. With this round, rosy Miss Betsey did Samuel Sewall fall in love. As he was a young man of good character, industrious in his business, and a member of the church, the mintmaster very readily gave his consent.

"Yes, you may take her," said he, in his rough way, " and you'll find her a heavy burden enough ! "

On the wedding day, we may suppose that honest John Hull dressed himself in a plum-colored coat, all the buttons of which were made of pine-tree shillings. The buttons

of his waistcoat were sixpences and the knees of his small-
clothes were buttoned with silver threepences. Thus
attired he sat with great dignity in Grandfather's chair;
and being a portly old gentleman he completely filled it
from elbow to elbow. On the opposite side of the room, 5
between her bridesmaids, sat Miss Betsey. She was
blushing with all her might and looked like a full-blown
peony or a great red apple.

There, too, was the bridegroom, dressed in a fine purple
coat and gold-lace waistcoat, with as much other finery 10
as the Puritan laws and customs would allow him to put on.
His hair was cropped close to his head, because Governor
Endicott had forbidden any man to wear it below the ears.
But he was a very personable young man, and so thought
the bridesmaids and Miss Betsey herself. 15

The mintmaster also was pleased with his new son-in-law;
especially as he had courted Miss Betsey out of pure love
and had said nothing at all about her portion. So when
the marriage ceremony was over, Captain Hull whispered
a word to two of his menservants, who immediately went 20
out and soon returned lugging in a large pair of scales.
They were such a pair as wholesale merchants use for
weighing bulky commodities, and quite a bulky commodity
was now to be weighed in them.

"Daughter Betsey," said the mintmaster, "get into one 25
side of these scales."

Miss Betsey — or Mrs. Sewall, as we must now call her
— did as she was bid, like a dutiful child, without any
question of the why and wherefore. But what her father
could mean, unless to make her husband pay for her by the 30
pound (in which case she would have been a dear bargain),
she had not the least idea.

"And now," said honest John Hull to the servants, "bring that box hither."

The box to which the mintmaster pointed was a huge, square, ironbound, oaken chest. The servants tugged with might and main but could not lift this enormous receptacle and were finally obliged to drag it across the floor. Captain Hull then took a key from his girdle, unlocked the chest, and lifted its ponderous lid. Behold! it was full to the brim of bright pine-tree shillings, fresh from the mint; and Samuel Sewall began to think that his father-in-law had got possession of all the money in the Massachusetts treasury. But it was only the mint-master's honest share of the coinage.

Then the servants, at Captain Hull's command, heaped double handfuls of shillings into one side of the scales while Betsey remained in the other. Jingle, jingle, went the shillings, as handful after handful was thrown in, till plump and ponderous as she was, they fairly weighed the young lady from the floor.

"There, son Sewall!" cried the honest mintmaster, resuming his seat in Grandfather's chair, "take these shillings for my daughter's portion. Use her kindly and thank Heaven for her. It is not every wife that's worth her weight in silver!"

— Grandfather's Chair.

1. What is money used for? What metals do we use in making our coins? What besides metals is used in making money? What did the colonists use for money?

2. What were pine-tree shillings? How did Captain Hull come to have a chest full of silver? How did the colonists obtain the metal?

3. Tell what happened at the Sewall-Hull wedding.

4. Explain: barter, commodity, wampum, quintal, buccaneer, shilling, receptacle.

THE CAT'S PILGRIMAGE

By James A. Froude

THE cat set off by herself to learn how to be happy and to be all that a cat could be. It was a fine sunny morning. She determined to try the meadow first and after an hour or two, if she had not succeeded then, to go off to the wood.

A blackbird was piping away on a thorn bush as if his heart was running over with happiness. The cat had breakfasted and so was able to listen without any mixture of feelings. She didn't sneak. She walked boldly up under the bush, and the bird, seeing she had no bad purpose, sat still and sang on.

"Good morning, blackbird; you seem to be enjoying yourself this fine day."

"Good morning, cat."

"Blackbird, it is an odd question, perhaps. What ought one to do to be as happy as you?"

"Do your duty, cat."

"But what is my duty, blackbird?"

"Take care of your little ones, cat."

"I haven't any," said she.

"Then sing to your mate," said the bird.

"Tom is dead," said she.

"Poor cat!" said the bird. "Then sing over his grave. If your song is sad you will find your heart grow lighter for it."

"Mercy!" thought the cat. "I could do a little singing

with a living lover but I never heard of singing for a dead one. But you see, bird, it isn't cat's nature. When I am cross I mew. When I am pleased I purr; but I must be pleased first. I can't purr myself into happiness."

5   "I am afraid there is something the matter with your heart, my cat. It wants warming. Good-by." The blackbird flew away, and the cat looked sadly after him.

"He thinks I am like him, and he doesn't know that a cat is a cat," said she. "As it happens now, I feel a great 10 deal, for a cat. If I hadn't a heart I shouldn't be unhappy. I'll try that great fat fellow."

The ox lay placidly chewing, with content beaming out of his eyes and playing on his mouth. "Ox," she said, "what is the way to be happy?"

15   "Do your duty," said the ox.

"Bother," said the cat, "duty again! What is it, ox?"

"Get your dinner," said the ox.

"But it is got for me, ox, and I have nothing to do but eat it."

20   "Well, eat it then, like me."

"So I do, but I am not happy for all that."

"Then you are a very wicked, ungrateful cat."

The ox munched away. A bee buzzed into a buttercup under the cat's nose. "I beg your pardon," said the cat, 25 "it isn't curiosity — what are you doing?"

"Doing my duty; don't stop me, cat."

"But, bee, what is your duty?"

"Making honey," said the bee.

"I wish I could make honey," sighed the cat.

30   "Do you mean to say you can't?" said the bee. "How stupid you must be! What do you do then?"

"I do nothing, bee. I can't get anything to do."

"You won't get anything to do, you mean, you lazy cat! You are a good-for-nothing drone. Do you know what we do to our drones? We kill them, and that is all they are fit for. Good morning to you."

"Well, I am sure," said the cat, "they are treating me civilly! I would better have stopped at home. at this rate. Stroke my whiskers! heartless! wicked! good for nothing! stupid! and only fit to be killed! This is a pleasant beginning, anyhow. I must look for some wiser creatures than these are. What shall I do? I know! I know where I will go."

It was in the middle of the wood. The bush was very dark, but she found him by his wonderful eye. Presently as she got used to the light she distinguished a sloping roll of feathers, a rounded breast, surmounted by a round head set close to the body without an inch of neck intervening. "How wise he looks!" she said. "What a brain! what a forehead! His head is not long, but what an expanse and what a depth of earnestness!"

The owl sloped his head a little on one side, the cat slanted hers upon the other. The owl set it straight again, the cat did the same. They stood looking this way for some minutes; at last, in a whispering voice, the owl said, "What are you who presume to look into my repose? Pass on upon your way and carry elsewhere those prying eyes."

"O wonderful owl," said the cat, "you are wise, and I want to be wise; and I am come to you to teach me." A film floated backward and forward over the owl's eyes; it was his way of showing that he was pleased. "I have heard in our schoolroom," went on the cat, "that you sat on the shoulder of Pallas and she told you all about it."

"And what would you know, O my daughter?" said the owl.

"Everything," said the cat, "everything. First of all, how to be happy."

5 "Mice content you not, my child, even as they content not me," said the owl. "It is good."

"Mice, indeed!" said the cat; "no, parlor cats don't eat mice. I have better than mice and no trouble to get it, but I want something more."

10 "The body's meat is provided. You would now fill your soul."

"I want to improve," said the cat. "I want something to do. I want to find out what the creatures call my duty."

15 "You would learn how to employ those happy hours of your leisure — rather, how to make them happy by a worthy use. Meditate, O cat! meditate! meditate!"

"That is the very thing," said she. "Meditate! that is what I like above all things. Only I want to know how; 20 I want something to meditate about. Tell me, owl, and I will bless you every hour of the day as I sit by the parlor fire."

"I will tell you," answered the owl, "what I have been thinking of ever since the moon changed. You shall take 25 it home with you and think about it too, and the next full moon you shall come again to me; we will compare our conclusions."

"Delightful! delightful!" said the cat. "What is it? — I will try this minute."

30 "From the beginning," replied the owl, "our race have been considering which first existed, the owl or the egg. The owl comes from the egg, and the egg from the owl."

"Mercy!" said the cat.

"From sunrise to sunset I ponder on it, O cat! When I reflect on the beauty of the complete owl I think that must have been first, as the cause is greater than the effect. When I remember my own childhood I incline the other way."

"Well, but how are we to find out?" said the cat.

"Find out!" said the owl. "We can never find out. The beauty of the question is that its solution is impossible. What would become of all our delightful reasonings, O unwise cat, if we were so unhappy as to know?"

"But what in the world is the good of thinking about it, if you can't find an answer?"

"My child, that is a foolish question. It is good, because thinking about profound things may stimulate wonder. It is in wonder that the owl is great."

"Then you don't know anything at all," said the cat. "What did you sit on Pallas's shoulder for? You must have gone to sleep."

"Your tone is overflippant, cat, for philosophy. The highest of all knowledge is to know that we know nothing."

The cat made two great arches with her back and her tail. "Bless the mother that laid you," said she. "You were dropped by mistake in a goose nest. You won't do. I don't know much, but I am not such a creature as you, anyhow. A great white thing!" She straightened her body, stuck her tail upon end, and marched off with much dignity.

But though she respected herself rather more than before, she was not on the way to the end of her difficulties. She tried all the creatures she met without advancing a step. They had all the old story, "Do your duty." But each had its own and not one could tell her what hers was. Only one point they all agreed upon — the duty of getting their dinner when they were hungry. The day wore on and she began to think she would like hers.

5 It was a great day in the fox's cave. The eldest cub had the night before brought home his first goose and they were just sitting down to it as the cat came by. "Ah, my young lady! what, you in the woods! Bad feeding at home, eh? Come out to hunt for yourself?"

10 The goose smelt excellent; the cat couldn't help a wistful look. She was only come, she said, to pay her respects to her wild friends. "Just in time," said the fox. "Sit down and take a bit of dinner; I see you want it. Make room, you cubs; place a seat for the lady."

15 "Why, thank you," said the cat. "Yes; I acknowledge it is not unwelcome. Pray don't disturb yourselves, young foxes. I am hungry. I met a rabbit on my way here. I was going to eat him but he talked so prettily I let him go."

20 The cubs looked up from their plates and burst out laughing. "For shame, young rascals," said the father. "Where are your manners? Mind your dinner and don't be so rude."

"Fox," she said, when dinner was over and the cubs were
25 gone to play, "you are very clever. The other creatures are all stupid." The fox bowed. "Your family were always clever," she continued. "I have heard about them in the books they use in our schoolroom. It is many years since your ancestor stole the crow's dinner."

30 "Don't say stole, cat; it is not pretty — obtained by superior ability."

"I beg your pardon," said the cat; "it is all from living

with men. That is not the point. Well, but I want to know whether you are any wiser or any better than foxes were then."

"Really," said the fox, "I am what nature made me. I don't know. I am proud of my ancestors and do my best 5 to keep up the credit of the family."

"Well, but fox, I mean do you improve? Do I? Do any of you? The men are always talking of doing their duty, and that, they say, is the way to improve and to be happy. And as I was not happy I thought that had, 10 perhaps, something to do with it; so I came out to talk to the creatures. They also had the old chant — duty, duty, duty; but none of them could tell me what mine was, or whether I had any."

The fox smiled. "Another leaf out of your schoolroom," 15 said he. "Can't they tell you there?"

"Indeed," she said, "they are very absurd. They say a great deal about themselves, but they only speak disrespectfully of us. If such creatures as they can do their duty and improve and be happy, why can't we?" 20

"They say they do, do they?" said the fox. "What do they say of me?" The cat hesitated. "Don't be afraid of hurting my feelings, cat. Out with it."

"They do all justice to your abilities, fox," said she; "but your morality, they say, is not high. They say you 25 are a rogue."

"Morality!" said the fox. "Very moral and good they are! And you really believe that? What do they mean by calling me a rogue?"

"They mean you take whatever you can get, without 30 caring whether it is just or not."

"My dear cat, it is very well for a man, if he can't bear

his own face, to paint a pretty one on a panel and call it a looking-glass, but you don't mean that it deceives you!"

"Teach me," said the cat. "I fear I am weak."

"Who gets justice from the men unless they can force it? Ask the horses that draw their plows. I don't mean it is wrong of the men to do as they do, but they need not deny it."

"You surprise me," said the cat.

"My good cat, there is but one law in the world. The weakest goes to the wall. The men are sharper-witted than the creatures and so they get the better of them and use them. They may call it just if they like, but when a tiger eats a man I guess he has just as much justice on his side as the man when he eats a sheep."

"And that is the whole of it," said the cat. "Well, it is very sad. What do you do with yourself?"

"My duty, to be sure," said the fox; "use my wits and enjoy myself. My dear friend, you and I are on the lucky side. We eat and are not eaten."

"Except by the hounds now and then," said the cat.

"Yes, by brutes that forget their nature and sell their freedom to the men," said the fox bitterly. "In the meantime my wits have kept my skin whole hitherto, and I bless nature for making me a fox and not a goose."

"Are you happy, fox?"

"Happy! yes, of course. So would you be if you would do as I do and use your wits. My good cat, I should be miserable as you if I found my geese every day at the cave's mouth. I have to hunt for them, lie for them, sneak for them, fight for them; cheat those old fat farmers and bring out what there is inside me; and then I am happy — of course I am."

"It has a rough end, this life of yours, if you keep clear of the hounds, fox," said the cat.

"What! a rope in the yard! Well, it must end some day, and when the farmer catches me I shall be getting old and my brains will be taking leave of me, so the sooner I go the better, that I may disgrace myself the less. Better be jolly while it lasts than sit mewing out your life and grumbling at it as a bore."

"Well," said the cat, "I am very much obliged to you. I suppose I may even get home again. I shall not find a wiser friend than you and perhaps I shall not find another good-natured enough to give me so good a dinner. But it is very sad."

"Think of what I have said," answered the fox. "I'll call at your house some night; you will take me a walk round the yard and then I'll show you."

"Not quite," thought the cat, as she trotted off; "one good turn deserves another, that is true; and you have given me a dinner. But they have given me many at home and I mean to take a few more of them; so I think you mustn't go round our yard."

"Ah! I see everybody likes what he was bred to," sighed the cat. "Train the cat as a cat should go and she will be happy and ask no questions. As for me, I must not seek for what is impossible. Since I have been bred to nothing, I must try to like that, but I consider myself an unfortunate cat."

1. What was really wrong with the cat's way of living that made her unhappy? To whom did she go for advice?

2. What did the owl tell the cat? What did the fox advise? Was the advice of either good? Discuss. Explain the reference to Pallas and the owl; to the fox and the crow.

SOLOMON AND THE BEES

By John G. Saxe

WHEN Solomon was reigning in his glory,
    Unto his throne the Queen of Sheba came —
So in the Talmud you may read the story —
    Drawn by the magic of the monarch's fame,
5 To see the splendors of his court and bring
Some fitting tribute to the mighty king.

Nor this alone; much had Her Highness heard
    What flowers of learning graced the royal speech;
What gems of wisdom dropped with every word;
10   What wholesome lessons he was wont to teach
In pleasing proverbs; and she wished, in sooth,
To know if Rumor spoke the simple truth.

Besides the queen had heard — which piqued her most —
    How through the deepest riddles he could spy;
15 How all the curious arts that women boast
    Were quite transparent to his piercing eye;
And so the queen had come — a royal guest —
To put the sage's cunning to the test.

And straight she held before the monarch's view,
20   In either hand, a radiant wreath of flowers;
The one, bedecked with every charming hue,
    Was newly culled from nature's choicest bowers;
The other, no less fair in every part,
Was the rare product of divinest art.

"Which is the true, and which the false?" she said.
　　Great Solomon was silent.　All amazed,
Each wondering courtier shook his puzzled head,
　　While at the garlands long the monarch gazed,
As one who sees a miracle, and fain, 　　　　　　　　　5
For very rapture, ne'er would speak again.

"Which is the true?" once more the woman asked,
　　Pleased at the fond amazement of the king;
"So wise a head should not be hardly tasked,
　　Most learnèd liege, with such a trivial thing!" 　　10
But still the sage was silent; it was plain
A deepening doubt perplexed the royal brain.

While thus he pondered, presently he sees,
　　Hard by the casement — so the story goes —
A little band of busy, bustling bees, 　　　　　　　　15
　　Hunting for honey in a withered rose.
The monarch smiled and raised his royal head;
"Open the window!" — that was all he said.

The window opened at the king's command,
　　Within the room the eager insects flew 　　　　　　20
And sought the flowers in Sheba's dexter hand!
　　And so the king and all the courtiers knew
That wreath was nature's — and the baffled queen
Returned to tell the wonders she had seen.

　　1. Words:　Talmud = Book of Jewish laws;　fond = Foolish;
dexter = Right.
　　2. Many stories are based on the fact that men of wisdom are
keen observers.　Why are you glad to see Solomon outwit the queen?
Why did she ask Solomon the question she did?

KING ROBERT OF SICILY

BY LEIGH HUNT

KING ROBERT of Sicily, brother of Pope Urban and of the Emperor Valemond, was a prince of great courage and renown. But he had a temper so proud and impatient that he did not choose to bend his knee to Heaven itself, but would sit twirling his beard and looking with something worse than indifference round about him during the gravest services of the church.

One day while he was present at vespers his attention was excited by some words in the *Magnificat*, in consequence of a sudden dropping of the choristers' voices. Being far too great and warlike a prince to know anything about Latin, he asked a chaplain near him the meaning; and being told that the words meant, "He hath put down the mighty from their seat and hath exalted the humble," he observed that men like himself were not so easily put down, much less supplanted by poor creatures whom people called "humble."

The chaplain, doubtless out of pure astonishment and horror, made no reply; and His Majesty, partly from the heat of the weather and partly to relieve himself from the rest of the service, fell asleep.

After some lapse of time the royal "sitter in the seat of the scornful," owing as he thought to the sound of the organ but in reality to a great droning fly in his ear, woke up in more than his usual state of impatience; and he was preparing to vent it, when to his astonishment he perceived the church empty. Every soul was gone excepting a deaf old woman who was turning up the cushions.

He addressed her to no purpose. He spoke louder and louder and was proceeding as well as rage and amaze would let him to try if he could walk out of the church without a 5 dozen lords before him, when, suddenly catching a sight of his face, the old woman uttered a cry of "Thieves!" and shuffling away closed the door behind her.

King Robert looked at the door in silence, then round about him at the empty church, then at himself. His 10 cloak of ermine was gone. The coronet was taken from his cap, the very jewels from his fingers. "Thieves, verily!" thought the king, turning white from shame and rage. "Here is conspiracy — open rebellion! Horses shall tear them all to pieces. What, ho, there! Open the door! 15 Open the door for the king!"

"For the constable, you mean," said a voice through the keyhole. "You're a pretty fellow!"

The king said nothing.

"Thinking to escape in the king's name," said the voice, 20 "after hiding to plunder his closet. We've got you."

Still the king said nothing.

The sexton could not refrain from another gibe at his prisoner.

"I see you there," said he, "by the big lamp, grinning 25 like a rat in a trap."

The only answer King Robert made was to dash his enormous foot against the door and burst it open. The sexton, who felt as if a house had given him a blow in the face, fainted away, and the king, as far as his sense of 30 dignity allowed him, hurried to his palace, which was close by.

"Well," said the porter, "what do *you* want?"

"Stand aside, fellow!" roared the king, pushing back the door with the same gigantic foot.

"Seize him!" cried the porter.

"On your lives!" cried the king. "Look at me, fellow! Who am I?"

"A madman and a fool; that's what you are!" cried the porter. "Hold him fast!"

In came the guards with an officer at their head who had just been dressing his curls at a looking-glass. He had the looking-glass in his hand.

"Captain Francavilla," said the king, "is the world run mad? Or what is it? Your rebels pretend not even to know me! Go before me, sir, to my rooms!" And as he spoke, the king shook off his assailants as a lion does curs and moved onward.

Captain Francavilla put his finger gently before the king to stop him; and then looking with a sort of staring indifference in his face, said in a very mincing tone, "Some madman."

King Robert tore the looking-glass from the captain's hands and looked himself in the face. It was not his own face.

"Here is witchcraft!" exclaimed King Robert. "I am changed." And for the first time in his life, a sensation of fear came upon him, but nothing so great as the rage and fury that remained.

"Bring him in — bring him in!" now exclaimed other voices, the news having got to the royal apartments. "The king wants to see him."

King Robert was brought in; and there, amidst roars of laughter, he found himself face to face with another

King Robert, seated on his throne, and as like his former self as he himself was unlike, but with more dignity.

"Hideous impostor!" exclaimed Robert, rushing forward to tear him down.

The court, at the word "hideous," roared with greater laughter than before; for the king in spite of his pride was at all times a handsome man, and there was a strong feeling at present that he had never in his life looked so well.

Robert when halfway to the throne felt as if a palsy had smitten him. He stopped and essayed to vent his rage but could not speak.

The figure on the throne looked him steadily in the face. Robert thought it was a wizard but hated far more than he feared it, for he was of great courage.

It was an Angel. But the Angel was not going to disclose himself yet nor for a long time.

"Since thou art royal-mad," said the new sovereign, "and in truth a very king of idiots, thou shalt be crowned and sceptered and be my fool. Fetch the cap and bauble and let the King of Fools have his coronation."

Robert felt that he must submit.

While the attendants were shaving his head, fixing the cap, and jeeringly dignifying him with the bauble-scepter, he was racking his brain for schemes of vengeance. What exasperated him most of all, next to the shaving, was to observe that those who had flattered him most when a king were the loudest in their contempt now that he was the court zany.

At length the king ordered the fool to be taken away, in order to sup with the dogs. Robert was stupefied, but he found himself hungry against his will and gnawed the bones which had been cast away by his nobles.

The proud King Robert of Sicily lived in this way for two years, always raging in his mind, always sullen in his manners, and, without the power to resent it, subjected to every indignity which his former favorites could heap on him. For the new monarch seemed unjust to him only. He had all the humiliations, without any of the privileges, of the cap and bells and was the dullest fool ever heard of.

All the notice the king took of him consisted in his asking now and then in full court when everything was silent, "Well, fool, art thou still a king?" Robert for some weeks loudly answered that he was. But finding that the answer was but a signal for a roar of laughter he converted his speech into the silent dignity of a haughty and royal attitude; till observing that the laughter was greater at this dumb show he ingeniously adopted a manner which expressed neither defiance nor acquiescence, and the Angel for some time let him alone.

Meantime everybody but the unhappy Robert blessed the new, or as they supposed him, the altered, king; for everything in the mode of government was changed. Taxes were light, the poor had plenty, work was reasonable. Half the day throughout Sicily was given to industry and half to health and intellectual enjoyment, and the inhabitants became at once the manliest and tenderest, the gayest and most studious, people in the world. Wherever the king went he was loaded with benedictions, and the fool heard them and wondered. And thus for the space of time we have mentioned he lived, wondering and sullen and hating, and hated and despised.

At the expiration of these two years, or nearly so, the king announced his intention of paying a visit to his brother the Pope and his brother the Emperor, the latter agreeing to come to Rome for the purpose. He went accordingly with a great train all clad in the most magnificent garments; but the fool was arrayed in foxtails and put side by side with an ape dressed like himself. The people poured out of their houses, and fields, and vine- 5 yards, all struggling to get a sight of the king's face and to bless it. The ladies strewed flowers and the peasants' wives held up their rosy children, which last sight seemed particularly to delight the sovereign.

The fool, bewildered, came after the court pages, by the 10 side of his ape, exciting shouts of laughter; though some persons were a little astonished to think how a monarch so kind and considerate to all the rest of the world should be so hard upon a sorry fool. But it was told them that this fool was the most perverse and insolent of men toward 15 the prince himself. Then, although their wonder hardly ceased, it was full of indignation against the unhappy wretch and he was loaded with every kind of scorn and abuse. The proud King Robert seemed the only blot and disgrace upon the island. 20

The fool had still a hope that when His Holiness saw him the magician's arts would be at an end. The good man, however, beheld him without the least recognition; so did the Emperor. When he saw them both gazing with unfeigned admiration at the exalted beauty of his former 25 altered self and not with the old faces of pretended good will and secret dislike, a sense of awe and humility for the first time fell gently upon him. Instead of getting as far as possible from his companion the ape, he approached him closer and closer, partly that he might shroud himself 30 under the very shadow of his insignificance, partly from a feeling of absolute sympathy and a desire to possess, if not one friend in the world, at least one associate who was not an enemy.

It happened that day that it was the same day on which two years before Robert had scorned the words in the *Magnificat*. Vespers were performed before the sovereigns. The music and the soft voices fell softer as they came to the words, and Robert again heard, with far different feelings, "He hath put down the mighty from their seat and hath exalted the humble." Tears gushed into his eyes, and to the astonishment of the court the late brutal fool was seen with his hands clasped upon his bosom in prayer and the water pouring down his face in floods of penitence.

Holier feelings than usual had pervaded all hearts that day. The king's favorite chaplain had preached from the text which declares charity to be greater than faith or hope. The Emperor began to think mankind really his brothers. His Holiness wished that some new council of the Church would authorize him to set up, above the Ten Commandments, and in more glorious letters, the new, eleventh, or great Christian commandment, "Behold I give unto you a new commandment, Love one another." In short, Rome felt that day like angel-governed Sicily.

When the service was over the unknown King Robert's behavior was reported to the unsuspected King-Angel, who had seen it but said nothing. The sacred interloper announced his intention of giving the fool his discharge; and he sent for him accordingly, having first dismissed every other person. King Robert came in his foolscap and bells and stood humbly at a distance before the strange, great, charitable Unknown, looking on the floor and blushing. He had the ape by the hand, who had long courted his good will, and who having now obtained it clung to his human friend in a way that to a Roman might have seemed ridiculous, but to the Angel was affecting.

"Art thou still a king?" said the Angel, putting the old question, but without the word "fool." 5

"I am a fool," said King Robert, "and no king."

"What wouldst thou, Robert?" returned the Angel in a mild voice.

King Robert trembled from head to foot and said, "Even what thou wouldst, O mighty and good stranger, 10 whom I know not how to name — hardly to look at!"

The stranger laid his hand on the shoulder of King Robert, who felt an inexpressible calm suddenly diffuse itself over his being. He knelt down and clasped his hands to thank him. 15

"Not to me," interrupted the Angel in a grave but sweet voice; and kneeling down by the side of Robert, he said, as if in a church, "Let us pray."

King Robert prayed and the Angel prayed, and after a few moments the king looked up and the Angel was gone; 20 and then the king knew that it was an Angel indeed.

And his own likeness returned to King Robert but never an atom of his pride; and after a blessed reign he died, disclosing this history to his weeping nobles and requesting that it might be recorded in the Sicilian annals. 25

1. Who, according to this story, first related the incident? What and where is Sicily?

2. What got King Robert into difficulty? How was he punished? Was he unjustly punished? How long did his punishment last? When did it cease? How could Robert have freed himself earlier?

3. Plan a moving-picture scenario for the story. Where would you break it up for the various scenes?

4. Read Longfellow's "King Robert of Sicily."

MOTH AND RUST

A CERTAIN mountain spring had four sons, three of
whom were steady-going, well-to-do brooks — the
first being in the violet-growing business, the second a
scene maker, while the third had hired himself out to a
5 woolen-spinner; but Steme, the youngest, had all his
days been a care and vexation to his father. He had all
the antic tricks of his cousins, the fogs and mists, and the
fickle disposition of his mother, who was of the Fire family.

One moment he drew himself out to the length of a giant,
10 as if he had been so much gutta percha or India rubber;
the next he made himself so small that you lost him altogether. Now he sang, roared, puffed, bellowed, shrieked,
and whistled, till the family were wild with his noise.
A little after, he was gone — mum as a mouse, however
15 you called him, and never any two days alike, excepting
in the fact that he was at all times idle and useless; till
one fine morning his father, being utterly out of patience,
hustled him out of Fairyland with, "See here, my lad!
it is time you sought your fortune."

20 "It is very odd," said Steme to himself. "I am sure I
could do something if there were not some mistake somewhere." And coming just then to a house which had on
the doorplate the words, "WISEST MAN," he rang the
bell, thinking perhaps the question could be settled there.
25 But the Wisest Man only said, "If you were of any use,
somebody would have discovered it before."

So Steme traveled on till he came to the court of the
king, where was a great hubbub; and as no one would pay
him the least attention, Steme grew sulky, and coiling
himself up, hid away in the teakettle. "Now if anybody
wants me, let him find me," said he; and you would never 5
have known that he was there, unless by the way the kettle
cover clattered now and then.

The court was in a hubbub because of the king's spectacles. And whether he had changed them at the tailor's
where he ordered the trimming for the Lord High Fiddle- 10
stick's green-satin gown, or at the jeweler's where his crown
was being mended, or at the grocer's where he had stopped
for a glass of milk, His Royal Highness was quite unable
to decide.

Only these could never be the spectacles that usually 15
rested on his royal nose; for whenever he looked through
them he could see nothing but Moth and Rust — moths
eating the bedcovers, the hangings, the carpets, the silks
and velvets, the wool and linen, the lace and embroidery,
in every part of His Majesty's dominions — rust on the gold 20
and silver, the marble and granite, the oak and walnut, the
houses and ships, everywhere in his kingdom.

The king grew nervous. "We are all coming to poverty,"
said His Royal Highness; and though it was drawing
toward Christmas he did little but peep through the 25
spectacles and look dismal.

Of course all the court looked dismal too. The courtiers
got a crick in the neck by going about with heads on one
side like His Majesty.

The Lord High Fiddlestick, being of a jolly disposition, 30
was obliged to shut himself up and laugh privately by the

hour to take the fun out of him before waiting on His
Royal Highness; while the ladies wore their old gowns to
court and said where the king could hear them, "Oh,
we are obliged to piece and patch in these days. Between
5 that dreadful Moth and the more dreadful Rust we are all
coming to poverty, you know."

In this dilemma they sent for the Wisest Man, who
came at once, looking so profound that the king took
courage and said, "What shall we do? Tell us, now."

10 "Hum!" said the Wisest Man. "Let us go back to first
principles. If there was nothing to eat there would be no
moths and if there was nothing to consume there would be
no rust — do you see?"

"Yes — certainly — of course," said all the courtiers,
15 but the king only groaned.

"But as there is silk and satin, velvet and linen, gold and
diamonds, everywhere in the kingdom, I really don't see
what you are to do about it," concluded the Wisest Man;
and he marched away home again.

20 This was cold comfort and the king groaned more deeply
than ever. But the king's son said to himself, "If there is
no help for it, why cannot we contrive to grow rich faster
and so keep ahead of the leak?"

So he sent for all the rich men in the kingdom.

25 "How did you grow rich?" asked the prince.

"By trading," answered they all together.

"Trade more, then, and we shall not all come to poverty,"
said the prince.

"Alas! Your Highness!" answered the rich men, "we
30 send away now just as much wheat and oil, and bring home
just as much silk and gold, as we can find horses and wagons
for carrying and houses for storing."

"Work faster, then," suggested the prince.

"We work as fast as flesh and blood is able," answered the rich men together as before.

"Now is my time," said Steme to himself. "Here is work a little more to my taste than violet growing!" and he began to clatter the cover of the kettle.

"Who is there?" asked the prince.

"Steme," gurgled the kettle.

"And what can you do, Steme?" said the prince.

"Carry as many tons as you like and run sixty miles an hour," spluttered the kettle.

"That is a likely story!" cried the prince. "Curled up there in a kettle, whoever you are!"

"Try me," said Steme, coming out of the kettle.

So the prince ordered a load that would have broken the backs of forty horses to be strapped behind Steme, who darted off with it as if it had been a feather, shrieking, snorting, and puffing, as he always did when his blood was up; and though he had a three days' journey before him he was back in a few hours, fresher than when he started.

"More loads! more tons!" bellowed Steme. "Longer journeys! I want to go farther. I want to go faster. I can run twice as fast! Huzza!"

"Ah! this is better," said the prince, setting all the men in the palace to load Steme more heavily. "Not much chance here for Moth and Rust."

Presently back came Steme roaring for more loads. All the men in the kingdom were set at work. Twice as much wheat and oil were sent out, and four times as much silk and gold were brought in, as ever before. "Not much danger of poverty now," exclaimed the courtiers, and even the king smiled till he thought to put on his spectacles, when he saw more Moth and more Rust eating twice as fast as before.

"That is because you don't work fast enough," shouted Steme. "Who ever saw such wheels and looms? Let me spin! Give me thousands of wheels! I can weave! Give me looms! Give me spindles! — millions of spindles — hundreds of thousands of looms!"

So the men worked night and day to make spindles and wheels and looms for Steme, and a thousand workmen could not spin and weave the tenth part of what Steme did in a day.

But the king looking through his spectacles saw Moth and Rust busy as ever at the very wheels and spindles and looms themselves.

"Still it is your fault," shouted Steme. "You don't get about fast enough. Your horses creep like snails. Give me horses with iron backs — hundreds of them — thousands! I will draw your carriages. Give me paddles — twenty and thirty in a hand! I will row your boats."

So Steme drove the carriages and rowed the boats, and as people went dashing and tearing about everywhere, they panted to each other, "What a wonderful nation we have grown to be! No chance for Moth and Rust now!"

But looking through his spectacles the king saw moths by the million and rust on everything.

"Your fault still!" snorted Steme. "Why don't you read more? Why not have more books? Let me make your books. Everybody shall have them. Everyone shall read and be wise. Some one will then find out the remedy for Moth and Rust."

So Steme made books by the ton and carried them everywhere, thundering continually, "More, more! faster, faster! not half enough yet!" But still the king saw moths and rust increase, and on Christmas Eve he had no heart for Christmas trees but wandered away in the forest and walked there by himself till just at dark he met a stranger.

"Who are you, and where are you going?" asked the king; for the man had such a broad, jolly, smiling face that the king knew it was none of his court.

"I am Merry Christmas," said the stranger, "and I am going to the cottage in the forest."

The king wondered why Merry Christmas had passed his palace, where were a hundred Christmas trees, to stop at the cottage where they could have nothing more than a pine branch; and he walked on too.

In the cottage lived an old woman and a little girl. Against the chimney hung the little one's stocking and on the table before the fire was a chicken nicely browned. The mouths of the dame and the little one watered, for they had not roast chicken for dinner every day, but just as Merry Christmas opened the door there stepped in before him and the king a poor little hungry, shivering boy.

"Sit down," said the dame; "we were waiting for you. And let us thank our Lord for all His grace."

"Why, there is hardly meat enough for two," cried the king. "Such a little chicken!"

"But hush!" said Merry Christmas. "I carve!"

And looking at him, the king understood how there would not only be enough for three but that it would taste better than the choicest bit of turkey on His Majesty's

own table; and when Merry Christmas sat down on the
hearth there was such a glow in the pine chips, and such
a light in the tallow candle, and such a brightness through
all the room — which came out of Merry Christmas and had
5 nothing to do with either fire or candle — that the three at
the table rejoiced like birds or babies without understanding why.

"How is this?" thought the king; and then, looking
again more sharply, he spied written on everything in the
10 little room, "We give of what we have to-day to whoever
needs, and trust to God for to-morrow."

"Oh," said Merry Christmas, chuckling, "no preventive
like that against Moth and Rust!" But the king went home
sorrowful, for he was very rich.

1. What did Steme's brothers do? Explain how each could
perform his work. Why did his father not like Steme?

2. Where do you first discover the author's trick of misspelling
"Steme"? How do you spell it? Does "Steme" work for us to-
day? How? Where?

3. What younger brothers of his now drive automobiles, ships,
and factory wheels?

4. What does "Moth and Rust" stand for? What should the
king have learned in the cottage? If we take Merry Christmas's
advice can we save "Steme" a great deal of labor? Explain your
answer.

THE MICE AND THE WEASELS

THE Weasels and the Mice waged perpetual warfare with each other in which much blood was shed. The Weasels, however, were always the victors. The Mice thought the cause of their frequent defeats was their lack of army leaders and army discipline. Accordingly, they chose from among themselves the Mice most renowned for their family descent, strength, and counsel, to say nothing of courage in battle and knowledge of the tactics of war. With this done the army was properly disciplined. Then the herald Mouse proclaimed war by challenging the Weasels to open combat.

The newly chosen generals bound their heads with straw, that they might be more conspicuous to all their troops. Scarcely had the battle commenced, however, when a great rout overwhelmed the Mice, who scampered off as fast as they could to their holes. But the generals were not so successful in making their escape, because of the straw ornaments on their heads. All the officers to the last mouse were captured and eaten by the Weasels.

The more honor the more danger.

— *Æsop's Fables.*

A LITTLE LAUGHTER

'Twas the saying of an ancient sage that humor was the only test of seriousness, and seriousness of humor. For a subject which would not bear jesting was suspicious; and a jest which would not bear a serious examination was certainly false wit.

— SHAFTESBURY.

THE RENOWNED WOUTER VAN TWILLER
(*See opposite page*)

A DUTCH GOVERNOR

BY WASHINGTON IRVING

Washington Irving (1783–1859) was the first American author to gain international fame as a writer. His first book that won him a reputation was his *Knickerbocker's History of New York*, from which the following extract is taken. It was supposed to be the writing of an old Dutchman, Diedrich Knickerbocker. It is a queer mixture of fact and nonsense, of history and broad humor.

THE renowned Wouter (or Walter) van Twiller was descended from a long line of Dutch burgomasters, who had successively dozed away their lives and grown fat upon the bench of magistracy in Rotterdam and who 5 had comported themselves with such singular wisdom and propriety that they were never either heard of or talked of — which, next to being universally applauded, should be the object of ambition of all magistrates and rulers.

There are two opposite ways by which some men make 10 a figure in the world : one by talking faster than they think, and the other by holding their tongues and not thinking at all. By the first, many a smatterer acquires the reputation of a man of quick parts ; by the other, many a dunderpate, like the owl, the stupidest of birds, comes 15 to be considered the very type of wisdom.

This, by the way, is a casual remark which I would not for the universe have it thought I apply to Governor van Twiller. It is true he was a man shut up within himself, like an oyster, and rarely spoke except in monosyllables ; 20 but then it was allowed he seldom said a foolish thing. So invincible was his gravity that he was never known to laugh, or even to smile, through the whole course of a long and prosperous life. Nay, if a joke were uttered in his presence that set light-minded hearers in a roar, it was observed to throw him into a state of perplexity. 5

With all his reflective habits he never made up his mind on a subject. If any matter were propounded to him on which ordinary mortals would rashly determine at first glance, he would put on a vague, mysterious look, shake his capacious head, smoke some time in profound 10 silence, and at length observe that he "had doubts about the matter," — which gained him the reputation of a man slow of belief and not easily imposed upon. What is more, it gained him a lasting name; for to this habit of the mind has been attributed his surname of Twiller, which 15 is said to be a corruption of the original *dwijfler*, or, in plain English, *doubter*.

The person of this illustrious old gentleman was formed and proportioned as though it had been molded by the hands of some cunning Dutch statuary as a model of 20 majesty and lordly grandeur. He was exactly five feet six inches in height and six feet five inches in circumference. His head was a perfect sphere and of such stupendous dimensions that Dame Nature, with all her sex's ingenuity, would have been puzzled to construct a neck capable of 25 supporting it; wherefore she wisely declined the attempt and settled it firmly on the top of his backbone, just between his shoulders. His body was oblong and particularly capacious. His legs were short, but sturdy in proportion to the weight they had to sustain; so that when 30 erect he had not a little the appearance of a beer barrel on skids.

His face, that infallible index of the mind, presented a vast expanse unfurrowed by any of those lines and angles which disfigure the human countenance with what is termed expression. Two small gray eyes twinkled feebly in the midst, like two stars of lesser magnitude in a hazy firmament; and his full-fed cheeks, which seemed to have taken toll of everything that went into his mouth, were curiously mottled and streaked with dusky red, like a spitzenburgh apple.

His habits were as regular as his person. He daily took his four stated meals, appropriating exactly an hour to each; he smoked and doubted eight hours; and he slept the remaining twelve of the four and twenty.

Such was the renowned Wouter van Twiller — a true philosopher, for his mind was either elevated above, or tranquilly settled below, the cares and perplexities of this world. He had lived in it for years without feeling the least curiosity to know whether the sun revolved round it or it round the sun; and he had watched for at least half a century the smoke curling from his pipe to the ceiling without once troubling his head with any of those numerous theories by which a philosopher would have perplexed his brain in accounting for its rising above the surrounding atmosphere.

— Knickerbocker's History of New York.

1. What is humorous about the description of van Twiller's person? His face? His habits? His thinking?

2. Can you explain what van Twiller could not; viz., the reason smoke rises?

3. There was a real Wouter van Twiller who was a Dutch governor of New York. What parts of Irving's description of him may be true? What parts are undoubtedly nonsense?

4. What other books or stories did Irving write?

THE TWINS

By H. S. Leigh

IN FORM and feature, face and limb,
　　I grew so like my brother
That folks got taking me for him
And each for one another.
It puzzlèd all our kith and kin,　　　　　　5
It reached a fearful pitch;
For one of us was born a twin
Yet not a soul knew which.

One day, to make the matter worse,
Before our names were fixed,　　　　　　10
As we were being washed by nurse
We got completely mixed.
And thus you see by fate's decree,
Or rather nurse's whim,
My brother John got christened me　　　　15
And I got christened him.

The fatal likeness even dogged
My footsteps when at school,
And I was always getting flogged —
For John turned out a fool.　　　　　　20
I put this question fruitlessly
To everyone I knew,
"What *would* you do if you were me,
To prove that you were *you?*"

Our close resemblance turned the tide
Of my domestic life,
For somehow my intended bride
Became my brother's wife.
In fact year after year the same
Absurd mistakes went on,
And when I died the neighbors came
And buried brother John.

1. Mistaking one person for another has been the source of much fun. Many old plays and stories are built on this theme. And of course "twins" offers a fine chance for a bad confusion. What was the difficulty in the case of the two brothers of this poem?

HOW TO TELL BAD NEWS

Mr. H. Good morning, steward, good morning. How are things going on at home?

Steward. Bad enough, Your Honor. The magpie's dead.

Mr. H. Poor Mag! So he's gone. How came he to die?

Steward. Overate himself, sir.

Mr. H. Did he, indeed! Greedy villain! Why, what did he get he liked so well?

Steward. Horseflesh, sir; he died of eating horseflesh.

Mr. H. How came he to get so much horseflesh?

Steward. All your father's horses, sir.

Mr. H. What! Are they dead too?

Steward. Aye, sir; they died of overwork.

Mr. H. Why were they overworked, pray?

Steward. Carrying water, sir.

Mr. H. Carrying water! And what were they carrying water for?

Steward. Sure, sir, to put out the fire.

Mr. H. Fire! What fire? 5

Steward. Oh, sir, your father's house is burned to the ground.

Mr. H. My father's house burned down! How did it get afire?

Steward. I think it must have been the torches. 10

Mr. H. Torches! What torches?

Steward. At your mother's funeral.

Mr. H. Alas! alas! My mother dead?

Steward. Yes, poor lady, she never looked up after it.

Mr. H. After what? 15

Steward. The loss of your father.

Mr. H. What! My father gone too?

Steward. Yes, poor gentleman; he took to his bed as soon as he heard of it.

Mr. H. Heard of what? 20

Steward. The bad news, sir, and please Your Honor.

Mr. H. What! More miseries? More bad news? Oh, no! You can add nothing more.

Steward. Yes, sir; the bank has failed and you are not worth a dollar in the world. I made bold, sir, to come 25 and tell you about it, for I thought you would like to hear the news.

---

1. This story has been told in several ways. You may have heard it in some other form. Sometimes it is in dialect, as between a colored servant and his master. What is the humor in it?

HANGING A PICTURE

By Jerome K. Jerome

YOU never saw such a commotion up and down a house as when my Uncle Podger undertook to do a job. A picture would have come home from the frame maker's and be standing in the dining room, waiting to be put up, and Aunt Podger would ask what was to be done with it, and Uncle Podger would say: "Oh, you leave that to *me*. Don't you, any of you, worry yourselves about that. *I'll* do that."

And then he would take off his coat and begin. He would send out the girl for six pennyworth of nails, and then one of the boys after her to tell her what size to get, and from that he would gradually work down and start the whole house.

"Now you go and get me my hammer, Will," he would shout; "and you bring me the rule, Tom; and I shall want the stepladder, and I had better have a kitchen chair, too; and Jim, you run round to Mr. Goggles and tell him, 'Pa's kind regards and hopes his leg's better; and will he lend us his spirit level?' And don't you go, Maria, for I shall want somebody to hold me the light. And when the girl comes back she must go out again for a bit of picture cord. And, Tom — where's Tom? — Tom, you come here; I shall want you to hand me up the picture."

And then he would lift up the picture, and drop it, and it would come out of the frame, and he would try to save the glass, and cut his finger; and then he would spring round the room looking for his handkerchief. He would not find his handkerchief, because it was in the pocket of the coat he had taken off and he did not know where he had put the coat, and all the house had to leave off looking for his tools and start looking for his coat while he would sit down and nurse his cut finger and storm at everybody.

"Doesn't anybody in the whole house know where my coat is? I never came across such a set in all my life — upon my word I didn't. Six of you! — and you can't find a coat that I put down not five minutes ago! Well, of all the —"

Then he'd get up and find that he had been sitting on it and would call out: "Oh, you can give it up! I've found it myself, now. Might just as well ask the cat to find anything as expect you people to find it."

And when half an hour had been spent in tying up his finger, and a new glass had been got, and the tools and the ladder and the chair and the candle had been brought, he would have another go, while the whole family, including the girl and the washerwoman, stood round in a semicircle ready to help. Two people would have to hold the chair, and a third would help him up on it and hold him there, and a fourth would hand him a nail, and a fifth would pass him up the hammer, and he would take hold of the nail and drop it.

"There!" he would say in an injured tone, "now the nail's gone."

Then we all would have to go down on our knees and grovel for it while he would stand on the chair and grunt and want to know if he was to be kept there all the evening.

The nail would be found at last, but by that time he would have lost the hammer.

"Where's the hammer? What did I do with the hammer? I declare! Seven of you gaping around there, and you don't know what I did with the hammer."

We would find the hammer for him, and then he would have lost sight of the mark he had made on the wall where the nail was to go in, and each of us had to get up on the chair beside him and see if we could find it, and we would each discover it in a different place, and he would call us all fools one after another and tell us to get down. And he would take the rule and remeasure and find that he wanted half of thirty-one and three-eighths inches from the corner, and would try to do it in his head, and would go mad.

And we would all try to do it in our heads and all arrive at different results and sneer at one another. And in the general row the original number would be forgotten and Uncle Podger would have to measure it again.

He would use a string this time; and at the critical moment, when he was leaning over the chair and trying to reach a point three inches beyond what was possible for him to reach, the string would slip and down he would slide on the piano, a really fine musical effect being produced by the suddenness with which his head and body struck all the notes at the same time.

At last Uncle Podger would get the spot fixed again, and put the point of the nail on it with his left hand, and take the hammer in his right hand. And with the first blow he would smash his thumb, and drop the hammer with a yell on somebody's toes. Aunt Maria would mildly observe that the next time Uncle Podger was going to hammer a nail into the wall, she hoped he'd let her know, so that she could pay her mother a visit while it was being done.

"Oh! you women, you make such a fuss over everything," Uncle Podger would answer. "Why, I like doing a little job of this sort."

Then he would have another try; and at the second blow the nail would go clean through the plaster and half the [5] hammer after it, and Uncle Podger would fall over against the wall with such force as to flatten his nose. Then we would find the rule and the string again, and a new hole was made, and the whole performance was repeated. At last, about midnight, the picture would be up — very [10] crooked and insecure, the wall for yards around looking as if it had been smoothed down with a rake, and everybody worn and wretched — everybody except Uncle Podger.

"There you are," he would say, stepping heavily off the [15] chair and surveying with evident pride the mess he had made. "Why, some people would have had a man in to do a little thing like that!"

— *Three Men in a Boat.*

1. What cartoons have you seen whose fun depended on situations similar to the above? Bring some funny newspaper cartoons to class, and tell what is humorous in them.

2. Draw a pencil sketch of the above scene, a part of it, or a cartoon of Uncle Podger.

3. What do names have to do with humorous writing? Suppose Podger's name had been Smith or Jones. Would the selection be so funny?

HELPS TO READ

By John Byrom

A CERTAIN artist — I forget his name —
Had got for making spectacles a fame,
Or, "Helps to Read," as, when they first were sold,
Was writ upon his glaring sign in gold;
5   And for all uses to be had from glass,
His were allowed by readers to surpass.

There came a man into his shop one day:
"Are you the spectacle contriver, pray?"
"Yes, sir," said he; "I can, in that affair,
10   Contrive to please you if you want a pair."
"Can you? Pray do then." So at first he chose
To place a youngish pair upon his nose,
And — book produced to see how they would fit —
Asked how he liked 'em. "Like 'em? Not a bit."

15   "Then, sir, I fancy — if you please to try —
These in my hand will better suit your eye."
"No, but they don't." "Well, come, sir, if you please,
Here is another sort; we'll e'en try these —
Still somewhat more they magnify the letter.
20   Now, sir?" — "Why, now I'm not a bit the better!"
"No? Here, take these that magnify still more.
How do they fit?" "Like all the rest before."

In short they tried the whole assortment through,
But all in vain for none of 'em would do.
The operator, much surprised to find
So odd a case, thought, "Sure the man is blind."
"What sort of eyes can yours be, friend?" said he.   5
"Why, very good ones, friend, as you may see."
"Yes, I perceive the clearness of the ball —
Pray, let me ask you, can you read at all?"

"No, you great blockhead! if I could, what need
Of paying you for any 'Helps to Read'?"   10
And so he left the maker in a heat,
Resolved to post him for an arrant cheat.

1. This is an instance of fun based on a total misunderstanding.
What was the misunderstanding between the optician and his customer?

2. Make up a similar situation that would serve as the basis for a funny story.

THE KETTLE AND THE CRICKET

By Charles Dickens

THE kettle began it. Don't tell me what Mrs. Peerybingle said. I know better. The kettle began it, full five minutes by the Dutch clock in the corner before the cricket gave a chirp.

It seemed as if there was a kind of match between the kettle and the cricket. And this is what led to it and how it came about The kettle was set upon having its own way. It wouldn't allow itself to be placed upon the top bar. It wouldn't hear of resting upon the knobs of coal.

It would lean forward with a drunken air and dribble, a very idiot of a kettle, on the hearth. It was quarrelsome, and hissed and spluttered at the fire. To sum all up, the lid turned topsy-turvy. It dived in sideways, down to the very bottom.

Mrs. Peerybingle got it up again at last, but the kettle looked sullen and pig-headed enough even then. It looked at Mrs. Peerybingle as if to say: "I won't let the water boil. Nothing shall make me."

But Mrs. Peerybingle dusted her chubby little hands against each other, and sat down before the kettle laughing. Meanwhile the jolly blaze rose up and fell, flashing and gleaming, and now it was that the kettle began to spend the evening. It threw off all crossness and burst into a stream of song. It was a song so cozy and jolly that never nightingale yet had the least idea of it. So plain, too! Bless you, you might have known it like a book.

"It's a dark night," sang the kettle. "The fallen leaves are lying by the way. Above, all is mist and darkness. Below, all is mire and clay. There's hoar frost on the finger post. There's thaw upon the track. The ice isn't water and the water isn't free. And you couldn't say that anything is what it ought to be. But he's coming, coming, coming —"

"And is here if you like," the cricket chimed in. It gave a chirrup, chirrup, chirrup of great size. If it had burst like an overcharged gun and chirruped its little body into fifty pieces, it would only have seemed natural.

The kettle had had the last of its solos. It kept on with the same ardor, but the cricket took first fiddle and kept it. How it chirped! Its sharp, shrill voice sounded through the house and seemed to twinkle in the outer darkness like a star. Yet they went very well together, the cricket and the kettle. It was like a race.

Chirp, chirp, chirp! Cricket a mile ahead. Hum, hum, hum-m-m! Kettle making play like a great top. Chirp, chirp, chirp! Cricket around the corner, fresher than ever. ₅ Hum, hum, hum-m-m! Kettle slow and steady. Chirp, chirp, chirp! Cricket going in to finish him. Hum, hum, hum-m-m! Kettle not to be finished.

At last they got so jumbled together in the hurry-skurry of the race that whether the kettle chirped or the ₁₀ cricket hummed, or both chirped and hummed, it would have taken a clearer head than yours or mine to have told. But of this there is no doubt. The kettle and the cricket sent each his fireside song of comfort into a ray of the candle. This shone out through the window and a long ₁₅ way down the lane.

And this light, bursting on a certain person who came near it through the gloom, told the whole thing to him. It cried, "Welcome home, old fellow! Welcome home, my boy!" ₂₀

— *The Cricket on the Hearth.*

1. This is a different kind of humor from the previous selections. Contrast it with one of them. Is it as funny? Is it quieter? Is it merely pleasant without being humorous to you?

2. Bring to class a short clipping from a paper or a magazine, which you consider good humor.

3. What do you know about the writings of Charles Dickens? Have you ever read any of his stories?

PIANO MUSIC

FIRST a soft and gentle tinkle,
    Gentle as the raindrop's sprinkle,
    Then a stop,
    Fingers drop.

Now begins a merry trill,
Like a cricket in a mill;
Now a short, uneasy motion,
Like a ripple on the ocean.

See the fingers dance about,
Hear the notes come tripping out;
How they mingle in the tingle
Of the everlasting jingle,
Like to hailstones on a shingle,
Or the ding-dong, dangle-dingle
Of a sheep bell! Double, single,
Now they come in wider gushes,
Up and down the player rushes,
Quick as squirrels, sweet as thrushes.

Now the keys begin to clatter
Like the music of a platter
When the maid is stirring batter.

O'er the music comes a change,
Every tone is wild and strange:

Listen to the lofty tumbling;
Hear the mumbling, fumbling, jumbling,
Like the rumbling and the grumbling
Of the thunder, from its slumbering
Just awaking.   Now it's taking 5
To the quaking, like a fever-and-ague shaking;
Heads are aching, something's breaking.

Goodness gracious!   Ain't it wondrous,
Rolling round above and under us,
Like old Vulcan's stroke so thunderous? 10

Now 'tis louder, but the powder
Will be all exploded soon;
For the only way to do,
When the music's nearly through,
Is to muster all your muscle for a bang, 15
Striking twenty notes together with a clang;
Hit the treble with a twang,
Give the bass an awful whang,
And close the whole performance
With a slam — bang — whang! 20

1. This poem is one of the old favorites in books of elocution. Notice how the words fit into the character of the music that is being played.   The same device is used in parts of Browning's *Pied Piper;* but the best-known examples of its use are Southey's *The Cataract of Lodore* and Poe's *The Bells.*

BIG BUSINESS

By Stephen Leacock

I KNEW, in Toronto — it is long years ago — a singularly bright young man whose name was Robinson. He had had some training in the iron-and-steel business, and when I knew him was on the lookout for an opening.

I met him one day in a great hurry, with a valise in his hand.

"Where are you going?" I asked.

"Over to England," he said. "There is a firm in Liverpool that have advertised that they want an agent here, and I'm going over to apply for the job."

"Can't you do it by letter?" I asked.

"That's just it," said Robinson, with a chuckle; "all the other men will apply by letter. I'll go right over myself, and get there as soon or sooner than the letters. I'll be the man on the spot, and I'll get the job."

He was quite right. He went over to Liverpool, and was back in a fortnight with English clothes and a big salary.

But I cannot recommend his story to my friends. In fact, it should not be told too freely. It is apt to be dangerous.

I remember once telling this story of Robinson to a young man called Tomlinson, who was out of a job. Tomlinson had a head two sizes too big, and a face like a bun. He had lost three jobs in a bank and two in a broker's office, but he knew his work, and on paper he looked a good man.

I told him about Robinson, to encourage him, and the story made a great impression.

"Say, that was a great scheme, eh?" he kept repeating. He had no command of words, and always said the same thing over and over.

A few days later I met Tomlinson on the street with a valise in his hand.

"Where are you going?" I asked.

"I'm off to Mexico," he answered. "They're advertising for a Canadian teller for a bank in Tuscapulco. I've sent my credentials down, and I'm going to follow them right up in person. In a thing like this, the personal element is everything."

So Tomlinson went down to Mexico, and he traveled by sea to Mexico City, and then with a mule train to Tuscapulco! But the mails, with his credentials, went by land and got there two days ahead of him.

When Tomlinson got to Tuscapulco he went into the bank and he spoke to the junior manager and told him what he came for.

"I'm awfully sorry," the junior manager said, "I'm afraid that this post has just been filled." Then he went into an inner room to talk with the manager. "The tellership that you wanted a Canadian for," he asked, "didn't you say that you have a man already?"

"Yes," said the manager, "a brilliant young fellow from Toronto; his name is Tomlinson, I have his credentials here — a first-class man. I've wired him to come right along, at our expense, and we'll keep the job open for him ten days."

"There's a young man outside," said the junior, "who wants to apply for the job."

"Outside?" exclaimed the manager. "How did he get here?"

"Came in on the mule train this morning; says he can do the work and wants the job."

"What's he like?" asked the manager.

The junior shook his head. "Pretty dusty-looking customer," he said; "shifty looking."

"Same old story," murmured the manager. "It's odd how these fellows drift down here, isn't it? Up to something crooked at home, I suppose. Understands the working of a bank, eh? I guess he understands it a little too well for my taste. No, no," he continued, tapping the papers that lay on the table, "now that we've got a first-class man like Tomlinson, let's hang on to him. We can easily wait ten days, and the cost of the journey is nothing to the bank as compared with getting a man of Tomlinson's stamp. And, by the way, you might telephone to the Chief of Police and get him to see to it that this loafer gets out of town straight off."

So the Chief of Police shut up Tomlinson in the calaboose and then sent him down to Mexico City under a guard. By the time the police were done with him he was dead broke, and it took him four months to get back to Toronto; when he got there, the place in Mexico had been filled long ago. *— Frenzied Fiction.*

1. Stephen Leacock, a professor in McGill University, Montreal, is the author of several books that are filled with laughs.

2. A bright man gets a job in a new way. A dull man tries the same way and fails miserably. That is the humorous situation made use of here. How are the characters fitted into it?

MAN AND HIS SHOES

HOW much a man is like his shoes!
  For instance, both a soul may lose;
Both have been tanned, and both made tight
By cobblers; both get left and right;
Both need a mate to be complete,   5
And both are made to go on feet.
They both need heeling, oft are sold,
And both in time will turn to mold.
With shoes the last is first; with men
The first shall be the last, and when   10
The shoes wear out they're mended new.
When men wear out they're men dead, too!
They both are trod upon, and both
Will tread on others, nothing loath;
Both have their ties, and both incline,   15
When polished, in the world to shine;
And both peg out.   Now would you choose
To be a man, or be his shoes?

1. Using the same word in two meanings is *punning*.   A pun is one of the oldest forms of humor.   The humor of this selection depends on its many puns.   How many do you discover in it?   Explain the double meaning in each.

OLD–WORLD STORIES

From an ancient Persian tale to a skating match in modern Holland — centuries stand between the two. And many things came to pass in the Old World in this period. The group of stories that follow include this range of time. They are interesting tales of fable and fact — the very stuff that the real history of our civilization is made of.

LAFAYETTE IS INTRODUCED TO SILAS DEANE
(*See opposite page*)

THE STORY OF LAFAYETTE

By Alma Holman Burton

THE chateau of Chavaniac was in the province of Auvergne, in the south part of France. It was a lofty castle, with towers and narrow windows from which cannon once frowned down upon besieging foes. There 5 was a deep moat around it, with a bridge which was drawn up in time of war so that no man, on horseback or on foot, could pass in at the gate without permission of the guard.

Low hills crowned with vineyards stood near the castle, 10 and beyond the hills stretched mountains whose peaks seemed to pierce the sky. In all France there was not a more charming spot than Chavaniac, and among all the nobles of the court there was no braver man than its master, the Marquis de Lafayette.

15 One day the drawbridge was let down over the moat and the gallant marquis rode away to the war in Germany. After taking part in several engagements he was shot through the heart in a skirmish at Minden. His comrades buried him on the field. The drums were muffled, the 20 band played a funeral dirge, and three rounds of musketry announced that the hero's body had been lowered into the grave.

In the midst of the mourning for the dead marquis, on September 6, 1757, his only son was born.

25 The little orphan, according to the custom in France, received a long name at his christening, but his loving

mother said that his everyday name should be Gilbert de Lafayette.

When Gilbert was old enough, his mother walked with him instead of leaving him to the care of servants. Sometimes they climbed a high hill to see the sun set over the towers of the chateau. Then she told him how the De Lafayettes, long before Columbus discovered America, had helped to banish the English kings from France, and how his own father had died for the glory of his country.

Sometimes as they walked through the halls of the castle she showed Gilbert the coats of mail which his ancestors had worn, and she told him about the swords and banners and other trophies which the De Lafayettes had won in battle.

"I would not have you less brave than they, my son," she would say.

The boy longed for the time to come when he might show his mother how very brave he was. He grew tall and strong and carried himself like a prince. He wanted to be worthy of his great ancestors.

The year he was eight there was much excitement about a wolf which prowled in the forest, killing the sheep in the pastures and frightening the peasants nearly out of their wits. Gilbert made this wolf the object of all his walks. He would persuade his mother to sit in some shady spot while he should go a little way into the forest.

"I will return in an instant, dear mother," he always said; and lest he might alarm her he walked quite slowly until a turn in the road hid him from view. Then he marched quickly into the dark wood.

He did this for many days, seeing only frisking squirrels and harmless rabbits. But one morning as he sped along a narrow path, his eyes wide open and his ears alert to catch every sound, he heard a cracking in the underbrush.

The wolf was coming! He was sure of it. His mind was made up in an instant. He would spring forward quicker than lightning and blind it with his coat while with his arms he would choke it to death.

"It will struggle hard," he thought. "Its feet will scratch me but I shall not mind; and when all is over I shall drag it to the feet of my mother. Then she will know, and the peasants will know, that I can rid the country of these pests."

He stood listening. His breath came fast. Again he heard the breaking of the bushes. "I ought first to surprise the beast by coming upon it quickly," he whispered. He tore off his coat and held it firmly as he hurried on. Soon he saw the shaggy hide and the great eyes shining through the thicket. He leaped forward with outstretched coat and — what do you think? — he clasped in his arms a calf that had strayed from the barnyard!

It was a rude disappointment for the boy. He returned to his mother, who was already alarmed at his absence, and confessed that he had tried to kill the wolf but had found only a calf.

"Ah, you were brave, my son," she cried. "I am quite sure that you would have ended the days of that terrible wolf had he but given you the chance."

The young Marquis de Lafayette was a born soldier. He loved to hear the boom of cannon and the rattle of muskets on the drill ground. When he was just nineteen years old he became captain of an artillery company.

But he said to himself, "Kings make war for conquest.

I wish that I might enlist and serve for a more worthy object."

That same year an English nobleman, the royal duke of Gloucester, chanced to visit France. He had displeased his brother, King George III, and for that reason had been 5 banished from England.

Lafayette attended a dinner party given in honor of the royal guest. While they sat about the table eating and drinking, a guard announced that a messenger was at the door with dispatches for His Royal Highness. 10

"Ah, news from England!" exclaimed the duke.

"Show the man in," ordered the officer in command.

A courier with dust on his garments entered the room, and bowing low delivered a bundle of letters.

"I beg Your Highness to read without ceremony," said 15 the commander.

The duke glanced over the papers for some time in silence. He looked grave. At last he said, "My courier has brought dispatches about our colonies in America."

"Ah," said one, "are the colonies acting badly?" 20

"Yes, they demand to vote their own taxes."

"How absurd! Why the people in France do not vote their own taxes."

"You must know," said the duke, "that many years ago one of the kings of England gave a charter to our people 25 which granted them the right to impose their own taxes. They now elect representatives to a parliament where they decide how much money should be used by the government."

"What do these Americans complain of, then?" asked 30 Lafayette.

"Taxation without representation," answered the duke.

"They insist that as loyal subjects they should be allowed either to send representatives to our parliament or to have a parliament of their own. Neither privilege has been granted. Our parliament imposes taxes on them, and when they refuse to pay the taxes the king sends soldiers to force them to do so. These dispatches inform me that the rebels have driven our troops out of a town called Boston and that delegates from the thirteen colonies have met at another town, called Philadelphia, and adopted a declaration of independence." After a pause the duke added, "I am not so sure, gentlemen, but the Americans are in the right. They are fighting as free-born Englishmen."

"The Americans *are* in the right," said Lafayette to himself; and while the other officers were making merry he was silent. As soon as he could do so he excused himself from the table. He hastened to his room and locked the door.

"This is indeed the hour I have sought," he murmured. He sat down to think. Presently he arose and paced the floor until it was almost morning. When at last he threw himself on the bed to sleep, he had resolved to leave the pleasures of rank and fortune that he might use his sword in the defense of liberty.

About this time the American Congress sent Silas Deane to France to seek aid; and Lafayette asked Baron de Kalb to go with him to visit the envoy.

De Kalb, who could speak both English and French, told Silas Deane that the Marquis de Lafayette wished to join the American army.

"We have no money to pay our officers," said Deane.

"I will serve without money," repeated De Kalb after Lafayette.

"We have no ship to carry you or your men," said Deane.

"I will buy a ship," was the answer.

Still the American hesitated to accept the services of such a boyish-looking officer.

But in the end Silas Deane gave Lafayette a contract [5] to sign, in which Lafayette promised to serve in the army of the United States whenever he was wanted.

When the venerable Benjamin Franklin came to Paris, Lafayette was the first to greet him. He was enchanted with the famous philosopher, whose simple manners and [10] plain dress befitted well the herald of a republic.

"Now indeed is our time of need," said Franklin.

Lafayette waited to hear no more. He bought a ship and ordered it to be equipped.

The voyage across the ocean was stormy and long. [15] Lafayette spent most of the time trying to learn to speak English.

His good ship *Victory* cast anchor near Charleston, South Carolina, and the party landed about midnight.

They found shelter at a farmhouse and on the following [20] day proceeded to Charleston. There Lafayette purchased carriages and horses to ride nine hundred miles to Philadelphia, where the Continental Congress was in session. When the carriages broke down because of the bad roads, the officers mounted the horses and continued their journey. [25]

"I am more determined than ever," Lafayette said to De Kalb, "to help these people preserve the liberties they have enjoyed."

He reached Philadelphia on July 27, 1777.
— *Lafayette, The Friend of American Liberty*.

1. Relate briefly the life of Lafayette to 1777.   Find from history what Lafayette did after he reached America.

HOSPITALITY REWARDED

ON a certain hill in a far-distant country there are two beautiful trees, a linden and an oak. At the foot of the hill there is an ugly marsh, and a little farther away there is a lake. A wonderful story is told about the trees and the lake.

A long, long time ago Jupiter and Mercury were traveling through that country to see how the people lived and whether they were kind-hearted and brave and true as all people ought to be. The two travelers were dressed in coarse garb and went from place to place on foot, and nobody guessed who they were.

Late one day they reached a thriving village in the midst of a beautiful plain. They were footsore and covered with dust, and no sooner had they entered the village than children and men began to hoot and throw stones at them.

They walked through the streets seeking some place of shelter for the night but no one would show them the least kindness. Some of the people were so rude as to set dogs upon them, and they were finally driven out of the village.

As they walked sadly along in the deepening twilight they came to a humble thatched cottage by the side of the road. An old man whose name was Philemon was sitting by the door and his wife, Baucis, was standing by his side with her knitting in her hand. The house was a very poor one but the two old people appeared to be contented and happy.

As soon as Philemon saw the travelers coming slowly up the hill he ran out and greeted them with kindly words. "Come in and rest yourselves," he said. "Come in, and my wife, Baucis, will give you some food, for I know that you are tired and hungry." 5

The strangers followed the old couple into their hut. Philemon gave them seats just inside the door and Baucis hurried to prepare some food for them. The good woman raked out the coals that lay among the ashes on the hearth, laid some dry sticks upon them, and soon had a blazing 10 fire. Then she ran into the garden and gathered some fresh vegetables; she cut a slice of meat from the side of bacon that hung in the chimney corner; she filled the great dinner pot and swung it above the flames.

While the food was cooking she drew out the little 15 table and covered it with a snow-white cloth. On the bench where her guests were to sit she placed a cushion filled with soft and fragrant seaweed. Then she placed on the table sweet-smelling herbs, and radishes, and cheese, and eggs cooked in the ashes. 20

When all was ready, the stew, smoking hot, was dipped from the kettle and served in coarse earthen dishes. Some milk was brought in a yellow pitcher, and apples and wild honey were added for dessert. But better than all these were the kind faces of Baucis and Philemon — their looks 25 of welcome, their attention to every need of their unknown visitors. The guests sat down at the table and the good old people stood behind them, ready to serve them and satisfy their wants. When the milk was poured out they were astonished to see that the pitcher was as full as ever. 30

"Wonder of wonders!" whispered good Baucis. "Did you ever hear of anything so strange?"

"Wife," answered Philemon, amazed and trembling, "I guess these are no common men. They are Mighty Beings come down from above."

Then both fell upon their knees and begged pardon for the coarseness of the food and the rudeness of the table and the dishes. "They are the best that we have," they said. "Gladly would we give you something better, but we cannot."

Jupiter raised them to their feet and smiled upon them. "The richest man in all the land could not have done more than you have done for our comfort," said he. "But what shall we say for the people of the village who drove us from their doors and refused to give us shelter for the night?"

"I beg that you will not be too harsh with them," said Philemon. "They did not know who it was whom they treated so rudely."

"Nay," said Jupiter, "but people who show no acts of kindness to poor and needy strangers are not likely to have the right feelings toward even the Mighty Ones from whom they receive all the good things of life. They shall be punished."

In the morning, after the two noble guests had eaten their breakfast they made ready to go on their way.

"Walk with us to the top of yonder hill," said Jupiter. Philemon and Baucis gladly obeyed.

When they had reached the top of the steep slope Mercury bade them look around. To their great wonder they saw that the village had disappeared and that a broad lake had taken its place. No house had been left standing save their own humble cottage.

"My good friends," said Jupiter, "you shall be rewarded

for your kindness to strangers. Is there not some favor that we can grant you?"

Then Philemon and Baucis both answered, "Let us finish our lives here where we have lived so long, and when the time comes for us to die let us both pass from life together." 5

"You shall have your wish," said Jupiter.

Even while he spoke Philemon and Baucis saw a wonderful change come over their humble dwelling. Lofty columns took the place of the corner posts, the thatch was changed to a gilded roof, and the doors were hung with 10 ornaments of gold. The cottage was transformed into a beautiful temple.

For many years the two old people were the keepers of the temple. But one day as they were standing outside and looking up into the sky, they felt themselves stiffen 15 so they could not stir. They had hardly time to say, "Good-by, dear Philemon," and "Good-by, dear Baucis," when they were changed into two noble trees — he into an oak and she into a linden.

Long, long ago the temple fell in ruins and was forgotten, 20 but the trees still stand side by side on the slope of the hill. When the wind rises the poor people who pass that way hear the rustle of the leaves and see the branches caress each other; and they fancy that they hear the trees saying, "Dear Baucis!" — "Dear Philemon!" 25

— Retold from Ovid's *Metamorphoses*.

1. Find from a book of myths what positions Jupiter (Zeus) and Mercury (Hermes) held among the gods.

2. Myths have been told to account for almost everything. What does this one undertake to explain?

3. What was the wish of Baucis and Philemon? What would you wish for if you had been in their place?

4. What does the story teach us as to hospitality?

THE VISION OF BELSHAZZAR

By George Gordon Byron

THE king was on his throne,
  The satraps thronged the hall;
A thousand bright lamps shone
  O'er that high festival.
A thousand cups of gold,
  In Judah deemed divine —
Jehovah's vessels hold
  The godless heathen's wine!

In that same hour and hall,
  The fingers of a hand
Came forth against the wall,
  And wrote as if on sand:
The fingers of a man —
  A solitary hand —
Along the letters ran,
  And traced them like a wand.

The monarch saw and shook,
  And bade no more rejoice;
All bloodless waxed his look,
  And tremulous his voice,
"Let the men of lore appear,
  The wisest of the earth,
And expound the words of fear,
  Which mar our royal mirth."

Chaldea's seers are good,
But here they have no skill;
And the unknown letters stood,
Untold and awful still.
And Babel's men of age   5
Are wise and deep in lore;
But now they were not sage,
They saw — but knew no more.

A captive in the land,
A stranger and a youth,   10
He heard the king's command,
He saw that writing's truth.
The lamps around were bright,
The prophecy in view:
He read it on that night —   15
The morrow proved it true.

"Belshazzar's grave is made,
His kingdom passed away,
He, in the balance weighed,
Is light and worthless clay;   20
The shroud, his robe of state,
His canopy, the stone;
The Mede is at his gate,
The Persian on his throne!"

1. Lord Byron based his poem on a Bible story. See the fifth chapter of Daniel. Who was the captive that read the handwriting on the wall? Why was he called to interpret it? What was the interpretation?

2. The Medes and the Persians under Darius captured Babylon 538 B. C. The kingdom of Babylon has passed away but the city is still in existence. Where is it?

THE SONS OF FERIDOUN

By James Baldwin

IN VERY ancient times, when the world was young and
men lived long, there was a king of Persia whose name
was Feridoun. He had ruled his country wisely and well
for more than five hundred years; and still, although his
5 hair was white with age, his eyes were sharp as the eagle's,
his arms were strong as bars of iron, and his feet were swift
as those of the gazelle.

He went constantly from one part of his kingdom to
another, doing whatever he could to make his people
10 happy. He sought out the things that were hidden, he
righted that which was wrong, he ruled by kindness and
love. Persia, during his reign, was like a garden of beauty
watered by rivers of contentment and peace. But as the
years passed and Feridoun grew older and older, it was
15 plain that he could not live and reign forever. Then his
wise men and counselors began to ask each other, "Who
shall be the ruler of our country when he is no more?"

Now Feridoun had three young sons, fair and tall and
strong, the joy and pride of his old age. But they were
20 as yet known only by the pet names of their babyhood, for
he had not tested their hearts. At length, however, when
they had come to the strength of manhood, he thought it
time to determine which of the three was most worthy to
sit on his throne. So he bade them get ready for a long
25 journey that they might visit the king of Yemen, who was
his friend.

The young men gladly obeyed him. They set out for Yemen with a great company of servants and warriors, with horses and camels and elephants as countless as the stars. The king of Yemen, when he learned of their coming, went forth to greet them; and his train was as grand as their own — glittering with silver and gold, and gorgeous as the plumage of a pheasant.

For one whole year the sons of Feridoun dwelt in Yemen. And they wooed and won for themselves the three daughters of the king — princesses as fair as the moon and as sweet as roses at the dawn of a summer day. At length, when the time came for them to return to their father, the king of Yemen loaded their camels and their elephants with much treasure and gave to each an umbrella of gorgeous beauty as a sign of kingly authority.

Now when Feridoun learned that his sons were on their way home, he went out to meet them and to prove their hearts. "For," he said, "I will thus learn which is the worthiest to succeed me as ruler of the world."

By his art in magic he caused the form of a dragon to rise from the earth — a form without substance, yet terrible to see — a dragon with eyes of fire and tongue of flame. This he placed in a narrow mountain pass, through which his sons would ride.

When the young men with their train appeared, the dragon of magic leaped out like a whirlwind. It beat upon the ground and raised a great dust, through which none could see. It roared terribly, like a lion of the desert. There was then great confusion among the horses, the camels, the elephants, and all who followed in the company of the princes.

"What enemy is this who threatens us?" cried the eldest;

and he rode forward a little way. But when he saw the fiery eyes and the dreadful form of the dragon, he dropped his spear upon the ground and fled in great haste. "A wise and prudent man will not fight with dragons," he said.

5 Then the second brother rode forward. The dragon leaped at him as though it would tear him in pieces. But he stood his ground, and said, "Since it is my business to fight, shall I be more afraid of a dragon than of a trained knight?" And he strung his bow and made ready to shoot.

10 Just then, however, the youngest brother came riding up. He saw the dragon in his path; he heard its terrible roaring, but he neither fled nor advanced. "Ho, you, whoever you may be!" he cried. "Do you know that you are in the path of lions? Beware! For we are the sons 15 of Feridoun, the mightiest of kings. Save yourself while you may!"

When Feridoun heard this he was satisfied, for he had tried the hearts of his sons. The dragon vanished from sight and the three brothers rode onward through the pass, 20 wondering at what they had seen. Soon, to their great joy, they saw their father coming to meet them, and in his train were thousands of warriors with elephants and trumpets.

The brothers made haste to alight from their steeds; they ran forward to greet him; they kissed the ground before 25 his feet. A thousand cymbals were clashed, a thousand trumpets were sounded, and ten thousand voices shouted for joy. Feridoun gently lifted his sons to their feet. He kissed their foreheads and gave unto them the honor which they deserved. And when they were come to the 30 city and the royal house, he prayed to God to bless them. Then he led them into his great hall and seated them upon golden thrones beside his own.

"O my sons," he said, "listen to me! The dragon which you saw in the mountains was naught but the work of magic. It was the means by which I sought to test your hearts. And now I will give to you names such as are befitting to men. 5

"The eldest shall be called Selim, the prudent. For a man who does not flee from danger is foolhardy rather than brave; and this, my son, when he found himself face to face with a dragon did not hesitate to betake himself to flight. The second shall be called Tur, the coura- 10 geous. For he showed his valor even from the start and was ready to give battle even though he might perish. The youngest shall be called Irij, the judicious. For he is a man both prudent and brave. He chooses the middle way, where there is safety and also honor." 15

Then Feridoun parted the world and gave three parts to his sons. To Selim he gave the lands of the setting sun, to Tur he gave China and the land of the Turks, but to Irij he gave Iran, which is Persia, with the throne of might and the crown of power. 20

— Retold from the *Shah Nameh* of Firdusi.

1. In what continent is the scene of this story laid? Who are the chief actors in it? What did they do?

2. Which of the three sons was favored in the division of the world? Why was he so favored? Do you think he deserved better treatment than his brothers?

3. A similar division of the world among three sons occurs frequently in stories of the East. You recall in this connection the repeopling of the world by the three sons of Noah, following the flood (Genesis 10: 19).

THOR'S JOURNEY

This is a story of the Norse gods, of northern Europe. It differs from the myths of southern Europe in that, like the climate, it is sterner and severer.

ONE spring the giants had been behaving very badly. The storm giants had gone to the far north and troubled the great eagle, Hraesvelger. They made him fly many times, although they knew that every time he lifted his wings the icy winds rushed out from his feathers and froze the twelve great rivers of the north. The frost giants laughed to see great blocks of ice floating down to destroy the homes of men, and the mountain giants tossed snow and ice from their shoulders upon the plowed fields. The cold lasted so long that farmers could hardly prepare the ground for seed. After the seed had been sown the cold winds kept it from sprouting. After it had begun to grow the storms beat down the young crops and seemed likely to destroy them all.

Except Balder the Good, and Frey, the gentle sun god, rough Thor was the only god who really cared for the farmers. He was sometimes very boisterous but he had a kind heart. It made him sad to see the poor farmers work so hard and get so little, and he wanted to do something to help them. So he harnessed his two goats to his iron chariot; took his iron gloves, his girdle of strength, and his hammer; and with Loki for a traveling companion set out for the land of the giants.

At the close of the first day they came to a cottage in the

edge of a wood. They stopped and asked food and shelter for themselves and their goats. Shelter the poor people gladly gave them, but they had no food. It was a long way to another house and Thor and Loki were tired and hungry. Thor raised his hammer and killed his goats. 5 The cottager dressed the meat, his wife cooked it, and there was soon a great platter of goat's flesh steaming on the table.

Thor asked the man and his wife and their two children to have supper with himself and Loki. It was a rare treat 10 to the children, who had seldom tasted meat. Thor said the bones must be left unbroken and thrown into the goatskins, which he had spread before the fireplace, because he had a use for them afterward.

While Thor was talking with the father and mother, 15 Loki whispered to the children that the choicest part was hidden within the bones. The boy, Thialfi, broke a thigh bone, ate the marrow, and threw the pieces on the heap with the others.

In the morning Thor and Loki rose early and began to 20 prepare for their journey. The cottager and his family wondered what Thor would do with his iron chariot, since the goats had been killed and eaten. They were amazed to see him strike the goatskins with his hammer, and astonished to see the goats jump up as lively as if they them- 25 selves had had warm shelter and good food instead of having made supper for others.

Thor harnessed the goats to his chariot and started to drive away, but one of the goats limped badly. Thor saw at once that its thigh bone had been broken. He raised 30 his hammer in anger. The poor people fell on their knees and begged for mercy. Thialfi confessed his disobedience,

and Thor forgave the offense on condition that Thialfi
and his sister Roskva should be his servants forever.
As there was no other way to save the lives of either themselves or their children, the parents consented. Then Thor
5 relented a little and said the children might come home
often. He charged the man to take good care of his goats
until his return; and with Loki, Thialfi, and Roskva, he
started on foot for the land of the giants.

The four traveled all day through a bleak and desolate
10 country. At sunset the prospect was still more dismal,
and to add to their discomfort a thick gray mist settled
down upon them. For a long time they wandered about
in search of shelter for the night. At last Thor saw the
dim outline of a queer-shaped house. The entrance was
15 very wide and high and seemed to take up the whole
side of the house. They went in but found it empty.
They lay down on the floor and soon fell asleep.

They were waked by a strange trembling of the house.
They were frightened by rumbling noises frequently re-
20 peated and greatly prolonged. Believing this to be an
earthquake and fearing the walls might fall and crush
them, Thor sent Loki, Thialfi, and Roskva into a wing of
the house, while he grasped his hammer and guarded the
main entrance.

25 In the early morning they continued their journey.
They had gone but a little way when they saw a steep hill
directly in their path. As they came nearer they noticed
that the hill trembled and they heard again the rumbling
noises of the night before. Suddenly they heard a great
30 sigh and saw a giant raise his head. Then they knew
that what had seemed a hill was the prostrate body of a
giant and that the trembling of the house and the sounds

they had mistaken for an earthquake had been caused by his snoring.

The giant looked about as if he had lost something. His eyes rested upon Thor and his companions and he exclaimed, "What have you little fellows done with my glove?" Before they could answer that they had not seen his glove he said, "Oh, here it is!" and reaching out picked up the house in which they had spent the night. The wing in which they had taken refuge from the supposed earthquake was the thumb of the glove.

The giant recognized Thor and seemed very glad to see him. He kindly asked where they were going, and when he found they were on the way to Utgard, the realm of the giants, he offered to be their guide and said his name was Skrymir.

They walked all day together. At night Skrymir said he was more sleepy than hungry and gave his bag of food to Thor to divide with his companions. Thor pulled the string and tugged at the knot but could not unfasten the bag. With an abundant supply of food in his hands he could neither eat nor give to the others.

Worn out with walking and long fasting, the gods and their servants tried to rest. But the giant had begun to snore and sleep was impossible. Disgusted and angry, Thor drew tighter his girdle of strength and hurled his hammer at the giant's head. Skrymir woke enough to rub the place with his hand and ask sleepily whether a leaf had fallen on his head.

At midnight the snoring was terrific. Thor dealt a fearful blow on the giant's crown. Skrymir, roused from sleep, said that he thought an acorn had fallen.

Toward morning it seemed to the tired gods that they

must get a little sleep. Thor threw his hammer with all his might at the giant's temple. Skrymir rose and said quietly: "Some birds must have dropped a piece of stick from their nest, for my temple is bruised. We must go now, I to the north and you to the east. You will soon come to Utgard. There you will find men larger than I. Be careful not to offend them." The giant disappeared in the woods and the gods kept on as directed.

At noon they came in sight of Utgard. No one noticed their approach. When they knocked at the gate no one came to admit them. So they slipped between the bars and went to the palace of the prince of the giants.

He was sitting on his throne and many of his warriors and courtiers were resting on stone benches in the great hall. For a long time no notice was taken of the intruders and then all the giants stared in surprise at the unbidden guests. The prince addressed them as "little people," and said: "I know you, Thor, and you can do more than one would think from your appearance. Now tell me what each one can do; for no one is welcome here unless he is good for something."

Loki, who was almost famished, boasted of his ability to eat.

The prince at once ordered meat, and the trial began between Loki and the prince's cook, Logi. A wooden platter filled with meat was placed between them. Loki ate rapidly and met his opponent at the middle of the dish; but to his great surprise he found that while he had eaten the meat, Logi had devoured meat, bones, and platter too.

Thialfi said he was swift of foot.

"Very well," said the prince; "run a race with Hugin."

At the first trial Hugin reached the goal a little in

advance of Thialfi. "Very good," said the prince; "try again."

The second time Thialfi was still further behind; and at the third trial he had run only half the course when Hugin reached the goal.   5

Thor, who was very thirsty, said he could drink a great deal.

The prince ordered a servant to bring a drinking horn, which he said some could empty at one draught, many at two, and he was a poor drinker indeed who could not drain 10 it at three. Thor looked at the horn. It was long but very narrow, and he thought his task an easy one. But the first draught barely uncovered the rim, the second only a little more, and the third lowered the liquid perhaps two or three inches. Much chagrined, Thor set the horn down 15 and began to boast of his strength.

The prince told him to pick up the gray cat that lay at the foot of the throne.

At the first trial he hardly moved the cat. Then he seized her firmly about the middle and made her arch her 20 back. The third time he lifted one paw from the ground.

Very angry, Thor's eyes flashed lightnings. "Let me wrestle with one of your courtiers," he cried.

The prince thoughtfully stroked his beard. "Try first," he replied, "what you can do against my old nurse, Elli." 25

A feeble, bent old woman entered the hall and took strong Thor in her grasp. Thor used all his might but she compelled him to sink down on one knee.

"Enough!" cried the prince. "Sit down now to the feast."   30

The strangers were well cared for that night, and the next morning the prince himself led them out as far as the wood.

"This," said he, "is the boundary of my domain. You would never have crossed it had I known your power. Let me tell you the tricks I have played on you.

"It was I who met you in the forest. Three times Thor struck me with his hammer. The first blow would have killed me had I not shoved a mountain between us. The second was a terrible shock though the mountain broke the force of the blow. The third crashed through the mountain and bruised my temple.

"Loki had an excellent appetite; but my cook, Logi, is wildfire, which swallows up everything in its path.

"Thialfi runs well; but Hugin, my thought, has no rival.

"The end of the long drinking horn touched the ocean. Thor drank so much that every shore was uncovered.

"The gray cat was the Midgard serpent. Thor lifted her so far that the great serpent almost escaped its prison at the bottom of the sea.

"Elli, my poor old nurse, is old age, who at last conquers everyone. Even Thor could not overcome her.

"Go now, and come no more within my realm. Mine are the eternal rocks and ice rivers. Though you rend them with thunderbolts there will be no place for your precious grains to take root."

Thor raised his hammer to punish the giant, but he was gone. The glittering walls of the palace had vanished.

—Retold from the *Edda*.

1. Did Thor succeed in his mission? What did he succeed in doing? How were his companions of assistance to him? What day of the week is named for Thor? For Freya?

2. Norse mythology is filled with the struggles of the gods with the giants. The giants represented the terrible forces of nature peculiar to a north country. With what forces did Thor contend?

HENRY HUDSON'S QUEST

By Burton Egbert Stevenson

OUT from the harbor of Amsterdam
   The *Half Moon* turned her prow to sea;
The coast of Norway dropped behind,
   Yet northward still kept she
Through the drifting fog and the driving snow,   5
Where never before man dared to go:
"O Pilot, shall we find the strait that leads to the Eastern
   Sea?"
"A waste of ice before us lies — we must turn back," said he.

Westward they steered their tiny bark,   10
   Westward through weary weeks they sped,
Till the cold gray strand of a stranger-land
   Loomed through the mist ahead.
League after league they hugged the coast,
And their Captain never left his post: 15
"O Pilot, see you yet the strait that leads to the Eastern
   Sea?"
"I see but the rocks and the barren shore; no strait is
   there," quoth he.

They sailed to the north — they sailed to the south —   20
   And at last they rounded an arm of sand
Which held the sea from a harbor's mouth —
   The loveliest in the land;
They kept their course across the bay,
And the shore before them fell away: 25

"O Pilot, see you not the strait that leads to the Eastern
　　Sea?"
"Hold the rudder true! Praise Christ Jesu! the strait is
　　here," said he.

5 Onward they glide with wind and tide,
　　Past marshes gray and crags sun kissed;
They skirt the sills of green-clad hills,
　　And meadows white with mist —
But alas! the hope and the brave, brave dream!
10 For rock and shallow bar the stream:
"O Pilot, can this be the strait that leads to the Eastern
　　Sea?"
"Nay, Captain, nay; 'tis not this way; turn back we must,"
　　said he.

15 Full sad was Hudson's heart as he turned
　　The *Half Moon's* prow to the south once more;
He saw no beauty in crag or hill,
　　No beauty in curving shore;
For they shut him away from that fabled main
20 He sought his whole life long, — in vain:
"O Pilot, say, can there be a strait that leads to the Eastern
　　Sea?"
"God's crypt is sealed! 'Twill stand revealed in His own
　　good time," quoth he.

1. To find a northwest passage to the Indies was the ambition of
the early navigators who explored the coast of the Western World.
Hudson, like the others, tried in vain to find it. What body of
water in the far north did he find? How is the *Half Moon* connected
with our history?

(This poem is used by special permission of the author.)

THE FRENCH CHILDREN'S CRUSADE

By Maude Barrows Dutton

The Crusades is the name of the religious wars waged by the Christians against the Mohammedans, during the Middle Ages. In 1212, 30,000 French children and 40,000 German children set out to march to Jerusalem and to convert the Turks on the way. Most of the children perished or were sold into slavery.

ONE summer afternoon long ago, in the time of the crusades, a little shepherd lad was sitting on the hillside watching his sheep. A tiny lamb had just wandered from the fold and the boy had chased it and brought it back safe to its mother. Hot and breathless from his long 5 run he threw himself down on the cool grass in the shade and shut his eyes. When he opened them again he found a stranger bending over him. He wore a long cloak about his shoulders, sandals laced across his bare feet, and carried a staff in his hand. 10

The shepherd boy sprang to his feet. He had heard about the crusades but he had never before seen a real pilgrim.

"Good lad," the old man at last spoke, "can you tell me where I can get a bite of food? I have come a long way 15 and am faint with hunger."

Stephen, for that was the shepherd boy's name, opened his leathern wallet and drew forth a piece of dry bread and some cheese. "Take my supper," he cried, "for I am not hungry. But tell me, have you really been on a crusade 20 and have you truly seen Jerusalem?"

The pilgrim sat down on the grass beside the boy and ate the bread and cheese silently. But when he had finished he turned to Stephen. — Yes, he had been on a crusade, and he told the boy all about it. As he spoke of the Holy City and the fighting with the Turks, the boy's eyes grew large and bright with excitement. The pilgrim then drew nearer and put his arm on Stephen's shoulder.

"My lad," he said slowly, "I am come here to tell you not of my life but of yours. You have been called to preach a children's crusade. You shall gather the children of France together and lead them to Jerusalem. This is the will of God."

Then picking up his staff he left a very much astonished little shepherd boy sitting on the hillside. But Stephen did not sit there long. He soon ran home to tell his bewildered parents the strange story. The next morning he began to preach to the children of the village.

But Stephen soon decided to leave the little village and go to Paris. In the church of Saint Denis, the patron saint of Paris, the French kings had been buried. Here, too, was kept the sacred oriflamme, the holy flag of the French realm. And here it was that the twelve-year-old Stephen, his shepherd's crook in his hand and his wallet at his side, began preaching the Children's Crusade.

Never had there been such excitement among the children of any land. Other lads sprang up in other villages to preach the same Children's Crusade. Young nobles came from their castles and peasant children from the hayfields to form in bands to march to Palestine. At their head went a youth carrying a flag made like the oriflamme, the symbol of Saint Denis. Vendôme was the gathering place selected by Stephen, and in June some fifteen hundred boys and girls were found there, ready for the crusade. Many of their fathers and mothers, with tears in their eyes, begged the children to come back to their homes, but the children pointed to the red crosses on their shoulders and replied, "God wills it." 5

So finally the day dawned when the crusade should start. Stephen rode at the head of the ranks in a chariot. Most of the children came afoot, carrying flags and singing hymns as they marched. It was a terrible crusade. The children were not used to the long days of tramping in the 10 hot sun and many of them died along the way. They were journeying toward Marseilles, where Stephen had seen in a vision that the Lord would open up a dry way for them across the sea. In vain they watched the blue water for this path to open. At length two merchants offered to 15 take them in their ships.

Amid singing and flying of banners the children embarked in seven vessels. The wind filled the white sails and thousands of French boys and girls waved farewell to their native land. 20

How little they dreamed that they were in reality saying farewell, never to return! A terrible storm arose and two of the vessels were wrecked off the coast of Italy and went down with all on board. The others sailed madly on but not to Jerusalem. The merchants who owned the ships 25 were slave dealers. They bore the innocent children to the coast of Africa and there sold them all into slavery. Not one came to the Holy Land. Not one returned to France. Did Stephen drown at sea or was he sold into slavery? No one knows. This was the sad story of the French 30 Children's Crusade. — *Little Stories of France.*

1. Read the next story with this one, and discuss the two together.

A CHILD CRUSADER'S STORY

WE THREE, Nicholas who cannot talk, Alain, and Denis, started along the roads with other children to go to Jerusalem. We have been walking a long time.

White voices called us in the night. They called all little children. They were like the voices of the birds that have died in winter; and at first we saw many poor birds stretched on the frozen earth, many little birds with red throats. Then we saw the first flowers and the first leaves, and we plaited crosses with them. We sang in the villages as we used to do at New Year's. And all the children ran to us. And we went forward like a flock.

There were men that cursed us, not knowing the Lord. There were women that held us back by our arms and questioned us and covered our faces with kisses. And then there were good souls that brought us wooden bowls of warm milk, and fruits. And everyone pitied us. For they do not know where we are going, and they have not heard the voices.

On the land there are thick forests, and rivers and mountains, and paths full of briers. And beyond the land is the sea which we are going to cross very soon. And beyond the sea is Jerusalem.

We have neither governors nor guides. But for us, all roads are right. Though Nicholas cannot speak, yet he walks like us, Alain and Denis. All lands are alike dangerous for children, yet we are not afraid. Everywhere there are thick forests and rivers and mountains and thorns.

Oh, how beautiful are all earthly things! We do not remember anything, for we have never been taught. Yet we have seen old trees and red rocks. Sometimes we pass into long shadows. Sometimes we walk until evening in the bright meadows. We have shouted Jesus' name into ⁵ the ears of Nicholas, and he knows it well. But he cannot say it. He rejoices with us in what we see. For his lips can open with joy, and he fondles our shoulders.

Men said that we should meet ogres and werewolves in the woods. It was not true. No one has frightened us; ¹⁰ no one has hurt us. The lonely and the sick come to look at us and old women light lights for us in their cabins. The church bells are rung for us. Peasants get up from their furrows to watch us. The animals, too, look at us and do not run away. ¹⁵

Since we have been walking the sun has grown warmer, and we no longer pick the same flowers. But all stalks may be plaited in the same shapes and our crosses are always fresh. So we are of good hope, and soon we shall catch sight of the blue sea, and beyond the blue sea is Jerusalem. ²⁰

And the Lord will let all of us little children come to His tomb. And the white voices will be joyful in the night.

1. Who led the French Children's Crusade? What caused him to lead it? How many French children joined in it? Where were they going?

2. Tell what happened to the young crusaders.

3. Who tells the "Child Crusader's Story"? What did the three do on the way?

HOW CALAIS WAS SAVED

By Jean Froissart

The town of Calais held out for almost a year against an English army led by King Edward III. Then, as the people were starving, they asked King Edward to let them go in safety if they gave up the town. When he refused, his knights told him that English soldiers could expect no mercy if their king showed none to others.

Froissart's *Chronicles* are a history of his own time — he knew many of the people, and saw many of the happenings, described.

THEN the king said: "Sirs, I will not stand out against all of you. So, Sir Walter Manny, you shall go and tell the Captain of Calais that all the mercy he shall have now from me is this: let six of the chief burgesses of the
5 town come out bareheaded, barefooted, and barelegged, with halters about their necks, and with the keys of the town and castle in their hands; let these six men put themselves altogether in my power, and I will have mercy on the rest."

10 Then Sir Walter went out again, and found the Captain of Calais, Sir John of Vienne, still on the wall, waiting for an answer. And Sir Walter told him all the mercy that he could get from the king.

"Well, sir," quoth Sir John, "I beg you to wait here for a
15 little while, till I can go into the town and tell this to the townsfolk, who sent me hither."

Then Sir John went into the market place and rang the town bell; and at once men and women began to assemble there, and Sir John told them all that he had done, and said: "Sirs, there are no better terms to be had; so take counsel among yourselves and make your answer at once."

Then all the people began to weep and to be so sorrowful that the hardest heart, seeing them, would have had pity on them; the Captain himself wept for pity. At last the 5 richest burgess of the town, Eustace of St. Pierre, rose up and said openly: "Sirs, great and small, it would indeed be a great wrong to allow the people of this town to die by famine or otherwise when there is a means to save them. I think that whoever kept them from this harm would 10 greatly please our Lord God. For my own part, I have faith in God to believe that he will pardon me if I die in this quarrel, to save others; and so I will be the first to put my life in peril."

When he had said this they all gave him great honor and 15 many of them kneeled down at his feet, weeping and sighing. Then another honest burgess stood up and said, "I will keep company with my good friend Eustace." He was called John of Aire. Then up rose James of Wissant, who was rich in goods and lands, and said that he would go 20 with his two cousins. And so did Peter of Wissant, his brother; and then two others said they would do the same. So they all went and dressed themselves as the king had commanded.

Then the Captain went with them to the gate of the city, 25 and men, women, and children made great lamentation at their departing. So they passed out of the gate, which was closed again behind them, and came to Sir Walter Manny where he waited for them between the gate and the barriers. And the Captain said to Sir Walter Manny, "Sir, as Captain 30 of Calais I deliver here to you, by the consent of all the people of the town, these six burgesses; and I truly swear to you that they are and were to-day, the most honorable, rich, and well-known burgesses of the town of Calais. And so, gentle knight, I beg of you to pray the king to have mercy on them, that they may not die."

5 Quoth Sir Walter, "I cannot say what the king will do, but I will do for them the best I can." Then the barriers were opened and the six burgesses went to the king, and the Captain went back to the town.

When Sir Walter presented the burgesses to the king
10 they kneeled down, held up their hands, and said : " Gentle king, behold us here, six men, who were burgesses of Calais and great merchants ; we have brought you the keys of the town and of the castle, and we submit ourselves entirely to your will and pleasure, that we may save the rest of
15 the people of Calais, who have suffered great misery. Sir, we beseech your grace in your great nobility to have mercy and pity on us."

At this all the earls and barons and others who were there wept for pity. But the king looked on them with anger, for
20 he hated the people of Calais very bitterly, on account of the great loss and annoyance they had formerly caused him at sea.

Then he commanded their heads to be cut off ; and though every man there begged the king to show them
25 mercy, he would hear no one who spoke for them. Then Sir Walter Manny said: "Ah, noble king, for the love of Heaven, restrain your passion. You have the name of being truly noble of mind ; therefore do not now do a thing that will blemish your good name and give folk cause to
30 speak evil of you. Everyone will say it is a great cruelty to put to death these worthy men who have willingly put themselves in your power to save their townsfolk."

But the king turned away from him, gnashing his teeth, and commanded the hangman to be sent for, and said, "The people of Calais have caused many of my men to be slain, and therefore these men shall die likewise."

Then the queen, Philippa, kneeled down and wept pite- 5 ously, saying, "Oh, gentle sir, since I came to you across the sea, at great peril, I have asked you for nothing. So now I humbly beg you, for the honor of the Son of blessed Mary, and for the love of me, that you will show mercy to these six burgesses." The king looked at the queen and 10 stood still a little while, thinking. Then he said, "Oh, lady, I wish that you had been in some other place at this time; for you have made a request of me that I cannot deny you. Therefore I give these six men to you, to do whatever you please with them." 15

So the queen had them brought into her own room, and had the halters taken from their necks, and new clothes given them, and their dinner served to them at their leisure. Then she gave them each six nobles, and had them safeguarded out of the English camp and set at liberty. 20

— *Chronicles*.

1. Where is Calais located? How far is it from England? Why should the English wish to capture it?

2. Why did King Edward wish the six burgesses to be bareheaded, etc.? What do you think of these six men? What is your opinion of Sir Walter Manny? Of the king?

3. What excuse did the king give for wishing the six burgesses to die? Who spoiled his plan? Explain line 19, page 330.

4. Is there anything in the story itself to suggest that the events took place in the Middle Ages?

THE SKATING MATCH

By Mary Mapes Dodge

The Netherlands, or Holland, as it is often called, is a very low country. Much of it is below sea level. Dikes fence the sea out and shut the rivers up into their channels. Canals connect streams and lakes. In the winter everybody skates. Farmers skate to market, and children skate to school. The following story tells of a great skating match in which forty Dutch boys and girls race on the ice.

THE twentieth of December came at last, bringing with it the perfection of winter weather. All over the level landscape lay the warm sunlight. It tried its power on lake, canal, and river; but the ice flashed defiance, and showed no sign of melting. The very weathercocks stood still to enjoy the sight.

This gave the windmills a holiday. Nearly all the past week they had been whirling briskly; now, being rather out of breath, they rocked lazily in the clear, still air. Catch a windmill working when the weathercocks have nothing to do!

There was an end to grinding, crushing, and sawing for that day. It was a good thing for the millers. Long before noon they concluded to take in their sails and go to the race. Everybody would be there. Already the north side of the frozen Y was bordered with eager spectators; the news of the great skating match had traveled far and wide. Men, women, and children, in holiday attire, were flocking toward the spot.

The site selected for the race was a faultless plain of ice near Amsterdam, on that great *arm* of the Zuider Zee which Dutchmen, of course, must call the Eye. The townspeople turned out in large numbers. Strangers in the city deemed it a fine chance to see what was to be seen. 5 Many a peasant from the northward had wisely chosen the twentieth as the day for the next city trading. It seemed that everybody, young and old, who had wheels, skates, or feet at command, had hastened to the scene.

There were the gentry in their coaches, dressed like 10 Parisians fresh from the boulevards; Amsterdam children in charity uniforms; girls from the Roman Catholic Orphan House, in sable gowns and white headbands; boys from the Burgher Asylum, with their black tights and short-skirted, harlequin coats. 15

There were old-fashioned gentlemen in velvet knee breeches; old-fashioned ladies too, in stiff, quilted skirts, and bodices of dazzling brocade. These were accompanied by servants bearing foot stoves and cloaks. There were the peasant folk, arrayed in every possible Dutch costume; 20 simple village maidens concealing their flaxen hair under fillets of gold; women whose long, narrow aprons were stiff with embroidery; women with short corkscrew curls hanging over their foreheads; women with shaved heads and close-fitting caps; and women in striped skirts and 25 windmill bonnets; men in leather, in homespun, in velvet, and broadcloth; burghers in model European attire, and burghers in short jackets, wide trousers, and steeple-crowned hats.

The music has commenced! How the melody seems to 30 enjoy itself in the open air! The fiddles have forgotten their agony, and everything is harmonious. Until you look at the blue tent, it seems that the music springs from the sunshine, it is so boundless, so joyous.   Only the musicians are solemn.

Where are the racers?   All are assembled together near the white columns.   It is a beautiful sight — forty boys and girls in picturesque attire, darting with electric swiftness in and out among each other, or sailing in pairs and triplets, beckoning, chatting, whispering, in the fullness of youthful glee.

A few careful ones are soberly tightening their straps; others, halting on one leg, with flushed, eager faces, suddenly cross the suspected skate over their knee, giving it an examining shake, and dart off again.   One and all are possessed with the spirit of motion.   They cannot stand still.   Their skates are a part of them; and every runner seems bewitched.

Twenty boys and twenty girls.   The latter, by this time, are standing in front, braced for the start; for they are to have the first "run."   Hilda, Rychie, and Katrinka are among them.   Two or three bend hastily to give a last pull at their skate straps.   It is pretty to see them stamp to be sure that all is firm.   Hilda is speaking pleasantly to a graceful little creature in a red jacket and a new brown petticoat.

Why, it is Gretel!   What a difference those pretty shoes make, and the skirt, and the new cap!   Annie Bouman is there, too.   Even Janzoon Kolp's sister has been admitted; but Janzoon himself has been voted out by the directors, because he killed the stork and only last summer was caught in the act of robbing a bird's nest — a legal offense in Holland.

The race is about to begin. Twenty girls are formed in a line. The music has ceased.

A man, whom we shall call the crier, stands between the columns and the first judges' stand. He reads the rules in a loud voice: 5

"The girls and boys are to race in turn, until one girl and one boy have beaten twice. They are to start in a line from the united columns, skate to the flagstaff line, turn, and then come back to the starting point; thus making a mile at each run." 10

A flag is waved from the judges' stand. Madame van Gleck rises in her pavilion. She leans forward with a white handkerchief in her hand. When she drops it, a bugler is to give the signal for them to start.

The handkerchief is fluttering to the ground. Hark! 15
They are off!

No. Back again. Their line was not true in passing the judges' stand.

The signal is repeated.

Off again. No mistake this time. Whew! How fast 20 they go! The multitude is quiet for an instant, absorbed in eager, breathless watching.

Cheers spring up along the line of spectators. Huzza! Five girls are ahead. Who comes flying back from the boundary mark? We cannot tell. Something red, that 25 is all. There is a blue spot flitting near it, and a dash of yellow nearer still. Spectators at this end of the line strain their eyes, and wish they had taken their post nearer the flagstaff.

The wave of cheers is coming back again. Now we can 30 see. Katrinka is ahead.

She passes the Van Holp pavilion. The next is Madame

van Gleck's. That leaning figure gazing from it is a magnet. Hilda shoots past Katrinka, waving her hand to her mother as she passes. Two others are close now, whizzing on like arrows. What is that flash of red and gray? Hurrah, it is Gretel! She, too, waves her hand, but toward no gay pavilion.

The crowd is cheering; but she hears only her father's voice — "Well done, little Gretel." Soon Katrinka, with a quick, merry laugh, shoots past Hilda. The girl in yellow is gaining now. She passes them all — all except Gretel. The judges lean forward without seeming to lift their eyes from their watches. Cheer after cheer fills the air. The very columns seem rocking. Gretel has passed them. She has won.

"Gretel Brinker, one mile!" shouts the crier.

The judges nod. They write something upon a tablet which each holds in his hand.

While the girls are resting — some crowding eagerly around our frightened little Gretel, some standing aside in high disdain — the boys form in a line.

Mynheer van Gleck drops the handkerchief, this time. The buglers give a vigorous blast. Off start the boys!

Halfway already. Did you ever see the like!

Three hundred legs flashing by in an instant. But there are only twenty boys! No matter: there were hundreds of legs, I am sure. Where are they now? There is such a noise, one gets bewildered. What are the people laughing at? Oh! at that fat boy in the rear. See him go! See him! He'll be down in an instant; no, he won't. I wonder if he knows he is all alone; the other boys are nearly at the boundary line. Yes, he knows it. He stops. He wipes his hot face. He takes off his cap, and looks about him. Better to give up with a good grace. He has made a hundred friends by that hearty, astonished laugh. Good Jacob Poot! The fine fellow is already among the spectators, gazing as eagerly as the rest.

A cloud of feathery ice flies from the heels of the skaters 5 as they "bring to," and turn at the flagstaffs. Something black is coming now, one of the boys — it is all we know. Now they come nearer; we can see the red cap. There's Ben, there's Peter, there's Hans!

Hans is ahead. Young Madame van Gend almost 10 crushes the flowers in her hand; she had been quite sure that Peter would be first. Carl Schummel is next, then Ben, and the youth with the red cap. The others are pressing close. A tall figure darts from among them. He passes the red cap, he passes Ben, then Carl. Now it is 15 an even race between him and Hans. Madame van Gend catches her breath.

It is Peter! He is ahead! Hans shoots past him. Hilda's eyes fill with tears; Peter must beat. Annie's eyes flash proudly. Gretel gazes with clasped hands; four 20 strokes more will take her brother to the columns.

He is there! Yes; but so was young Schummel just a second before. At the last instant, Carl, gathering his powers, had whizzed between them and passed the goal.

"Carl Schummel, one mile!" shouts the crier. 25

Soon Madame van Gleck rises again. The falling handkerchief starts the bugle; and the bugle, using its voice as a bowstring, shoots off twenty girls like so many arrows.

It is a beautiful sight, but one has not long to look; before we can fairly distinguish them, they are far in the 30 distance. This time they are close upon one another. It is hard to say, as they come speeding back from the flag-staff, which will reach the columns first. There are new faces among the foremost — eager, glowing faces, unnoticed before. Katrinka is there and Hilda; but Gretel and Rychie are in the rear. Gretel is wavering; but when Rychie passes her, she starts forward afresh. Now they are nearly beside Katrinka. Hilda is still in advance; she is almost "home." Like an arrow, she is speeding toward the goal. Cheer after cheer rises in the air. Peter is silent; but his eyes shine like stars. "Huzza! Huzza!"

The crier's voice is heard again:

"Hilda van Gleck, one mile!"

A loud murmur of approval runs through the crowd, catching the music in its course, till all seems one sound, with a glad, rhythmic throbbing in its depths. When the flag waves, all is still.

Once more the bugle blows a terrific blast. It sends off the boys like chaff before the wind — dark chaff, I admit, and in big pieces.

It is whisked around at the flagstaff, driven faster yet by the cheers and shouts along the line. We begin to see what is coming. There are three boys in advance, this time, and all abreast — Hans, Peter, and Lambert. Carl soon breaks the ranks, rushing through with a whiff. Fly, Hans; fly, Peter; don't let Carl beat again! Carl the bitter, Carl the insolent. Van Mounen is flagging; but you are as strong as ever. Hans and Peter, Peter and Hans; which is foremost? We love them both.

Hilda, Annie, and Gretel, seated upon the long crimson bench, can remain quiet no longer. They spring to their feet, so different and yet one in eagerness. Hilda instantly reseats herself; none shall know how interested she is; none shall know how anxious, how filled with one hope. Shut your eyes, then, Hilda, hide your face with its rippling joy. Peter has beaten.

"Peter van Holp, one mile!" calls the crier.　　　　5

The same buzz of excitement as before, while the judges take notes; the same throbbing of music through the din; but something is different. A little crowd presses close about some object near the column. Carl has fallen. He is not hurt, though somewhat stunned. If he were less 10 sullen, he would find more sympathy in these warm young hearts. As it is, they forget him as soon as he is fairly on his feet again.

The girls are to skate their third mile.

How resolute the little maidens look as they stand in a 15 line! Some are solemn with a sense of responsibility; some wear a smile, half bashful, half provoked; but one air of determination pervades them all.

This third mile may decide the race. Still, if neither Gretel nor Hilda win, there is yet a chance among the rest 20 for the silver skates.

Each girl feels sure that, this time, she will accomplish the distance in one half the time. How they stamp to try their runners! How nervously they examine each strap! How erect they stand at last, every eye upon 25 Madame van Gleck!

The bugle thrills through them again. With quivering eagerness they spring forward, bending, but in perfect balance. Each flashing stroke seems longer than the last.

Now they are skimming off in the distance.　　　　30

Again the eager straining of eyes; again the shouts and cheering; again the thrill of excitement, as, after a few moments, four or five, in advance of the rest, come speeding back, nearer, nearer, to the white columns.

Who is first? Not Rychie, Katrinka, Annie, nor Hilda, nor the girl in yellow, but Gretel — Gretel, the fleetest sprite of a girl that ever skated. She was but playing in the earlier race; *now* she is in earnest, or, rather, something within her has determined to win. That lithe little form makes no effort; but it cannot stop — not until the goal is passed!

In vain the crier lifts his voice; he cannot be heard. He has no news to tell; it is already ringing through the crowd — *Gretel has won the silver skates!*

Like a bird, she looks about her in a timid, startled way. She longs to dart to the sheltered nook where her father and mother stand. But Hans is beside her; the girls are crowding around. Hilda's kind, joyous voice breathes in her ear. From that hour, none will despise her. Goose girl or not, Gretel stands acknowledged Queen of the Skaters.

With natural pride, Hans turns to see if Peter van Holp is witnessing his sister's triumph. Peter is not looking toward them at all. He is kneeling, bending his troubled face low, and working hastily at his skate strap. Hans is beside him at once.

"Are you in trouble, mynheer?"

"Ah, Hans! that you? Yes, my fun is over. I tried to make a new hole to tighten my strap; and this botheration of a knife has cut it nearly in two."

"Mynheer," said Hans, at the same time pulling off a skate, "you must use my strap!"

"Not I, indeed, Hans Brinker!" cried Peter, looking up,

"though I thank you warmly. Go to your post, my friend; the bugle will sound in a minute."

"Mynheer," pleaded Hans in a husky voice, "you have called me your friend. Take this strap — quick! There is not an instant to lose. I shall not skate this time; indeed, I am out of practice. Mynheer, you *must* take it," and Hans slipped his strap into Peter's skate, and implored him to put it on.

"Come, Peter!" cried Lambert from the line; "we are waiting for you."

"For Madame's sake," pleaded Hans, "be quick! She is motioning to you to join the racers. There, the skate is almost on; quick, mynheer, fasten it. The race lies between Master Schummel and yourself."

"You are a noble fellow, Hans!" cried Peter, yielding at last. He sprang to his post just as the handkerchief fell to the ground. The bugle sends forth its blast, loud, clear, and ringing.

Off go the boys!

"Just look!" cries a tough old fellow from Delft. "They beat everything — these Amsterdam youngsters. See them!"

See them, indeed! They are winged Mercuries, every one of them. What mad errand are they on? Ah, I know; they are hunting Peter van Holp. He is some fleet-footed runaway from Olympus. Mercury and his troop of winged cousins are in full chase. They will catch him! Now Carl is the runaway. The pursuit grows furious. Ben is foremost!

The chase turns in a cloud of mist. It is coming this way. Who is hunted now? Mercury himself. It is Peter, Peter van Holp! Fly, Peter! Hans is watching

you.   He is sending all his fleetness, all his strength, into
your feet.   Your mother and sister are pale with eagerness.
Hilda is trembling, and dare not look up.   Fly, Peter!
The crowd has not gone deranged; it is only cheering.
5 The pursuers are close upon you.   Touch the white column.
It beckons; it is reeling before you; it —

"Huzza!   Huzza!   Peter has won the silver skates!"

"Peter van Holp!" shouted the crier.   But who heard
him?   "Peter van Holp!" shouted a hundred voices; for
10 he was the favorite boy of the place.   "Huzza!   Huzza!"

Now the music was resolved to be heard.   It struck up
a lively air, then a tremendous march.   The spectators,
thinking something new was about to happen, deigned to
listen and to look.

15   The racers formed in single file.   Peter, being tallest,
stood first.   Gretel, the smallest of all, took her place at
the end.   Hans, who had borrowed a strap from the cake
boy, was near the head.

Three gayly twined arches were placed at intervals upon
20 the river, facing the Van Gleck pavilion.

Skating slowly and in perfect time to the music, the boys
and girls moved forward, led on by Peter.   It was beautiful
to see the bright procession gliding along like a living
creature.   It curved and doubled and drew its graceful
25 length in and out among the arches; whichever way Peter,
the head, went, the body was sure to follow.   Sometimes
it steered direct for the center arch; then, as if seized with
a new impulse, turned away, and curled itself about the
first one; then unwound slowly, and bending low, with
30 quick, snakelike curvings, crossed the river, passing at
length through the farthest arch.

When the music was slow, the procession seemed to crawl like a thing afraid; it grew livelier, and the creature darted forward with a spring, gliding rapidly among the arches, twisting, turning, never losing form, until, at the call of the bugle, it suddenly resolved itself into boys and ₅ girls standing in double semicircle before Madame van Gleck's pavilion.

Peter and Gretel stand in the center, in advance of the others. Madame van Gleck rises majestically. Gretel trembles, but feels that she must look at the beautiful lady. ₁₀ She cannot hear what is said. She is thinking that she ought to try and make a curtsy, when suddenly something so dazzling is placed in her hand that she gives a cry of joy.

Then she ventures to look about her. Peter, too, has something in his hands. "Oh, oh! how splendid!" she ₁₅ cries, and "Oh! how splendid!" is echoed as far as people can see.

Meantime the silver skates flash in the sunshine, throwing dashes of light upon those two happy faces.

— *Hans Brinker, or the Silver Skates.*

1. Describe the crowd and the scene before the race begins. What similar scene have you witnessed?

2. Explain by diagram how the race was conducted.

3. Who won the first heat for the boys? The second? The third? Answer the same questions for the girls.

4. What fine act of courtesy enabled Peter to stay in the race? Who is Gretel? Is she related to Peter? Why is Carl not liked?

5. Near what large city did the race take place? Find it on the map.

6. Tell of a race of any kind you have witnessed or taken part in.

TRUE SUCCESS

Have little care that life is brief,
And less that art is long,
Success is in the silences
Though fame is in the song.

— CHRISTINA ROSSETTI.

CARCASSONNE (*See page 354*)

LETTER TO HIS SON

By Robert E. Lee

YOU must study to be frank with the world; frankness is the child of honesty and courage. Say just what you mean to do on every occasion and take it for granted you mean to do right. If a friend asks a favor, you should
5 grant it if it is reasonable; if not, tell him plainly why you cannot; you will wrong him and wrong yourself by equivocation of any kind. Never do a wrong thing to make a friend or keep one; the man who requires you to do so is dearly purchased at a sacrifice. Deal kindly but
10 firmly with all your classmates; you will find it the policy which wears best. . . . If you have any fault to find with anyone, tell him, not others, of what you complain; there is no more dangerous experiment than that of undertaking to be one thing before a man's face and another behind
15 his back. We should live, act, and say nothing to the injury of anyone. It is not only best as a matter of principle but it is the path of peace and honor.

In regard to duty, let me, in conclusion of this hasty letter, inform you that nearly a hundred years ago there
20 was a day of remarkable gloom and darkness — still known as "the dark day" — a day when the light of the sun was slowly extinguished as if by an eclipse. The Legislature of Connecticut was in session, and as the members saw the unexpected and unaccountable darkness
25 coming on they shared in the general awe and terror. It was supposed by many that the last day — the day of

judgment — had come. Some one in the consternation of
the hour moved an adjournment. Then there arose an old
Puritan legislator, Davenport of Stamford, and said that
if the last day had come he desired to be found in his place
doing his duty and therefore moved that candles be brought 5
in, so that the House could proceed with its duty. There
was quietness in that man's mind, the quietness of heavenly
wisdom and inflexible willingness to obey present duty.

Duty, then, is the sublimest word in our language. Do
your duty in all things, like the old Puritan. You cannot 10
do more, you should never wish to do less. Never let me
and your mother wear one gray hair for any lack of duty
on your part.

1. Robert E. Lee (1807–1870) was one of the greatest military
geniuses America has produced. No small part of the success of the
Southern armies in the Civil War was due to his leadership. Above
all he was a true gentleman. Find out about his life in any encyclopedia.

2. Explain what Lee meant by frankness. Where must you
draw the line between frankness and disagreeable forwardness?

3. You see one of your classmates deliberately break a window
in the school. He denies all knowledge of the act. What is your
duty? Discuss fully.

4. What does the story of the Connecticut legislator illustrate?

(From *Library of Southern Literature*, published by The Martin and Hoyt Co., Atlanta,
Ga.)

ABOU BEN ADHEM

BY LEIGH HUNT

ABOU BEN ADHEM (may his tribe increase!)
    Awoke one night from a deep dream of peace,
And saw within the moonlight in his room,
Making it rich and like a lily in bloom,
5 An Angel writing in a book of gold;
Exceeding peace had made Ben Adhem bold,
And to the Presence in the room he said,
"What writest thou?" The Vision raised its head,
And with a look made of all sweet accord,
10 Answered, "The names of those who love the Lord."
"And is mine one?" said Abou. "Nay, not so,"
Replied the Angel. Abou spoke more low,
But cheerily still, and said, "I pray thee, then,
Write me as one that loves his fellow men."

15 The Angel wrote and vanished. The next night
It came again with a great wakening light,
And showed the names whom love of God had blessed,
And lo! Ben Adhem's name led all the rest.

1. What did Ben Adhem do to cause his name to be inscribed in the book of gold? Why was it at the head of the list?
2. Can you name any other virtue that might rank high in the list?
3. Do not name the person, but select some one — boy, girl, man, or woman — of whom you have a high opinion. Tell what there is about this person that you like.

THE NOBLE NATURE

BY BEN JONSON

IT IS not growing like a tree
  In bulk doth make man better be;
Or standing long an oak, three hundred year,
To fall a log at last, dry, bald, and sear.
      A lily of a day   5
      Is fairer far in May,
  Although it fall and die that night, —
  It was the plant and flower of light.
In small proportions we just beauties see;
And in short measures life may perfect be.   10

INGRATITUDE

BY WILLIAM SHAKESPEARE

BLOW, blow, thou winter wind,
  Thou art not so unkind
    As man's ingratitude;
Thy tooth is not so keen
Because thou art not seen,   5
    Although thy breath be rude.

Freeze, freeze, thou bitter sky,
Thou dost not bite so nigh
    As benefits forgot;
Though thou the waters warp,   10
Thy sting is not so sharp
    As friend remembered not.

AS GOOD AS HIS WORD

By MARTHA G. PURCELL

IN THE early days of Kentucky there dwelt in Lewis County a man by the name of Larkin Liles. He was the hardy son of a hardy race, who hunted and trapped. And while he knew not a letter of the alphabet, had never
5 attended school a day in his life, nor heard the golden rule, yet his rugged honesty and high sense of honor can never be surpassed.

On one occasion, when at Vanceburg in the above-named county, he became involved in a rough-and-tumble fight
10 with very serious results. For this offense he was tried, found guilty, and sentenced to serve one year in the penitentiary. It so happened that the sheriff of Lewis County at this time was a personal friend of "Jay Bird" Liles and knew the soul of honor hidden by the man's rough clothes.
15 After leaving the courtroom, the prisoner, in a voice husky with emotion, said, "Uncle Buck" — everyone called the sheriff of Lewis County by this title — "Uncle Buck, won't you let me go home and get in my winter's wood? I want to fix to have my corn crop gathered,
20 so as to fatten my hogs, so the children will have meat. Then I'll come over to Clarksburg and go with ye to the penitentiary."

Sheriff Parker asked, "How long will it take ye, Jay Bird?"

25 "About two weeks," he said.

Then the man in the sheriff shone forth, and he replied,

"Go ahead and do it." So well did he know the pride with which Jay Bird Liles kept a promise that he was confident of his return at the promised time.

The wood was cut, an arrangement was made concerning the crop, the good-by kiss was given to his weeping wife and helpless babes, and in just two weeks to the day and hour, Liles walked into the sheriff's office ready to be taken to Frankfort.

When he told Uncle Buck that he was ready to start, the sheriff shook his hand. On the morrow they would take the boat for Maysville and from there go by stage to Lexington and on to Frankfort. Jay Bird's voice trembled as he thought of the disgrace of being publicly taken by the sheriff to the penitentiary, and again he made a most singular request.

"Say, Uncle Buck, I'd rather not do it. You go that way, but let me take my gun and walk through the mountains to Frankfort, won't ye? I'd rather do that, and maybe I might kill some game on the road. I'll meet you at any spot, on any day you appoint."

What do you suppose the sheriff replied? Looking him straight in the eye he answered, "All right, Jay Bird, suit yourself. Frankfort lies in yon direction. You can't miss it. When you reach Frankfort go straight to the governor's office and tell him what you are there for — if I don't get there first."

Then this rugged mountaineer, this unlettered, unpolished son of the hills, started on foot to Frankfort, one hundred and fifty miles away. There he would hear the lock snap as it closed the door that would shut him in from freedom and friends.

Two days later, before the people of Frankfort were

abroad, a tall, gaunt, determined-looking backwoodsman in buckskin clothes and a coonskin cap, looking as if he belonged to the days of Daniel Boone, made his way to the governor's house and quietly seated himself on a stone. As Governor Clark started from the house after breakfast he was astonished to see this man of the mountains who quickly inquired, "Say, Mister, are you the governor?"

"Yes, my man, I am the governor. What can I do for you?"

"Well, governor, my name is Larkin Liles, and I came up here from Lewis County to get into the penitentiary for one year. Have you seen anything of Buck Parker?"

Utterly astounded Governor Clark asked, "Who is Buck Parker?"

"Why, Buck Parker is the high sheriff of Lewis County. I thought everybody knew that. We all call him 'Uncle Buck' Parker. He was to come by stage and meet me here. I walked through."

Governor Clark looked the man over carefully. Then Jay Bird continued anxiously, "Say, governor, the sheriff ain't here yet and I don't want to lose any time. Can't you let me into the penitentiary and tell Buck Parker where he can find me when he comes?"

More astonished than ever, Governor Clark said, "Have you had your breakfast, Mr. Liles?"

Jay Bird shook his head and explained that he had traveled all night and had come straight to the governor. The governor at once took him in, gave him his breakfast, and told him to go over to the capitol.

Ten hours later the sheriff came by stage and soon found Jay Bird at the governor's office. The governor immediately asked if it was a fact that this man, condemned to a year in the penitentiary, had trudged on foot, alone, all the way from Lewis County. When told it was just as Jay Bird had said, the governor asked, "Is the man crazy? Couldn't he have escaped?"

"Easily, and all the sheriffs, constables, and rewards could never have caught him. No, Jay Bird is not simple. He is honest."

The governor was so interested he asked for all the details. Then Uncle Buck told of the fight, the trial, and the conviction; of how Jay Bird had kept his word when permitted to go to say good-by to his loved ones; of his long life of honesty and hospitality; and of how he had begged to come alone on foot to Frankfort, rather than as a common, convicted felon.

With eyes dimmed by tears, the governor hastily affixed his name and the seal of the state to a small piece of paper. This he handed to Larkin Liles and said in a husky voice, "Mr. Liles, go home to your family and kiss the little ones for me. You shall never enter the penitentiary while Clark is governor of Kentucky."

— *Stories of Old Kentucky* (*adapted*).

1. There is nothing finer in life than rugged honesty. All true success is built upon it. Our whole commercial life depends on it. Why do stores give people goods on credit? Why do you feel safe in putting money in a bank?

2. Retell the story of Larkin Liles. What other story have you read or heard that is called to mind by this one?

3. Imagine that you were Governor Clark. What would you have done with Liles? Give the reasons for your doing so.

CLEON AND I

By Charles Mackay

CLEON hath a million acres — ne'er a one have I;
  Cleon dwelleth in a palace — in a cottage, I;
Cleon hath a dozen fortunes — not a penny, I;
But the poorer of the twain is Cleon and not I.

5 Cleon, true, possesseth acres — but the landscape, I;
Half the charms to me it yieldeth money cannot buy;
Cleon harbors sloth and dullness — freshening vigor, I;
He in velvet, I in fustian — richer man am I.

Cleon is a slave to grandeur — free as thought am I;
10 Cleon fees a score of doctors — need of none have I.
Wealth-surrounded, care-environed, Cleon fears to die;
Death may come — he'll find me ready — happier man
    am I.

Cleon sees no charms in Nature — in a daisy, I;
15 Cleon hears no anthems ringing in the sea and sky —
Nature sings to me forever — earnest listener, I;
State for state, with all attendants, who would change?
    Not I.

1. Wherein does the poet claim he is richer than Cleon? How do you suppose Cleon came to lose these finer things of life? Is it possible for a man to be wealthy without being like Cleon? Discuss your answer.

2. Explain: twain, sloth, fustian, fees, anthems.

CARCASSONNE

By Gustave Nadaud

I'M growing old; I've sixty years;
    I've labored all my life in vain;
In all that time of hopes and fears
    I've failed my dearest wish to gain:
I see full well that here below   5
    Bliss unalloyed there is for none.
My prayer will ne'er fulfillment know;
    I never have seen Carcassonne!

You see the city from the hill,
    It lies beyond the mountains blue;   10
And yet to reach it one must still
    Five long and weary leagues pursue,
And to return as many more!
    Ah! had the vintage plenteous grown! —
The grape withheld its yellow store,   15
    I shall not look on Carcassonne!

They tell me every day is there
    Not more nor less than Sunday gay;
In shining robes and garments fair
    The people walk upon their way;
One gazes there on castle walls
    As grand as those of Babylon,
A bishop and two generals!
    I do not know fair Carcassonne!

The curé's right.   He says that we
  Are ever wayward, weak, and blind;
He tells us in his homily
  Ambition ruins all mankind.
Yet, could I there two days have spent,
  While still the autumn sweetly shone,
Ah me! I might have died content
  When I had looked on Carcassonne!

Thy pardon, Father, I beseech,
  In this my prayer if I offend;
One something sees beyond his reach
  From childhood to his journey's end.
My wife, our little boy, Aignan,
  Have traveled even to Narbonne;
My grandchild has seen Perpignan:
  And I — have not seen Carcassonne!

So crooned one day, close by Limoux,
  A peasant, double bent with age.
"Rise up, my friend," said I, "with you
  I'll go upon this pilgrimage."
We left next morning his abode,
  But (Heaven forgive him!) halfway on,
The old man died upon the road:
  He never gazed on Carcassonne.

1. Carcassonne represents an ambition that is never attained. The old man had looked forward all his life to visiting the place.   It was his ideal.   Explain this saying: "We all have our Carcassonnes."

2. Judging from the names, where is the scene of the poem laid? Who speaks all the stanzas except the last?   Then who appears?

3. Study the picture on page 344.   What do you think of it?

JOHN MAYNARD

By J. B. Gough

JOHN MAYNARD was well known in the lake district as a God-fearing, honest, and intelligent pilot. He was pilot on a steamboat from Detroit to Buffalo. One summer afternoon — at that time those steamers seldom carried boats — smoke was seen ascending from below, and the captain called out, "Simpson, go below, and see what the matter is down there."

Simpson came up with his face pale as ashes and said, "Captain, the ship is on fire."

Then, "Fire! fire! fire on shipboard!"

All hands were called up. Buckets of water were dashed on the fire, but in vain. There were large quantities of rosin and tar on board, and it was found useless to attempt to save the ship. The passengers rushed forward and inquired of the pilot, "How far are we from Buffalo?"

"Seven miles."

"How long before we can reach there?"

"Three quarters of an hour at our present rate of steam."

"Is there any danger?"

"Danger here! See the smoke bursting out! Go forward if you would save your lives."

Passengers and crew — men, women, and children — crowded the forward part of the ship. John Maynard stood at the helm. The flames burst forth in a sheet of fire, clouds of smoke arose. The captain cried out through his trumpet, "John Maynard!"

"Aye, aye, sir!"

"Are you at the helm?"

"Aye, aye, sir!"

"How does she head?"

5   "Southeast by east, sir."

"Head her southeast and run her on shore," said the captain.

Nearer, nearer, yet nearer, she approached the shore. Again the captain cried out, "John Maynard!"

10   The response came feebly this time, "Aye, aye, sir!"

"Can you hold on five minutes longer, John?" he said.

"By God's help, I will."

The old man's hair was scorched from the scalp. One hand disabled, his knee upon the stanchion, and his teeth
15 set, with his other hand upon the wheel, he stood firm as a rock. And he beached the ship. Every man, woman, and child was saved — except John Maynard.

— Adapted.

1. This is a story made famous by its author, a popular preacher of his day. It is a story that lives because it is fundamentally sound. No higher act can be performed than this: he gave his life that others might be saved. That is an ideal upon which religions are founded and civilizations are built. No wonder that literature has it for a favorite theme.

2. On what body of water did this catastrophe occur? What is especially terrible about a fire at sea? What is there about Maynard's act that makes it so appealing to us?

It is well to think well. It is divine to act well.

— Horace Mann.

THE HERITAGE

By James Russell Lowell

In this poem Lowell speaks chiefly of the heritage of the average person who works for a living.   After reading it one is proud that he has the privilege of working.

WHAT doth the poor man's son inherit?
  Stout muscles and a sinewy heart,
A hardy frame, a hardier spirit;
  King of two hands, he does his part
  In every useful toil and art;   5
A heritage, it seems to me,
A king might wish to hold in fee.

What doth the poor man's son inherit?
  Wishes o'erjoyed with humble things,
A rank adjudged by toil-won merit,   10
  Content that from employment springs,
  A heart that in his labor sings;
A heritage, it seems to me,
A king might wish to hold in fee.

What doth the poor man's son inherit?   15
  A patience learned of being poor;
Courage, if sorrow come, to bear it;
  A fellow feeling that is sure
  To make the outcast bless his door;
A heritage, it seems to me,   20
A king might wish to hold in fee.

THE HERITAGE

O rich man's son! there is a toil
    That with all others level stands;
Large charity doth never soil,
    But only whitens, soft white hands;
5   This is the best crop from thy lands —
A heritage, it seems to me,
Worth being rich to hold in fee.

O poor man's son! scorn not thy state;
    There is worse weariness than thine,
10 In merely being rich and great:
    Toil only gives the soul to shine,
    And makes rest fragrant and benign, —
A heritage, it seems to me,
Worth being poor to hold in fee.

15 Both, heirs to some six feet of sod,
    Are equal in the earth at last;
Both, children of the same great God,
    Prove title to your heirship vast
    By record of a well-filled past;
20 A heritage, it seems to me,
Well worth a life to hold in fee.

1. Make a list of the things the poor man's son inherits. What is the best opportunity of the rich man's son? What do both inherit finally?

2. Poor men's sons, as well as rich, often fail to cultivate patience, courage, a strong body, etc. What is the matter with them? Do riches have anything to do with real success? Explain your answer.

3. Explain what is meant by "heritage"; "hold in fee"; "fragrant and benign"; "fellow feeling."

A WISH

By Samuel Rogers

MINE be a cot beside the hill;
　　A beehive's hum shall soothe my ear;
A willowy brook that turns a mill,
With many a fall shall linger near.

The swallow oft beneath my thatch   5
Shall twitter from her clay-built nest;
Oft shall the pilgrim lift the latch
And share my meal, a welcome guest.

Around my ivied porch shall spring
Each fragrant flower that drinks the dew;   10
And Lucy at her wheel shall sing
In russet gown and apron blue.

The village church among the trees,
Where first our marriage vows were given,
With merry peals shall swell the breeze,   15
And point with taper spire to heaven.

　1. The author here describes the home he should prefer to have above all others.　Prove from the poem that he liked the outdoors; that he was hospitable; that he was religious.
　2. What work do you judge he would prefer to do?
　3. Explain lines 3, 5, 16.

WHO IS THE HAPPIEST MAN?

By James Baldwin

MANY hundreds of years ago there lived in Asia a
king whose name was Crœsus. The country over
which he ruled was not very large but its people were
prosperous and famed for their wealth. Crœsus himself
was said to be the richest man in the world; and to this
day it is customary to say of a very wealthy man that he is
"as rich as Crœsus." King Crœsus had everything that
could make him happy — lands and houses and slaves,
fine clothes to wear, and beautiful things to look at. He
could not think of anything to make him more contented.
"I am the happiest man in the world," he said.

It happened one summer that a great man from across the
sea was traveling in Asia. The name of this man was Solon,
and he was the lawmaker of Athens, in Greece. He was
noted for his great wisdom, and centuries after his death
the highest praise that could be given to any learned man
was to say, "He is as wise as Solon."

Solon had heard of Crœsus and his wealth and one day
he paid him a visit in his beautiful palace. Crœsus was
now happier and prouder than ever before, for the wisest
man in the world was his guest. He led Solon through the
palace and showed him the grand rooms, the fine carpets,
the rich furniture, the pictures, the books. Then he invited
him out to see his gardens and his orchards and his stables,
and he showed him thousands of rare and beautiful things
that he had collected from all parts of the world.

In the evening, as the wisest of men was dining with the richest of men, the king said to his guest, "Tell me, O Solon, who do you think is the happiest of all men?" He expected that Solon would answer, "King Croesus."

The wise man was silent for a minute; then he said, "I have in mind a poor man who once lived in Athens. His name was Tellus and I doubt if ever there was a happier man than he."

This was not the answer that Croesus wished. He hid his disappointment, however, and asked: "Why do you think so? What did Tellus have to make him happy?"

"He was an honest man," answered Solon, "and he labored hard for many years to bring up his children and give them a good education. When they were grown up and able to care for themselves he joined the Athenian army and gave his life bravely in the defense of his country. Can you think of anyone who is more deserving of happiness?"

"Perhaps not," answered Croesus, half choking with vexation, "but who do you think ought to rank next to Tellus in happiness?" He was sure that this time Solon would say, "Croesus."

"I have in mind two young men whom I knew in Greece," answered the wise man. "Their father died when they were only children and they were very poor. But they worked hard to keep the house together and to support their mother. Year after year they toiled, never suffering anything to interfere with their mother's comfort. When at length she died, they gave all their love to Athens, their native city, and nobly served her as long as they lived."

Then Croesus was angry. "Why is it that you place these poor working people above the richest of kings?"

he asked. "Why do you make me of no account and think nothing of my wealth and power?"

"O king," said Solon, " no man can say whether you are happy or not, until you die. For no one knows what misfortunes may befall you or what misery may be yours in days to come."

Many years after this, when Crœsus was much older and richer, there arose in Asia a powerful king whose name was Cyrus. At the head of a great army he marched through one country after another, overthrowing many a rich and ancient kingdom. Crœsus with all his wealth could not withstand this mighty warrior. His city was taken, his palace was burned, his orchards and gardens were destroyed, his treasures were carried away, and he himself was made prisoner.

"This stubborn fellow, Crœsus, has caused us much trouble by his resistance," said King Cyrus. "Take him and make an example of him for other little rulers who would dare to stand in our way."

The soldiers thereupon carried Crœsus to the market place, handling him pretty roughly all the while. There they built up a great pile of dry sticks and broken furniture from the ruins of his once beautiful palace, and on the top of it they tied the unhappy king. "Now we shall have a merry blaze," said the savage fellows, and one of them ran for a torch.

Poor Crœsus lay bleeding and bruised upon the pyre, without a friend to soothe his misery. Then he thought of the words which wise Solon had spoken long before, "No man can say whether you are happy or not, until you die." The memory of these words only added to his despair and he moaned aloud, "O Solon! Solon!"

It so happened that Cyrus was riding by at that very moment and heard his moans. "What does he say?" he asked the soldiers.

"He says nothing but 'Solon! Solon! Solon! O Solon!'" they answered. 5

Then the king came up nearer to the pyre and said to Crœsus, "What do you mean by calling 'Solon! Solon! Solon!' in that way?"

Crœsus was silent at first, but after Cyrus had repeated his question kindly, he told all about Solon's visit at the 10 palace and what he had said.

Cyrus listened and was much moved by the story. He thought of the words, "No man knows what misfortunes may befall you or what misery may be yours in days to come," and he wondered if he too might not sometime 15 lose all his power and be helpless in the hands of his enemies. "Is it not true," he asked himself, "that men ought to be merciful and kind to those who are in distress? I will do to Crœsus even as I would have others do to me." So he caused poor Crœsus to be set free, and ever afterwards he 20 treated him as an honored and trusted friend.

— Thirty More Famous Stories Retold.

1. Who was Crœsus? Solon? Cyrus?

2. Whom did Solon pick out as happy men? Why did he omit Crœsus? How did Solon's statement come true? Explain how Solon really saved Crœsus' life.

3. "Do as you would be done by." Which of the characters acted upon this proverb?

THE HAPPY MAN

By Sir Henry Wotton

HOW happy is he born and taught
    That serveth not another's will;
Whose armor is his honest thought,
    And simple truth his utmost skill!

5 Who hath his life from rumors freed;
    Whose conscience is his strong retreat;
Whose state can neither flatterers feed,
    Nor ruin make oppressors great.

That man is freed from servile bands
10   Of hope to rise or fear to fall;
Lord of himself, though not of lands,
    And having nothing, yet hath all.

DARE TO DO RIGHT

DARE to be honest, good, and sincere;
    Dare to please God and you never need fear.
Dare to be brave in the cause of the right;
Dare with the enemy ever to fight.
5 Dare to be patient and loving each day;
Dare speak the truth whatever you say.
Dare to speak kindly and ever be true;
Dare to do right and you'll find your way through.

A GOLDEN COPPERSMITH

BASIL GAVRILOFF MARINE, a Russian crown slave and by trade a coppersmith, was at the beginning of March returning to Petrograd from visiting his family at his native village. He arrived at Moscow on the night of the eleventh with ten of his companions, and as the railway train was already gone they were obliged to pass the night there and remain till three the next afternoon.

"The villagers are curious," Marine himself related, "and as we had never been at Moscow before, we determined to see all the curiosities of that ancient town. We entered the Cathedral of the Assumption and kissed all its holy relics. We ascended to the top of the belfry of Ivan Veliky and then proceeded to the Bird Market. Here we heard that a terrible fire was raging — that the Great Theater was burning. As it was only noon, we determined to be spectators and hastened to the spot."

They arrived just as the fire was at its height; the theater burnt from the interior and the flames spread rapidly, bursting from the roof and the windows in savage fury. At the time the fire broke out three workmen were engaged at the top of the building; it gained upon them so fast they had only time to reach the roof from a window, where they frantically rushed about without hope of escape, surrounded by flames which each moment gained upon them. Two of them in wild despair threw themselves from the roof and were instantly killed by falling on the pavement below.

The third remained, and suffocating with the smoke screamed for assistance in a manner that struck agony to the hearts of all who heard him. His death seemed inevitable. There was not a ladder of sufficient length to reach the roof of the building and the miserable man had the alternative of perishing by the flames or leaping down as his comrades had done. But even in this extremity his confidence did not forsake him and he sought refuge on that side where the wind blew the flames away from him. Marine and his companions all this time were spectators of the scene. "I held my tongue," said Marine, "but my heart beat painfully and I asked myself how I could save this poor soul."

"Companions," cried the brave fellow suddenly, "wait for me here while I try and save that man!" His comrades looked at him with surprise but without dissuading him from his purpose.

"God be with you!" said they, "for it is a good deed you are about to do." Without losing another moment Marine approached the authorities present and solicited permission to try and rescue the man from the frightful death which menaced him.

Permission obtained, he took off his cap and sheepskin coat and confided them to the care of the police. Accompanied by his brother and provided with a stout cord, he rushed to a ladder that was placed against the wall but which was very far from reaching the roof. Marine made the sign of the Cross and began to ascend. When he reached the summit he fastened the cord around his waist, and once more devoutly crossing himself, began to climb one of the pipes that led from the roof.

The crowd below, breathless with astonishment and fear,

eagerly watched each movement. Around him the flames were playing with intense fury, and above the terrible noise of the falling timbers were heard the fearful shrieks of the unfortunate man, who though he saw assistance coming to him dreaded it might be too late. Nothing daunted, Marine continued his perilous ascent. "It was cold," said he, "and there was a terrible wind, but yet I felt it not; for from the moment I determined upon trying to save the fellow, my heart was on fire and I was like a furnace."

His burning hands kept continually sticking to the frozen pipes, which somewhat retarded his progress; but still he courageously continued his way. "The pipe cracked," said he, "it was no longer firm — this dear pipe; but happily I had arrived at the cornice, where there was foot room."

His brother, who had remained all this time on the ladder, had made a hook fast to one end of the cord. Marine passed it to the man on the roof and desired him to fasten it somehow, securely. This he did by fixing it round one of the ornaments of the cornice. Marine doubled it to make it more secure and then made him slide down the pipe — himself giving the example. At the moment Marine reached the ladder and the man he had so nobly preserved was seen to glide down in safety, a remarkable movement was manifested by the crowd — a movement truly Russian. All heads were simultaneously uncovered and all hands made the sign of the Cross.

When Marine reached the ground the man was already halfway down the ladder and out of all danger. "I had hardly reached the ground," Marine related, "when a gentleman in a cloak and military casque approached me and gave me twenty-five silver rubles." A great number of others surrounded him and each gave him according to his means — some ten kopecks silver, others a ruble, and some only copper.

"Thanks, brave man!" was cried on all sides; "you are a courageous and good Christian; and may God long grant you health and bless you!"

"What became of the man I rescued," said Marine, "I do not know, but that is not my affair. Thanks to God, he is saved. A gentleman — an aid-de-camp — came to me, gave me a ticket, and took me in his sledge to the office of the Chancellerie, where he wrote down all that had taken place."

During this time Marine did not lose his presence of mind; he was only anxious about one thing — that the railway train should not leave without him. At three o'clock he was in the coach and on Friday, the thirteenth, he arrived at his destination, where he was waited for by his master, Monsieur Flottoff.

He requested permission for one day's leave to visit his aunt, who kept a small shop in the Vassili Ostroff, which was readily granted. When leaving her to return home he was astonished at being called to the house of the Grand Master of the Police, who accompanied him to the palace. The courage of which he had so lately given so strong a proof had been brought to the knowledge of the Emperor, who desired to see him. Never had he thought even in his wildest dreams that such an honor would be accorded to him, a simple man of the people.

The Emperor received Marine in his cabinet, and with the greatest kindness said, "Marine, I thank thee for the good and great action thou hast performed. But I wish to hear from thy own mouth how, with God's assistance, thou didst it."

Marine related the adventure to him in his own simple manner, and when he had finished, the Czar, who had listened to him with the greatest attention, embraced him 5 and said: "My son, may God bless you! And remember, if you ever stand in need of my assistance, come to me and it shall be accorded you." The Emperor then presented him with a medal and one hundred and fifty silver rubles, and Marine left the Czar's presence a happy man. 10

1. Tell the main points of the story. Why is the coppersmith called "golden"? What other story in this section has a lesson similar to this?

OPPORTUNITY

By John J. Ingalls

MASTER of human destinies am I!
    Fame, love, and fortune on my footsteps wait.
Cities and fields I walk; I penetrate
Deserts and seas remote, and passing by
    Hovel and mart and palace, soon or late   5
I knock unbidden once at every gate.
If sleeping, wake; if feasting, rise before
    I turn away. It is the hour of fate,
    And they who follow me reach every state
Mortals desire, and conquer every foe   10
    Save Death; but those who doubt or hesitate,
Condemned to failure, penury, and woe,
    Seek me in vain and uselessly implore.
    I answer not, and I return no more!

(From *Writings, Addresses, and Orations* by J. J. Ingalls, Franklin Hudson Publishing Co., Kansas City, Mo.)

COMMUNITY AND COUNTRY

Happy are all free peoples too strong to be dis-
possessed;
But blessed are those among nations who dare to
be strong for the rest!

— ELIZABETH BARRETT BROWNING.

THE MAN WITH HIS HAT IN HIS HAND

(See opposite page)

THE MAN WITH HIS HAT IN HIS HAND

By Clark Howell

This is a story of the World War. To train the volunteer and drafted soldiers, our government established cantonments in many places. One of these, Camp Gordon, was near Atlanta, and it was in that camp that the incident related occurred. It is a fine illustration of the spirit that makes our democracy possible.

THE Twenty-ninth Regiment of United States Volunteers was quartered at Atlanta. They had received orders for their departure. The troops were formed in full regimental parade in the presence of thousands of 5 spectators, among whom were anxious and weeping mothers, loving sisters and sweethearts, and a vast multitude of others who had gone to look, possibly for the last time, upon departing friends.

Of the enlisted men a great percentage were from Georgia, 10 most of them from simple farmhouses and the quiet and unpretentious hearthstones which abound in the rural communities. A few had seen service in Cuba, but most of them had volunteered as raw recruits from the farm. There were sturdy and rugged mountaineers from the Blue Ridge 15 counties — strong, steady, and intrepid, with the simplicity characteristic of the mountain fastnesses from which they came. There were boys from the wire grass — plain, unassuming, and unaffected, their eyes lighted with the fire of determination and their hearts beating in unison with 20 the loyalty of their purpose. The men moved like machines. The regiment of raw recruits had become in a few months a command of trained and disciplined soldiers. The very air was fraught with the impressive significance of the scene, which had its counterpart in many of the states where patriots enlisted faster than the muster roll was called.

Leaning against a tree was a white-haired mountaineer who looked with intent eyes and with an expression of the keenest sympathy upon the movements of the men in uniform. His gaze was riveted on the regiment, and the frequent applause of the visiting multitude fell apparently unheard on his ears. The regiment had finished its evolutions; the commissioned officers had lined themselves to make their regulation march to the front for their report and dismissal. The bugler had sounded the signal; the artillery had belched its adieu as the king of day withdrew beyond the hills; the halyard had been grasped, and the flag slowly fell, saluting the retiring sun. As the flag started its descent the scene was characterized by a solemnity that seemed sacred in its intensity. From the regimental band there floated the *Star-Spangled Banner*. Instinctively and apparently unconsciously, the old man by the tree removed his hat from his head and held it in his hand in reverential recognition until the flag had been furled and the last strain of the national anthem had been lost in the resonant tramp of the troops as they left the field.

What a picture that was — the man with his hat in his hand, as he stood uncovered during that impressive ceremony! I moved involuntarily toward him, and impressed with his reverential attitude, I asked him where he was from. "I am," said he, "from Pickens County"; and in casual conversation it developed that this raw mountaineer had come to Atlanta to say farewell to an only son who

stood in line before him and upon whom his tear-bedimmed
eyes might then be resting for the last time. The silent
exhibition of patriotism and loyalty had been prompted
by a soul as rugged but as placid as the great blue mountains which gave it birth and by an inspiration kindled
from the very bosom of nature itself.

There was the connecting link between the hearthstone
and the capitol. There was the citizen who, representing
the only real, substantial element of the nation's reserve
strength — "the citizen standing in the doorway of the
home, contented on his threshold" — had answered his
country's call — the man of whom Henry Grady so elo-
quently said: "He shall save the Republic when the drum
tap is futile and the barracks are exhausted." There was
that in the spontaneous action of the man that spoke of
hardships to be endured and dangers to be dared for
country's sake; there was that in his reverential attitude
that said, even though the libation of his heart's blood
should be required in far-off lands, his life would be laid
down as lightly as his hat was lifted to his country's call.
Denied by age the privilege of sharing the hardships and the
dangers of the comrades of his boy, no rule could regulate
his patriotic ardor, no limitation could restrain the in-
stincts of his homage.

1. Why was "The Man" present when the soldiers were preparing to break camp? What was there about him that attracted
Mr. Howell's attention?

2. Read the lines of the story upon which the picture on page 372
is based. Is the picture a fair illustration of the scene as you imagine
it?

3. Select another title for the story that will also refer to "The
Man." What do you think of the present title?

4. Read the last paragraph aloud and tell what it means to you.

OUR COUNTRY'S CALL

By John Greenleaf Whittier

UP THE hillside, down the glen,
   Rouse the sleeping citizen;
Summon out the might of men!

Like a lion growling low,
Like a night storm rising slow,   5
Like the tread of unseen foe —

It is coming — it is nigh!
Stand your homes and altars by;
On your own free thresholds die!

Clang the bells in all your spires;   10
On the gray hills of your sires
Fling to heaven your signal fires!

Oh! for God and duty stand,
Heart to heart and hand to hand,
Round the old graves of the land!   15

Whoso shrinks or falters now,
Whoso to the yoke would bow,
Brand the craven on his brow!

Freedom's soil hath only place
For a free and fearless race —   20
None for traitors false and base!

THE LANDING OF THE PILGRIMS

By Felicia D. Hemans

The Pilgrims set sail in the *Mayflower* from Delftshaven, Holland, July, 1620, and landed on the coast of Massachusetts, December 21, 1620.

THE breaking waves dashed high
    On a stern and rock-bound coast,
And the woods against a stormy sky
    Their giant branches tossed;

5 And the heavy night hung dark
    The hills and waters o'er,
When a band of exiles moored their bark
    On the wild New England shore.

Not as the conqueror comes,
10   They, the true-hearted, came;
Not with the roll of the stirring drums,
    And the trumpet that sings of fame;

Not as the flying come,
    In silence and in fear;
15 They shook the depths of the desert's gloom
    With their hymns of lofty cheer.

Amid the storm they sang,
    And the stars heard, and the sea;
And the sounding aisles of the dim woods rang
20   To the anthem of the free.

The ocean eagle soared
From his nest by the white wave's foam,
And the rocking pines of the forest roared;
This was their welcome home!

There was woman's fearless eye,   5
Lit by her deep love's truth;
There was manhood's brow, serenely high,
And the fiery heart of youth.

What sought they thus afar?
Bright jewels of the mine?   10
The wealth of seas, the spoils of war? —
They sought a faith's pure shrine!

Aye, call it holy ground,
The soil where first they trod!
They have left unstained what there they found —   15
Freedom to worship God!

1. If you are not familiar with the story of the Pilgrims, seek it out in histories. Your teacher or librarian will help you. Find out about the nationality of the Pilgrims; their travels before coming to America; their difficulties on the way.

2. Bring to class pictures of some of the following: Plymouth Rock; the *Mayflower;* an early Pilgrim house; Pilgrim man, woman, and child.

3. Explain the references in the poem to "band of exiles"; "hymns of lofty cheer"; "faith's pure shrine."

4. Were the Pilgrims the first settlers in America? Explain your answer.

5. Why did the Pilgrims leave their homes for the new land? What brought the people of other settlements to America?

A GREAT CITIZEN

By James Baldwin

TWO days before the battle of Bunker Hill the Continental Congress was sitting in the state house at Philadelphia.

The king of Great Britain had declared the American ⁵colonies to be in a state of rebellion and had sent soldiers to reduce them to subjection. It was for the Congress to provide some way of defense.

On this particular day, therefore, it passed the following resolution :

¹⁰ "*Resolved*, That a General be appointed to command all the Continental Forces, raised or to be raised for the defense of American liberty.

"That five hundred dollars per month be allowed for the pay and expenses of the General."

¹⁵ Who should the general be?

A delegate from Maryland arose and nominated George Washington of Virginia.

On the following day the president of the Congress informed Washington officially that he had been unan-²⁰imously chosen to be commander in chief of all the forces of the American colonies.

Washington arose and thanked the Congress for the honor which it had conferred upon him; and while declaring that he did not think himself equal to the duties ²⁵required of him, he asserted his readiness to do all that he could for "the support of the glorious cause."

"As to pay," he continued, "I beg leave to assure the Congress that as no pecuniary consideration could have tempted me to accept this arduous employment, I do not wish to make any profit from it. I will keep an exact account of my expenses. These, I doubt not, they will 5 discharge, and that is all I desire."

Thus the United American colonies entered upon a long and precarious war with the mother country. They had as yet no efficient army; they had no money; but they felt a supreme faith in the righteousness of their cause. 10

Upon George Washington of Virginia devolved the task of organizing, equipping, and conducting the army. Upon Robert Morris of Pennsylvania devolved the task of supplying the funds for the carrying on of the war. Without the patriotic labors of both these men, it is not un- 15 reasonable to believe that the colonies would have failed to achieve their liberty and the war would have ended in disaster.

Robert Morris was at the head of the largest commercial house in Philadelphia; he was the leading man of business 20 in America. In the Congress of 1775 he was active in pushing forward and sustaining the war, and people soon perceived that the country must very largely depend upon him for financial aid.

When the Declaration of Independence was proposed, 25 Robert Morris voted against it. He was in favor of independence, but he did not believe the time was ripe for it. When the day came for adopting the declaration, however, he signed and thus pledged his life and his fortune to the cause of liberty. 30

The months that followed were months of trial and great perplexity. How should the money be obtained to feed and clothe and arm the patriot forces commanded by Washington? It required all the skill and experience of Robert Morris to provide for the necessities of the new government. It required, also, an amount of self-sacrifice which few other men would have been willing to make. Often he was obliged to borrow large sums of money for which he became personally responsible. Through his exertions, three million rations of provisions were forwarded to the army just at the moment when such aid was most needed.

In the following year he was appointed superintendent of finance, or, as we should now say, Secretary of the Treasury for the United States. But the treasury was empty; the Congress was in debt two and a half million dollars; the army was destitute; there was no one who would lend to the government; without some immediate aid the war could not go on. Nevertheless people had confidence in Robert Morris, and it was that confidence which saved the day.

He began by furnishing the army with several thousand barrels of flour, pledging his own means to pay for it.

When Washington decided to make a bold campaign in Virginia against Lord Cornwallis, it was to Robert Morris that he looked for support.

"We are in want of food, of clothing, of arms," said the general. "We have not even the means of transporting the army from place to place or subsisting it in the field."

"I myself," said Robert Morris, "will see that you are provided."

He hastened to borrow of his friends all the money they were willing to spare for the cause of liberty. He pledged his own means to the last shilling. He directed the commissary to send forward all necessary supplies for the army in Virginia. He procured boats for transporting troops and provisions. He left nothing undone; he spared no pains to make the campaign in Virginia successful. Washington's victory at Yorktown was to a large degree 5 the result no less of his own skill and courage than of the energy and self-sacrifice of Robert Morris.

At the close of the war there was no money to pay off the soldiers and there was great dissatisfaction on every side. Robert Morris came forward, and by indorsing 10 certificates to the amount of three quarters of a million dollars relieved the public distress and made it possible to disband the army. While doing this, he again pledged himself personally to see that all the obligations that he had made in behalf of the government were properly 15 satisfied.

It is pleasant to remember that the money which he had so generously advanced in aid of the cause of liberty was finally paid back to him, and that his faith in the honesty of the government was not misplaced. 20

— American Book of Golden Deeds.

1. What is the name of the war that freed our American colonies from England? What was Washington's part in this war? Lord Cornwallis's? What particular battles are mentioned in this selection?

2. What did Robert Morris do that entitles him to be called "A Great Citizen"?

3. What is the Declaration of Independence? When was it approved by the representatives of the colonies?

4. This selection is more than a sketch of Morris's part in the war. It sketches briefly the whole War of Independence, and is worthy of your most careful study as a supplement to your history work.

AT VALLEY FORGE

By H. A. Brown

At no time during the Revolutionary War were the soldiers of Washington so hard pressed as during the winter of 1777–78. The little army was camping at Valley Forge, half clothed, half fed, half armed, and thoroughly discouraged. The winter was a severe one, and but for the leadership of their commanders the American cause might have failed just then. Valley Forge is an important name in American history.

THE wind is cold and piercing on the old Gulf Road, and the snowflakes have begun to fall. Who is this that toils up yonder hill, his footsteps stained with blood? His bare feet peep through his worn-out shoes, his
5 legs are nearly naked, his shirt hangs in strings, his hair is disheveled, his face wan and thin, his look hungry. On his shoulder he carries a rusty gun, and the hand that grasps the stock is blue with cold. His comrade is no better off, nor he who follows.
10 A fourth comes into view, and still another. A dozen are in sight. Twenty have reached the ridge, and there are more to come. See them as they mount the hill that slopes eastward into the Great Valley. A thousand are in sight, but they are only the vanguard of the motley com-
15 pany that winds down the road until it is lost in the cloud of snowflakes that have hidden the Gulf hills. Yonder are horsemen in tattered uniforms, and behind them cannon lumbering slowly over the frozen road.

Are these soldiers that huddle together and bow their

heads as they face the biting wind? Is this an army that comes straggling through the valley in the blinding snow? No martial music leads them in triumph into a captured capital. No city full of good cheer and warm and comfortable homes awaits their coming. No sound keeps time ⁵ to their steps save the icy wind rattling the leafless branches and the dull tread of their weary feet on the frozen ground. In yonder forest must they find their shelter and on the northern slope of these inhospitable hills their place of refuge.   ¹⁰

Trials that rarely have failed to break the fortitude of men await them here. The Congress whom they serve shall prove helpless to protect them, and their country herself seem unmindful of their sufferings. Disease shall infest their huts by day, and famine stand guard with them ¹⁵ through the night. Frost shall lock their camp with icy fetters, and the snows cover it as with a garment; the storms of winter shall be pitiless, — but all in vain. Danger shall not frighten nor temptation have power to seduce them. Doubt shall not shake their love of country, nor ²⁰ suffering overcome their fortitude. The powers of evil shall not prevail against them; for they are the Continental Army, and these are the hills of Valley Forge!

1. While the American soldiers were suffering cold and hunger in their little Pennsylvania camp, the British troops were comfortably housed in Philadelphia. The whole situation was a hard one for the Americans to bear. But Valley Forge was the darkness before dawn. In the spring of 1778 news came that France would help the colonists; and meanwhile Baron Steuben was busy drilling the men and making an army out of raw recruits. Write a sentence telling what you think Valley Forge stands for in our history.

CONCORD HYMN

By Ralph Waldo Emerson

On April 19, 1775, the American soldiers turned back the British in a sharp fight at Concord bridge. At Concord, and at Lexington a few hours before, the first blood was shed in battle for our country. Sixty years later a monument was erected beside the stream in honor of the fallen heroes. This poem was written as a part of the services dedicating the monument.

B Y THE rude bridge that arched the flood,
    Their flag to April's breeze unfurled,
Here once the embattled farmers stood,
    And fired the shot heard round the world.

5 The foe long since in silence slept;
    Alike the conqueror silent sleeps;
And Time the ruined bridge has swept
    Down the dark stream which seaward creeps.

On this green bank, by this soft stream,
10   We set to-day a votive stone;
That memory may their deed redeem,
    When, like our sires, our sons are gone.

Spirit, that made those heroes dare
    To die and leave their children free,
15 Bid Time and Nature gently spare
    The shaft we raise to them and thee.

1. Explain lines 3–4; 10–13. Report on the battles of Lexington and Concord.

THE HOUSE BY THE SIDE OF THE ROAD

By Sam Walter Foss

THERE are hermit souls that live withdrawn
  In the place of their self-content;
There are souls like stars, that dwell apart
  In a fellowless firmament;
There are pioneer souls that blaze their paths   5
  Where highways never ran —
But let me live by the side of the road
  And be a friend to man.

Let me live in a house by the side of the road
  Where the race of men go by —   10
The men who are good and the men who are bad,
  As good and as bad as I.
I would not sit in the scorner's seat
  Or hurl the cynic's ban —
Let me live in a house by the side of the road   15
  And be a friend to man.

I see from my house by the side of the road,
  By the side of the highway of life,
The men who press with the ardor of hope,
  The men who are faint with the strife,   20
But I turn not away from their smiles nor their tears,
  Both parts of an infinite plan —
Let me live in a house by the side of the road
  And be a friend to man.

I know there are brook-gladdened meadows ahead,
   And mountains of wearisome height;
That the road passes on through the long afternoon
   And stretches away to the night.
5 And still I rejoice when the travelers rejoice
   And weep with the strangers that moan,
Nor live in my house by the side of the road
   Like a man who dwells alone.

Let me live in my house by the side of the road,
10   It's here the race of men go by —
They are good, they are bad, they are weak, they are
    strong,
   Wise, foolish — so am I.
Then why should I sit in the scorner's seat,
15   Or hurl the cynic's ban?
Let me live in my house by the side of the road
   And be a friend to man.

1. This poem emphasizes the relation of the citizen to his community. Why would the speaker be a desirable neighbor?

2. What is a cynic? A hermit? A pioneer? Why could the "I" be none of these?

3. Would the speaker make a good politician? A good man for a local office? Give reasons for your answers.

4. Memorize at least one of the stanzas. Observe how long it takes you.

(From *Dreams in Homespun* by Sam Walter Foss. Used by special arrangement with Lothrop, Lee & Shepard Co., Publishers.)

OLD IRONSIDES

By Oliver Wendell Holmes

Old Ironsides was a pet name for the frigate *Constitution*, which won many victories in the War of 1812. Holmes wrote this poem to protest against dismantling the old ship in the early 30's — and he won his point.

AYE, tear her tattered ensign down!
    Long has it waved on high,
And many an eye has danced to see
    That banner in the sky;
Beneath it rung the battle shout, 5
    And burst the cannon's roar; —
The meteor of the ocean air
    Shall sweep the clouds no more.

Her deck, once red with heroes' blood,
    Where knelt the vanquished foe, 10
When winds were hurrying o'er the flood,
    And waves were white below,
No more shall feel the victor's tread,
    Or know the conquered knee; —
The harpies of the shore shall pluck 15
    The eagle of the sea!

Oh, better that her shattered hulk
    Should sink beneath the wave;
Her thunders shook the mighty deep,
    And there should be her grave; 20

Nail to the mast her holy flag,
Set every threadbare sail,
And give her to the god of storms,
The lightning and the gale!

1. What did Holmes suggest should be done with Old Ironsides?
This poem produced such a wave of enthusiasm that the naval authorities rebuilt the ship. She still lies in Boston harbor, a relic of
ancient days and a monument to the power of three stanzas of poetry.

2. In any encyclopedia, look up the *Constitution* and read the
story of her achievement.

3. Report also some interesting facts of Holmes's life.

GOD GIVE US MEN

By J. G. HOLLAND

GOD give us men. The time demands
  Strong minds, great hearts, true faith, and willing
    hands;
  Men whom the lust of office does not kill;
5 Men whom the spoils of office cannot buy;
  Men who possess opinions and a will;
  Men who have honor, men who will not lie;
  Men who can stand before a demagogue
  And damn his treacherous flatteries without winking;
10   Tall men, sun crowned, who live above the fog
In public duty and in private thinking!
  For while the rabble with their thumb-worn creeds,
Their large professions, and their little deeds,
Mingle in selfish strife, lo Freedom weeps,
15 Wrong rules the land, and waiting Justice sleeps!

DAILY SERVICE

By Susan Coolidge

WHO serves his country best?
　　Not he who for a brief and stormy space
Leads forth her armies to the fierce affray.
Short is the time of turmoil and unrest;
　　Long years of peace succeed it, and replace.　　5
　　　There is a better way.

Who serves his country best?
　　Not he who guides her senates in debate
And makes the laws which are her prop and stay;
Not he who wears the poet's purple vest,　　10
　　And sings her songs of love and grief and hate.
　　　There is a better way.

He serves his country best
　　Who joins the tide that lifts her nobly on;
For speech has myriad tongues for every day,　　15
And song but one; and law within the breast
　　Is stronger than the graven law on stone.
　　　There is a better way.

He serves his country best
　　Who lives pure life and doeth righteous deed,　　20
And walks straight paths however others stray,
And leaves his sons as uttermost bequest
　　A stainless record which all men may read.
　　　This is the better way.

No drop but serves the slowly lifting tide,
　　No dew but has an errand to some flower,
No smallest star but sheds some helpful ray,
And man by man, each given to the rest,
5　　Makes the firm bulwark of the country's power.
　　There is no better way.

1. What is the "better way"? What ways are less good?
2. To what previous passages do lines 15-17 refer?

"BREATHES THERE THE MAN"

By Sir Walter Scott

BREATHES there the man with soul so dead,
　　Who never to himself hath said,
　　"This is my own, my native land!"
Whose heart hath ne'er within him burned,
5　As home his footsteps he hath turned
　　From wandering on a foreign strand?
If such there breathe, go, mark him well;
For him no minstrel raptures swell;
High though his titles, proud his name,
10　Boundless his wealth as wish can claim, —
Despite those titles, power, and pelf,
The wretch, concentered all in self,
Living, shall forfeit fair renown,
And, doubly dying, shall go down
15　To the vile dust from whence he sprung,
Unwept, unhonored, and unsung.
　　　　　　　　— *The Lay of the Last Minstrel.*

1. Read this selection aloud as forcefully as you can. Ask your classmates to interpret any doubtful passages for you.

A CREED OF AMERICANISM

By William H. Ketler

THERE are many reasons why I should be proud of
my native land and loyal to it and its institutions.

My native land, the United States of America, was the
first to declare that all men have inalienable rights to life,
liberty, and the pursuit of happiness.   5

Carrying out this declaration, the United States has a
form of government in which we are all equal before the
law.   There is no position in the government to which any
of us may not attain.   Poor boys have attained the pres-
idency of the United States, a greater honor than the 10
throne held by any European monarch.

By the union of states our government gives each of us
a greater range of civilized country to travel in than any
other nation in history.   I, a citizen of New Jersey, have
equal rights in California with any citizen of that state, 15
and my life is as safe in California as it is in New Jersey.

My country gives me the right to think, speak, and write
my thoughts, and try to persuade my fellow citizens to think
as I do, provided that I do not incite them to violent
action and do not interfere with the liberty of any other 20
citizen.

My country permits me to worship God according to the
dictates of my conscience, and permits no union of church
and government nor any favors to any form of religious
belief.   25

My country with its public schools enables me to learn

the thoughts and understand the achievements of the great and wise men of all ages. This public school places the poor boy on a level with the rich boy and enables the attentive and studious boy to win the honors, regardless of 5 the wealth of his parents.

My country has a greater variety of climate than any other civilized country on earth, and by the freedom and ease with which I may go from one section to another I may quickly find the climate adapted to my particular 10 state of health.

My country is favored with much natural beauty and grandeur, inciting me to reverence for the God who spread all this wonderful picture land before me.

My country raises every plant and every beast needed 15 in any way to sustain my life and provide for my comfort.

My country has become a beacon light to all the other peoples of the earth, summoning them to leave the darkness of ignorance and dwell in the glorious light of liberty.

So again I pledge allegiance to you, the flag of my 20 native land, beautiful banner of the brave and the free, and I thank God, who gave me life, that I am able to say, I am an American.

1. This is not a creed to be memorized, but one to be studied for its compact information about our country.

2. How many items of excellence about the United States does the author mention? Take each and give the name of a country that does not possess that advantage.

3. Write a short creed (a pledge of good citizenship) for your own community. First set down a few good things your community has; then the things it lacks. Then fashion your creed to include both, ending with a pledge of citizenship.

THE ARK OF THE COVENANT

By Henry W. Grady

As you will remember from your Bible, the Ark of the Covenant was a sacred chest, made of acacia wood overlaid with gold, containing the Decalogue (Ten Commandments) of the Israelites. The term "Ark of the Covenant" has come to signify that which contains a most sacred possession.

In the following address by Henry Woodfen Grady (1851–1889), a famous Southern journalist and orator, our nation's Ark of the Covenant is first thought of as being the Capitol at Washington; but Mr. Grady, after contemplating the fine home life of an American citizen, decides that our *true* Ark of the Covenant is the Home.

A FEW Sundays ago I stood on a hill in Washington. My heart thrilled as I looked on the towering marble of my country's Capitol and a mist gathered in my eyes as, standing there, I thought of its tremendous significance and the powers there assembled, and the responsibilities 5 there centered — its president, its congress, its courts, its gathered treasure, its army, its navy, and its sixty millions of citizens.

It seemed to me the best and mightiest sight that the sun could find in its wheeling course — this majestic 10 home of a Republic that has taught the world its best lessons of liberty — and I felt that if wisdom, and justice, and honor abided therein, the world would stand indebted to this temple on which my eyes rested, and in which the ark of my covenant was lodged, for its final uplifting and 15 regeneration.

A few days later I visited a country home. A modest, quiet house, sheltered by great trees and set in a circle of field and meadow, gracious with the promise of harvest; barns and cribs well filled, and the old smokehouse odorous
5 with treasure — the fragrance of pink and hollyhock mingling with the aroma of garden and orchard, resonant with the hum of bees and poultry's busy clucking; inside the house thrift, comfort, and that cleanliness that is next to godliness; and the old clock that had held its steadfast
10 pace amid the frolic of weddings, and kept company with the watchers of the sick bed, and had ticked the solemn requiem of the dead; and the well-worn Bible that, thumbed by fingers long since stilled, and blurred with tears of eyes long since closed, held the simple annals of the family, and
15 the heart and conscience of the home.

Outside stood the master, strong and wholesome and upright; wearing no man's collar; with no mortgage on his roof, and no lien on his ripening harvest; picking his crops in his own wisdom, and selling them in his own time in his
20 chosen market; master of his lands and master of himself. Near by stood his aged father, happy in the heart and home of his son. And as they started to the house the old man's hand rested on the young man's shoulder, touching it with the knighthood of the Fourth Commandment, and
25 laying there the unspeakable blessing of an honored and grateful father.

As they drew near the door, the old mother appeared; the sunset falling on her face, softening its wrinkles and its tenderness, lighting up her patient eyes, and the rich music
30 of her heart trembling on her lips as in simple phrase she welcomed her husband and son to their home. Beyond was the good wife, happy amid her household cares. And the

children, strong and sturdy, trooping down the lane with the lowing herd, or weary of simple sport, seeking, as truant birds do, the quiet of the old home nest.

And I saw the night descend on that home. And the stars swarmed in the bending skies, and the father, a simple man of God, gathered the family about him, and read from the Bible the old, old story of love and faith, and then closed the record of that simple day by calling down the benediction of God on the family and the home!

And as I gazed, the memory of the great Capitol faded from my brain. Forgotten its treasure and its splendor. And I said, "Surely here — here in the homes of the people — is lodged the ark of the covenant of my country. Here is its majesty and strength. Here the beginning of its power and the end of its responsibility."

The home is the source of our national life. Back of the national Capitol and above it stands the home. Back of the President, and above him, stands the citizen. What the home is, this and nothing else will the Capitol be. What the citizen wills, this and nothing else will the President be.

1. Read this selection silently and try to picture the two scenes as the author saw them. What is the first picture? The second?

2. Describe the master of the country home as you see him. What is meant in line 24, page 395, by "the knighthood of the Fourth Commandment"?

3. Tell what the mother was like.

4. What is the conclusion of the author? Explain what is meant by the citizen's being above the President.

QUALITIES OF GOOD CITIZENSHIP

By Theodore Roosevelt

THE man who counts is the man who is decent and who makes himself felt as a force for decency, for cleanliness, for civic righteousness. He must have several qualities. First and foremost, of course, he must be honest, 5 he must have the root of right thinking in him. That is not enough. In the next place he must have courage. The timid good man counts but little in the rough business of trying to do well the world's work. And finally, in addition to being honest and brave he must have common sense. 10 If he does not have it, no matter what other qualities he may have, he will find himself at the mercy of those who, without possessing his desire to do right, know only too well how to make the wrong effective.

1. This is a very meaty, compact statement of what good citizenship is. What qualities did Roosevelt mention? What reason does he give for selecting each?

2. Memorize these thirteen lines. They are not only expressive of a great man but they will also help you to become a better citizen.

All private virtue is the public fund:
As that abounds the state decays or thrives;
Each should contribute to the general stock,
And who lends most is most his country's friend.
— *Jephson.*

GOOD BOOKS YOU SHOULD KNOW

HERE are the titles of a few good books whose acquaintance you will enjoy. If you come to know only a few of them your journey through this book will not have been made in vain.

Alcott's *Little Women*
Alden's *Adventures of Jimmy Brown*
Bachman's *Great Inventors and Their Inventions*
Baker's *Children's Books of Poetry*
Baldwin's *American Book of Golden Deeds*
Baldwin's *Fifty Famous Rides and Riders*
Baldwin's *Conquest of the Old Northwest*
Baldwin's *Story of Roland*
Baldwin's *Story of Siegfried*
Baldwin's *Thirty More Famous Stories Retold*
Baldwin and Livengood's *Sailing the Seas*
Brooks's *Boy Emigrants*
Burton's *Lafayette, The Friend of American Liberty*
Carpenter's *Geographical Readers*
Carpenter's *Readers on Commerce and Industry*
Cody's *Life and Adventures of Buffalo Bill*
Cooper's *Deerslayer*
Cooper's *Pilot*
Defoe's *Robinson Crusoe*
Dickens's *Cricket on the Hearth*
Dodge's *Hans Brinker, or the Silver Skates*
Dorrance's *Story of the Forest*

Doyle's *Refugees*
Du Chaillu's *Wild Life Under the Equator*
Dutton's *Little Stories of France*
Eggleston's *Hoosier Schoolboy*
Fabre's *Insect Adventures*
Foote and Skinner's *Makers and Defenders of America*
Guerber's *Story of the English*
Guerber's *Story of the Greeks*
Guerber's *Story of Modern France*
Guerber's *Story of Old France*
Guerber's *Story of the Romans*
Hawthorne's *Grandfather's Chair*
Hughes's *Tom Brown's School Days*
Macdonald's *Light Princess*
Munroe's *Dorymates*
Munroe's *Flamingo Feather*
Otis's *Toby Tyler*
Page's *A Captured Santa Claus*
Pitré's *Swallow Book* (Camehl)
Pyle's *Modern Aladdin*
Pyle's *Stolen Treasure*
Scott's *Ivanhoe*
Scott's *Tales and Verse* (Webster and Coe)
Stevenson's *Treasure Island*
Stoddard's *Red Mustang*
Swift's *Gulliver's Travels*
Twain's *Adventures of Tom Sawyer*
Van Dyke's *First Christmas Tree*
Verne's *Around the World in Eighty Days*
Verne's *Twenty Thousand Leagues Under the Sea*
Wilkins's *Weaver's Children*
Wyss' *Swiss Family Robinson*